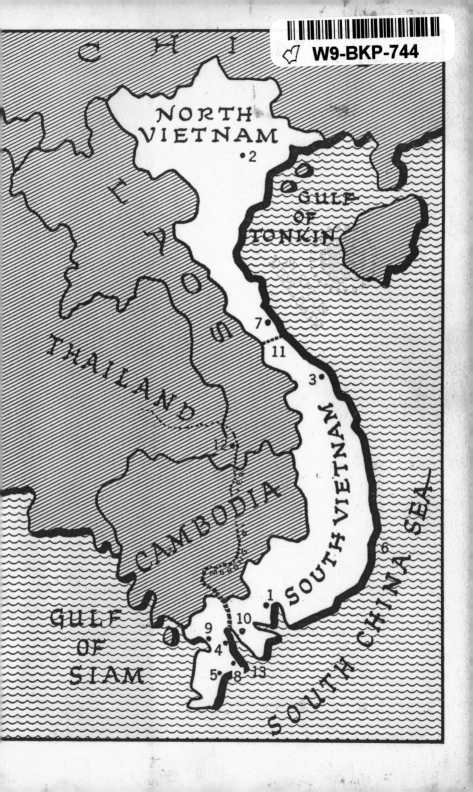

DATELINE: VIET NAM

"*DATELINE: VIET NAM*"

JIM G. LUCAS

AWARD HOUSE · NEW YORK 1966

AWARD HOUSE
Second Printing August, 1966

Copyright © 1966 by The E. W. Scripps Company

ALL RIGHTS RESERVED

AWARD HOUSE books are published by
Universal Publishing and Distributing Corporation
New York, New York

MANUFACTURED IN THE UNITED STATES OF AMERICA

Distributed by Crown Publishers, Inc., New York

Library of Congress catalog card number: 66-25709

Introduction

Jim Lucas and I first met in Saigon—fittingly enough. The occasion was lunch at the Caravelle Hotel's roof restaurant. That was in January of 1964. We were both a bit long in the tooth to be pursuing and reporting upon combat operations in Viet Nam. However, Jim is ten years longer in the tooth than I am, and the strenuous, continually dangerous life must have been considerably more debilitating to him than to me. I also had the advantage of half a year of Green Berets' training behind me. Yet, when I left Viet Nam, six months after that first meeting, to go home and write *The Green Berets*, Jim was still going strong, slogging through the mud of the Mekong Delta, reporting the war where it really was—out in the boondocks.

No newsman deserved the 1964 Ernie Pyle award for war reporting more than did Jim. As I read his dispatches in this book, I re-live my own experiences in the cauldron of a highly unconventional conflict of no fronts and no rears where you can get yourself dead very easily.

As Jim points out, early back in 1964 you could count on one hand the war correspondents constantly out in the bonnies with the troops, taking their chances with the game little Viet troopers and their hard-charging American advisers.

Our paths crisscrossed frequently, particularly when I made it to Jim's baliwick in Can Tho, headquarters of the war against the Viet Cong in the Mekong Delta. Often we would discuss the vicissitudes of being out in the field constantly. Our chief fear was that we would hold up some combat operation led by

Americans patient enough to let us tag along—our physical stamina was not up to that of the young troopers out to kill the Cong.

Jim and I had many friends in common and tried to retain some sort of professional stoicism when they died.

I remember reading one of Jim's columns datelined Can Tho, December 6, 1965, just a few hours before I was to give a talk before New York's prestigious Dutch Treat Club. Since my talk was to be "off the record," I expanded on the column. It mentioned my old friend Larry Thorne, the real life model for the hero of the first story of *The Green Berets*—Sven Kornie, as I called him.

In that column, Jim paid well-deserved tribute to this legendary member of the legendary Green Berets, who had been reported mysteriously "missing" though nobody wanted to talk about it. Well, it happened that during my second tour in Viet Nam, in October and November of 1965, I looked up Larry. He had been a prime mover in the Special Forces exercises at Fort Bragg—code-named Golden Hawk—after his 1964 stint in Viet Nam. Golden Hawk was designed to train Special Forces men in the techniques of interdicting Viet Cong infiltrators in their own territory—in other words going into North Viet Nam or Communist-dominated Laos and Cambodia and getting at the enemy in what they thought was their privileged sanctuary.

It may be news to Jim, even at this writing, but I learned that our mutual friend Larry Thorne was last seen (he is still presumed dead) in a fight with the Viet Cong along the Ho Chi Minh trail deep in Laos. The action took place on October 18th. I talked to Thorne a few days before he got it and had the satisfaction of knowing he was proud of the way he had been portrayed in *The Green Berets*.

In this book of Jim Lucas' columns you, the reader, will live through the day-by-day agony, despair and triumph of the Viet Nam war as fought by both the Vietnamese and their American advisers. Jim has never been known to pull punches, and his words give you the true picture of what it has been like for our fighting men as the conflict has escalated from an American "advisory" mission to a mortal engagement involving more than 300,000 American combat troops.

When I first returned from Viet Nam at the end of May of 1964, I was accused of exaggeration, if not downright fabrication, about the problems Americans faced trying to make many of the Vietnamese officers actually fight for their country. Secretary of Defense McNamara carried with him a refutation of a *U.S. News and World Report* piece I had written in Viet Nam at the end of May, emphasizing the troubles we were experiencing in making our "sensitive" allies, especially the Vietnamese Air Force, fight the Communists. The day I was due to report to a Pentagon debriefing on June 3rd, Jim saved me with his second article on the attitudes of the Vietnamese fighter and chopper pilots.

I had quoted my own experiences on VNAF (Viet Nam Air Force) missions and described the reluctance of the Viet pilots to get down low enough (putting themselves in ground-fire range, of course) to do any good whether on strafing runs or helicopter rescues. Pentagon toppers called me a liar. Then out came Lucas that day on the front page, breaking his second eyewitness report in a week on the VNAF, and confirmed my findings. It is men like Jim Lucas who keep the authorities reasonably honest in their releases about the Viet Nam war.

There are, alas, all too few Jim Lucases. Fortunately, Jim is still covering the heart and the heartbeat of the war in Viet Nam. All of us can depend only upon honest, first-hand, courageous reporting to keep us informed about what our men face in day-to-day battle. So all of us can thank this 52-year-old combat reporter for the fortitude and devotion to his craft which has carried him through nearly three years of telling us what really is going on in Viet Nam.

ROBIN MOORE

Part One

JANUARY - JUNE, 1964

FOREWORD (FROM AN ARTICLE WRITTEN AT THE
CONCLUSION OF MY FIRST SIX MONTHS IN VIET NAM
AND PUBLISHED NATIONALLY IN AUGUST, 1964)

The six months I spent in the Mekong Delta covering the Vietnamese war added up to rich and rewarding experience. It was not a particularly easy one. Not when you're 50 years old, out of shape and slightly overweight.

Fortunately, the youngsters made allowances for the old man, and that was a blessing. When I finally left in early June, I knew 90 per cent of the officers and enlisted men south of the Bassac River by their first names. Most of them knew me as "Jim." You treasure that kind of relationship with your news sources.

No newspaperman can be very proud of the American press in this show. In the six months I lived in the Delta, I was the only correspondent regularly assigned to—working and living with—combat troops. Now that I have come home there is no one. I can't explain why this is so.

This is the only war of recent memory which has not been covered to saturation. We flew more than 300 correspondents to Lebanon, where no shot was fired in anger. In Viet Nam, 16,000 Americans are involved, with thousands more on the way, and well over 200 have been killed.

Maybe I shouldn't complain. I had no competition. But after a while, I didn't particularly enjoy having the story to myself.

In other wars I've known there have been press camps—correspondents issued combat clothing, provided with transportation and food. None of that was available in Viet Nam. Accreditation was handled by the Vietnamese, not the Americans. You were accredited on a monthly basis. This meant returning to Saigon to renew your accreditation at the end of each month.

I did that once. Vietnamese red tape is every bit as bad as ours. It took two days to get your papers. The rub was, after going to all this trouble, no one ever asked to see my accreditation. They weren't interested. I decided I wasn't, either. No one ever bothered me, even though I still was carrying February's authorization in June.

The information office in Saigon had no provision for combat gear. You had to get your own. This meant buying fatigues, combat boots, etc., on the local market. My fatigues faded and shrank after the first washing. My combat boots came apart after one week in the paddies.

Eventually I acquired everything I needed from the troops. I had Army field boots, a bullet-proof vest, GI fatigues—the works —when I checked out. Other correspondents were envious of my boots, which had steel plates to protect against poisoned spikes. I never told where I got them.

I went to Viet Nam with a pocket full of American Express travelers' checks. I could cash them, of course, but I had to take Vietnamese piastres in change.

To eat with the U.S. Army or trade at the post exchange, I needed dollars. The Embassy finance office wouldn't help me.

"Mr. Lucas," the young lady in charge told me acidly, "as far as we are concerned, you are just another tourist."

In desperation I sought an appointment with Ambassador Henry Cabot Lodge. I had no intention of interviewing him that early in the game (this was January). We discussed my program briefly. As I started to leave, Ambassador Lodge—as I knew he would—asked if there was anything he could do for me. I took him up immediately.

"There is indeed," I said, "you can give me every dollar bill you can lay your hands on, and I'll give you travelers' checks in return."

Lodge raided the wallets of everybody on his staff, and I came out with $150 in U.S. green. Later I was able to arrange to cash my checks with the PX in Can Tho.

Within 10 days, I had arranged with Col. Sammie L. Homan, senior advisor to the 4th Vietnamese Corps, to make his compound in Can Tho my permanent base. My room cost me $1 a day. My meals came to $3.

Covering a war is a great deal like covering a courthouse. You get to know your sources and your beat. My beat was the Mekong Delta; my sources were the thousands of Americans assigned there.

I quickly worked out a schedule. Monday I paid my rent, got a haircut, went to the PX, etc. Tuesday morning I took off for Ca Mau, Soc Trang, Rac Gia, Sa Dec or wherever I felt the story was. I usually stayed with it until Friday. Saturday and Sunday were for writing. A field trip produced anywhere from six to 15 stories.

Clips were my currency. My home base in Washington kept them coming. The men I wrote about naturally wanted to see what I'd written.

The Americans with whom I worked and lived were almost dumbly grateful to have someone interested in them. They made working easy. Nothing was too good for me. Invariably, wherever I went, I got the best bunk, the best chow and the front seat in whatever jeep or truck was available for transportation.

In Can Tho my room was next to that of Lt. Col. John Roberts, who commanded Delta Battalion and had all the helicopters in the Delta. Robbie and I became close friends. I knew within seconds whenever there was action. Robbie always saw to it that I got a ride.

I came back to the U.S. because I had become fatigued, mentally and physically. I felt I had been too close to the forest to see the trees.

Back home I hope to take a longer, more dispassionate look at the whole picture. But I fully intend to go back.

JAN. 24, CAN THO

You know it's war when you see a young man dead.

Young men court danger as they court women, and for much the same reasons. They relish the chase and, occasionally, the conquest; pain puzzles them as much as it hurts them, and the thought of failure is insupportable.

They scorn the term, and sing ribald songs about it, but

13

secretly each wants to be a hero, in the finest and best sense of the word, and there's nothing wrong with that, because quiet heroism is the stuff of war.

This war is no different, nor was this young American. There are thousands involved, 6000 miles from home, but it lures the bravest and best—or perhaps the most foolhardy—and they all are supremely confident that they'll go home eventually and all this will be a horrid memory.

This man had volunteered for Viet Nam when he didn't have to, because possibly he was bored with garrison life and weary of the bars on Hotel Street back in Honolulu. Going to war, he figured, would give him a chance to "live."

Much about war, he found, was as tiresome and tedious as life in camp. You waited around a lot more than you had been led to believe you would, and when you got a mission, it usually turned out pretty tame.

He was a gunner on a UH-1B—the helicopters they call Hueys —and he considered it a grubby job because no one ever seemed to shoot at anything, like they used to do in the movies, and as older men who'd been in Korea and World War II seemed to remember they had done.

Day after day he sat at the open door of his chopper as it took off and landed, rifle at the ready, eyes sweeping the paddies, the villages and the canals that receded or rose up to meet him.

He was looking for signs of hostile activity, and the rules were very strict about when he could or could not shoot. Somehow, nothing he saw was covered by the rules.

He was the first man in his outfit to get it. They said solemnly it was a fluke, and no one would have realized the shot had been fired if it had missed.

But it didn't miss. It caught him in the throat and came out the back of his head and he slumped over and was dead.

The doctors said later the most he could have felt was the equivalent of a good, solid punch to the jaw. He was buckled in, so he didn't fall from his seat.

But his heart continued to pump for a while, and his blood

14

slipped out onto the floor and sloshed at the feet of his buddies on the trip back to their base.

They brought him in, and it shocked the guys he'd had breakfast with a few hours earlier and who'd sat beside him at the movies the night before. It was obvious he was beyond help, but they all wanted to help anyhow, so they moved things that didn't need moving, and hurried to help carry him to the ambulance. The ambulance took him away and, somewhere, an adjutant wrote up the notices they send to next of kin. Thus, automatically, the impersonal process that converts a man into a statistic got under way, and his friends began cleansing their minds of all but the finest memories of him.

At dinner they spoke of him quietly, in the past tense, and attributed to him virtues that undoubtedly would have surprised the young man who was now dead.

❋   ❋   ❋

It has always been like this, and always will be, in war. The death of one man settles nothing. There was still a mission to finish, and his chopper was needed, so someone took his place and it went back to work.

JAN. 25, CAU DUC

It's that mud—that damnable, man-eating mud—that turns this Mekong Delta war into a foul-smelling hell.

It's unavoidable. It pulls at a man, drags him down, holds him there.

❋   ❋   ❋

We've been on the march now better than 10 hours. We are five Americans and 300 Vietnamese, alone in a hostile area which the Communist Viet Cong have ruled for 18 months or longer.

There was sporadic sniper fire from tree fringes at the edge of abandoned villages. Two of our men were slightly wounded. One was hurt by a mine.

But mainly the Viet Cong held their fire until after we reached the wet paddies and turned toward the swamps. We

15

had hoped to stay on the dikes, but now we had to go into that putrid mud.

The lanky old sergeant from Dalton, Ga., has been in Viet Nam for a long time and he knows his enemy. Said Sgt. Vernon King:

"They'll not hit us with any force today or tomorrow. They make us go into the mud and that wears us out. Then, when we're too tired to take another step, they'll try to clobber us."

* * *

I was already dog-tired when we reached the banks of a small canal. The tide was out. It was no more than a few dozen yards across. Already some of our wiry little Vietnamese were on the other side. Others were still fording it.

Hesitantly I slid into the mud feet-first, and quickly sank almost to my waist. I tried to raise my legs and they wouldn't budge.

I struggled, and sank deeper. One leg twisted, painfully.

And then I panicked, doing the wrong things. Sergeant King had warned me: "When you're stuck in the mud, never reach out for a Vietnamese. They'll jerk you forward and maybe snap both your legs above the knees."

So when they came toward me to help, I fought back. They tried to hoist me on their shoulders. Failing this, one of them finally dug me out with his bare hands.

* * *

Then there were more paddies and more mud ahead and then the swamps.

But by now I had learned to keep walking, concentrating on every step, trying never to give the mud another chance.

All my life I've been afraid of snakes, and now suddenly I remembered that Viet Nam had deadly rice snakes and kraits. Yet almost absently I saw one under foot. I stepped over it, and it slithered away. Then I saw another, but held doggedly to my course.

Once the mud pulled my right boot half off. I jammed my hand into the mud—ignoring the snakes—and saved it. I forgot all about being afraid of snakes.

So I plodded on. The tide was in and I swam three small canals, pulling the leeches off my back when I got across.

By now it became apparent our senior U.S. officer, Capt. Chip Meyers of Carmel, Calif., was getting worried about my making the three more miles we had to go. And in that three miles were one more canal and a river to cross.

I had taken off my jacket to plunge into the last brackish canal when suddenly—miraculously—a chopper appeared overhead. Chip Meyers denied he had called for it.

The craft came down and I climbed aboard—exhausted and almost in a state of collapse.

"Sorry," I said. "I couldn't make it. I was holding them back."

"Nonsense," said Maj. John Valentic of Campbelltown, Pa. "This is a young man's war."

And soon I was airborne back to Cau Duc, to wash up, get clean clothes, coffee—and get scared of snakes all over again.

JAN. 30, THAT SAN

Up ahead, a hundred yards or so, a machine gun spoke—probingly, uncertainly at first and then in a steady stream. A grenade exploded with a muffled whoomp.

This was a night ambush we had prepared and there were 22 tense armed Vietnamese soldiers concealed in the brush.

"Anything that moves after 7 p.m. is fair game," Maj. Marcus D. Moreman of Waverly, Ala., had said. "We've had some good successes with our ambushes. Once you reach the kill zone, you shoot."

And this is the kill zone. Here neither side expects or gives quarter.

This is the Seven Mountains area along the Cambodian border, the only place in the Mekong Delta where there's high ground. In many ways it is remindful of Korea.

The Viet Cong and their allies, the Cambodian Communists (identified as MC for Mekong Communists), hold the Seven Mountains—four in Viet Nam and three in Cambodia, 10 miles away.

In their caves and caverns, some a mile long, they make their own ammunition, run hospitals and printing presses and fly their own flag. Almost nightly they build huge fires to let the people know they're here.

Tonight was no exception. Once we lobbed artillery shells at the fires. But at $35 a round, that is an expensive way to douse a flame, Moreman reflected. So now we let them burn.

And tonight we have something going in our favor. Four days ago four Buddhist monks, returning from Cambodia with 180,-000 piastres (about $1800) for a new pagoda, were brutally murdered at Lac Quoi just inside Viet Nam. Their heads had been cut off and tucked in their arms.

There is no proof the Viet Cong had done it; it could have been done by bandits. But a newspaper in Tri Ton, eight miles up the road, had accused the Viet Cong. And in the village of Nga Bau Lau, Vietnamese flags had appeared where none had ever been seen before. At the monks' funeral the Viet Cong were openly denounced in a geniune outpouring of grief. It would be a while before the enemy's propaganda people could repair the damage.

I had set out from That San at dusk, joining up with the Vietnamese at the foot of the mountain known at Nui Khet. The Vietnamese commander, Maj. Tu Duong Van, couldn't believe I had planned to go along. But Major Moreman had assured me it would be a unit of 22 men, and besides, two full companies wouldn't be far away. If we were overwhelmed, three shots in the air would be our distress signal.

"You're safer here than you'd be in the vaults of the Bank of England," said Capt. Michael Ilsemann of Cleveland.

We walked slowly, on lookout for booby traps. Some are 10 feet deep, set with bamboo spikes which could disembowel a man. And this area had not been scouted recently.

"They're crude and easy to spot," Moreman said to allay my apprehension. "Just keep your eyeballs peeled."

Just how, I wanted to know, could they be spotted.

"Follow in my tracks," he grinned. "If I drop out of sight, step over me. Or step on my head. I'm tall."

On the trees were signs that read: "Vietnamese soldiers, booby traps are meant only for your American masters. Please turn back."

Those signs are booby traps too, with grenades behind them.

We set up our ambush outside a village. I took my assigned post 10 yards off the trail, wishing I were anywhere else. First, I had to fight mosquitos. The lotion in the plastic bottle, I found, keeps them from biting. But they still dive-bombed me.

It's deathly quiet. I wait. One hour. Two. You remember that an American was bitten last week by a green mamba. I begin to wonder if there are any around here. I become convinced there are. I fight down the impulse to get away fast.

Still I wait, and begin to wonder if the others are still there. I've heard nothing for a half hour or more. Could they have gone off? Would they?

Then the shooting starts. It lets up, then starts again. Rifles bark. Machine guns chatter. Grenades explode. Noise in the village ceases. Even the dogs are silent.

The enemy had come in sampans up the canal, I learned later, and headed for the village with their supplies.

Then I heard them running, blindly, in panic.

It's quiet now. But the Viet Cong have been alerted, so finally I can move out.

Back on the trail we leave two Viet Cong dead.

FEB. 3, CHAU LANG

The little group of Americans here—military advisers with the Vietnamese, and myself—stood immobile, white-faced and tight-lipped.

From a village just over the mountain a few miles away word came to us that the Communist Viet Cong forces there had an American prisoner.

At least, the report said, he was a white man and the Viet Cong were parading him, shackled and manacled, and proclaiming he was an American. They had another prisoner, too, a Vietnamese officer.

19

The enemy was showing off these two before the villagers as proof of the Communists' prowess in battle, and evidence that they would win this war.

But the report, in all truth, was considered unreliable, and even if it were true there was little likelihood they'd still be there now. Besides, we had a job to do here, defending Chau Lang. So pursuit was out of the question.

Still, we couldn't get it out of our minds. If there really was an American over there—that close to us—a prisoner hoping desperately to be saved . . . Well, there were tears in our eyes.

It is a fact that the Viet Cong do hold seven of our Special Forces men as prisoners. They took four in one group, three in another, late last year.

Because they fear our Special Forces—who train guerrillas to whip the Communists at their own game—the Viet Cong will not be likely to free them soon. This reasoning made us all the more angry and frustrated.

We remembered how the Viet Cong had boasted of the tortures they would inflict on any who fell into their hands.

Reliable reports are that all of our men are still alive, although one previously was reported to have died. We know they have been mistreated. Frequently they are exhibited and publicly humiliated.

But captured documents indicate the enemy has had little luck in efforts to break their will, brainwash them, force them to sign confessions or betray their cause.

"Americans," the documents say in effect, "are surprisingly well disciplined. They have told us nothing beyond their names, ranks and serial numbers. All efforts to obtain information from them so far have been unsuccessful. Efforts will be continued."

Somehow this makes Americans sit up a little straighter.

"It's hardly surprising," said an American colonel the other night. "The men they've taken have been captains and master sergeants. Professionals who've been in the army a long time. Hell will freeze over before they get anything out of those men."

The Viet Cong pretend to hold more Americans than they

actually do. This apparently is intended to sway villagers. Reliable reports say they sometimes use stand-ins, who pose as Americans. They are known to have several French sympathizers with them. They may have Russians, Bulgarians and Romanians.

In at least two instances Frenchmen with Viet Cong sympathies have been taken into villages and exhibited in chains as prisoners of war; then they have made loud "confessions" denouncing "their own country," which is represented as the U.S. It fools the villagers.

That may have been what happened here. But we don't know. And because we don't, it hurts. No matter how we reason it, we seem to have let a buddy down. Maybe that's why so many of us skipped chow.

FEB. 5, CAN THO

Getting around in the Mekong Delta, I depend mostly on light planes and helicopters—if I can get on one.

There are, of course, roads, and we have vehicles. But such travel vastly increases the chances of getting shot or ambushed by the Communist Viet Cong forces.

Planes and helicopters are safer but can't always be depended on for the return trip. A big fracas breaks out somewhere else and they round up all the aircraft for the trooplift. So you sit and wait. Then, when one suddenly shows up two or three days later, you'd better hustle or it will take off without you. These pilots don't like sitting on the ground too long. Not with Viet Cong mortars around.

A trip in a helicopter is an experience. They take off almost straight up, and they waste no time doing it. Here at Can Tho there's a big canal, with a lot of barge traffic on it, and it runs right past the end of our runway. Sometimes the Commies park their barges right at the end of our runway and take pot shots at us.

This is why we take off straight-up. The favorite altitude is 3000 feet. Small arms fire has trouble reaching that far up.

21

The part that bothers me is taking off and landing. They leave the doors open. For anyone who has a phobia about heights this is unnerving.

I usually manage to get the seat facing the door. True, I am strapped in, and everybody assures me there is no chance of my falling out. But still I close my eyes.

Gunners sit on each side of the ship, leaning out that open door. They're buckled in. They have rifles and they are looking for Viet Cong. They do this until we get to 3000 feet, then they close the doors. I open my eyes.

Then I start worrying about going down and opening those doors again.

Another little problem is what we call the unsecured airfield. An unsecured airfield is one usually well out in some rice field, away from camp, and not regularly guarded.

Before we land, they've got to be secured. This is done by sending out a company of troops to flush the nearby paddies of Viet Cong. The trouble with this is that the enemy might have planted mines on the runway while nobody was looking, and there is no time to check on details like that.

Naturally we have to let down very carefully. I've experienced mighty gentle landings in these parts. Needless to say, I don't get out to stretch my legs on an unsecured field. Longest I ever stayed on one was about three minutes.

There's a chopper-run every day from Saigon to Can Tho, but the only people who get on have high priorities. This doesn't seem to disturb those who get left, however. I haven't met anyone yet who minded being stranded in Saigon.

Tra Vinh, however, is another matter. That's where I got stranded last. I was winging my way to Sa Dec, when they called for our chopper to go pick up some wounded. So they dropped me at Tra Vinh. I stayed there about three hours, eating delicious C-rations, and sure enough they came back.

I climbed aboard, and—the main battery was dead! The pilot had enough power, however, to work his radio; so pretty soon another chopper sat down beside us, hooked up a battery charger, and we took off. With the doors open. I worried all the way to Sa Dec about riding in a helicopter with a weak battery, but we got there—as this dispatch suggests.

FEB. 7, CHAU LANG

"I don't like this setup," said Special Forces Capt. Jerry Thorne as he surveyed the scene. "It would he hard to defend."

Thorne, a Finn who fought against the Russians and the Germans, is senior adviser to a Vietnamese Special Forces Battalion. He commands a party of 11 Americans who give the strange-talking little Finn their total respect.

They come from all parts of the U.S. Warren Whitman of Oaks, Pa., is barely out of high school. Sgt. Charles Deal of Sidney, Ohio, is a grizzled Army veteran with three children. Sgt. Frederick Robinson of Newport, Tenn., and Specialist Asker Green of Thomasville, Ga., are Negroes. Sgt. Francis Hinson of Holly Hill, S.C., is the son of a Southern Baptist preacher.

But they're all in this together, and they know—as does their Captain—that they could be wiped out if one man lets another down. They don't intend that to happen. They are strapping figures, all specialists in their trade, and loving—despite their grousing—the danger they share. They want the Viet Cong to come after them.

These men are new to Viet Nam. They left San Francisco Jan. 9. They're making adjustments all men make if left in the jungle to defend themselves. But they're making it rapidly, and with professional aplomb.

They know that Chau Lang already has been attacked once, and will be again. On Nov. 27 the Viet Cong launched their most recent attempt to take this camp, assaulting it with heavy mortars. Three Americans were wounded and two Vietnamese killed. But our side killed 150 of them.

Still Chau Lang is untenable. Even a layman can see that. It was established during the Diem regime. It now has no Vietnamese commander, the old one having been locked up for obviously political reasons. The village was built around an old Buddhist pagoda, which serves as a command post. There is only one road out of the village and it can be cut. That, however, doesn't worry Captain Thorne.

"We don't intend to get out," says. "We will stay and fight. That pagoda, if we are ever driven into it, is where we'll stay as long as there is one man alive."

Thorne walked to the edge of camp and peered with binoculars at Nui Cam, the big mountain at his rear. This night he would send out patrols, as usual, but this time with a special reason.

"There are 600 of them up there," he said. "You'll not see them. They stay in their caves. We fire artillery and mortars up there every night just to let them know we know.

"There's a kill order out for us, you know. They intend to destroy us. As long as that order is out, I'm not leaving camp. They meant to do it two nights ago. Our artillery stopped them. Maybe they'll try it tonight."

Thorne expects soon to be told to move his camp. As a commander, he will be glad to go. He wants room to maneuver in, to take the offensive.

These men live well. They buy all their food in nearby Tri Ton—an incredibly dirty town with a noisy market—but their cook served with the French and does wonders with victuals.

But sooner or later, these Americans here know, an attack will come. They'll be ready. For the next six months this is their world. Everything else is remote and unreal.

FEB. 10, THAT SAN

All three men are pros—professional Army men in a deadly game of life and death here in the Mekong Delta.

The night I talked with them, over coffee, they were waiting for the hour to go out on ambush with the Vietnamese forces to which they are attached.

Capt. Michael Ilsemann, West Point Class of 1957, was restless—and for reasons far afield from the mere prospects of meeting the Communist Viet Cong enemy.

He was waiting for word from the Euclid-Glenville Hospital

in Cleveland where his wife was expecting their first baby.

(In time he got that word. Mrs. Karen Ilsemann, his 26-year-old wife, gave birth to an eight-pound, 12-ounce son on Jan. 21. After he received the news, Captain Ilsemann messaged back that he was "terribly proud" of his blue-eyed, brown-haired baby. The baby was named Michael, Jr.)

More relaxed was Maj. Marcus Moreman of Waverly, Ala., senior adviser to a Vietnamese training battalion. He was opening his mail from home.

"I've got this aunt back in Alabama," he said with a smile. "She writes me every other day and it reads like something out of 'Gone With the Wind.' She can put more words on a post card with that script of hers than most people can put in a book."

This year—as he has done every year—Major Moreman bought the usual season tickets to Auburn University's football games. He has worked his way, being a steady customer, up to the 50-yard line. If he missed a season, he explained, "I'd have to go back behind the goal posts and start over again."

Capt. Robert Anspaugh of Fountain, Colo., is a former enlisted man with long military service. His wife and children are back home where he hopes some day to retire.

Presently he's the senior adviser to another battalion. And things aren't going too well.

He frets. The Viet Cong are all about. Only a couple of nights ago they attacked. And then they withdrew, but we don't know how far.

How, I asked, do you recognize a Viet Cong on sight?

"If he's wearing black, you shoot without question," said Major Moreman.

"If he's armed, go get him," suggested Anspaugh.

"I don't figure I'm making a mistake if he carries a grenade," contributed Ilsemann.

"A good rule," Moreman said, "is this: if he run from you, shoot. If he comes toward you, hold your fire—two seconds."

These men were living every day in an area surrounded by the enemy.

A few weeks ago they sent a truck for water. It never came back. It hit a mine and two men were killed.

Snipers frequently fire at them, yet these men like their jobs. They want to help the Vietnamese. Their faith in these native soldiers, well away from Saigon, is strong.

One thing the Americans are proud of is their new mess hall. Also, they have new quarters—including showers with hot water. Their food is good. They have movies several nights a week.

But this night they were going on ambush. Outside the immediate surroundings every man is their foe.

As Major Moreman said wryly, this is the only training area in the world where the enemy furnishes the training aids.

FEB. 11, THAT SAN

In all the Mekong Delta, so it seemed, no one else was astir.

We had come back from patrol to the village where we were to pick up our jeep, and it wasn't there.

The village was dark, save for the lanterns the peasants leave to ward off evil spirits. In some of the huts people were still up, but their doors were barred.

Our jeep finally came, barreling down the road, lights out, with a grinning Captain Tu at the wheel. We drove him to his camp, and now Maj. Marcus Moreman of Waverly, Ala., took over and we were on our way. Alternately he gunned and slowed down. This way, he said, we might confuse anyone hoping to shoot us.

Ahead loomed a bridge, guarded by the Vietnamese Self Defense Corps (SDC), a paramilitary group of locals with little military training. The bridge's gates were locked and big coils of barbed wire had been rolled in front of them.

"Let's hope," Major Moreman said, "that those guys are what we think they are. Let's hope they're still the regular guards."

Sometimes, he explained, the Viet Cong will overrun an outpost or a bridge guarded by these local vigilantes, and shoot up the next vehicle to appear.

"How can we be sure who they are?" I asked nervously.

"When they shoot you," the Major said.

The SDC appear, rubbing their eyes and grumbling, and Capt. Michael Ilsemann of Cleveland dismounts.

"Come on, Dat," he says to his interpreter, "let's see if we can talk them into letting us pass."

After a palaver, the gate swings open, the barbed wire is rolled back, and we are on the bridge. The gate behind us is locked and they haven't yet opened the other one. Moreman cradles a carbine in his lap. Then the far gate is opened, and we go through safely.

"Know your enemy," the textbooks all say, but here that doesn't apply. Here the enemy can be the farmer in the field, the shopkeeper, perhaps the village teacher. He may even be the man with the gun guarding the bridge.

The danger is particularly acute in a training area like this. The recruits are simply drafted into the Vietnamese Army (usually referred to by Americans as Arvin, for RVN, or Republic of Viet Nam). There is a security check of sorts, but it is not always thorough.

Recently a whole company of recruits completed their training, then defected with their weapons. Now the practice is to keep SDC recruits in a special compound until their loyalties are established.

These SDC posts are a prime Viet Cong target. Dozens of them in this area have been overrun, destroyed or abandoned. Some have been rebuilt, only to be destroyed again. They are ridiculous little forts of the type once favored by the French. A good-sized puff of wind could knock one down. A single mortar shell can obliterate one.

For all their training, the SDC are often reluctant to fight. For one thing, they are poorly paid. For another, they have their families with them. They fear the night, and stubbornly refuse to send out patrols.

In one afternoon, we found two SDC posts that had been abandoned without notice, and their forces concentrated in another post that seemed safer. There, the post commander's teeth chattered as he recounted an attack the previous night by 200 Viet Cong. Why had he not used his radio? He wasn't sure. He once had one, but. . .

Often SDC posts are destroyed because traitors in their ranks open the gates and let the Viet Cong in. When that happens, women and children die, too.

At best, the posts are of doubtful value, some say more trouble than they're worth.

"They're just re-supply points for the Viet Cong," bitterly summed up one American officer.

FEB. 17, CAN THO

Every war develops its own distinctive lingo. World War II gave us "snafu" (situation normal, all fouled up) and every veteran from Korea knows that "skosh" means "little," or "not very much."

In Viet Nam, if a thing is good, or even passably good, it's "outstanding," with emphasis on the second syllable. If it's not, one is "sorry 'bout that." This is said crisply, the implication being that you are not in the least bit sorry about anything.

If a man gets in hot water, he's in "deep trouble." If he's in real deep trouble, he's "up to his ears in alligators."

Some of our "cooperative" messes in the field are certainly up to their ears in alligators.

In the Army, only established units can have field messes. There are not many of them here. Most of our military advisory groups in the field are temporary setups.

This means they must run cooperative messes. Under this setup, the men pool their allowances and feed themselves.

Soldiers are not always the best bookkeepers. In a field mess, with Uncle Sam picking up the tab, a GI can go back for seconds or thirds as often as he wishes—which is sometimes often indeed.

In many of the cooperative messes they carried on this admirable old military tradition, particularly on those occasions the mess sergeant dished out steaks. The rub was, he had to buy them from the Saigon commissary where prices are approximately those of stateside, and they cost close to $1 a pound.

The members of one cooperative mess were stunned recently when a roving auditor informed them they were $11,000 in debt. They're now on reduced, almost starvation, rations. Just try getting more than one egg for breakfast!

Tape recorders, usually bought in Hong Kong or Tokyo, are the current status symbol. They come in all shapes and sizes, from tiny portable ones, used to exchange thoughts with loved ones, to huge complicated jobs capable of reproducing symphonies. Some men have close to $1000 invested in such gadgetry.

Every compound has them, and each evening the cacaphony of sound is deafening. The men exchange tapes. Copying a tape calls for turning up the sound. Get a half-dozen copying sessions under way in a limited area and it's a problem. There have been occasions when the Viet Cong could drop a mortar-round into this compound and it wouldn't be heard.

Cameras run a poor second. A surprisingly large number of officers and men favor guitars, which apparently are of good quality and easily obtained.

Many Americans were disturbed by a recent Army order forbidding them to take their annual 30-day leave in the United States. Not many would have gone anyhow—because of the strain of a second parting—but it was good to know they could.

A few did arrange to meet their wives in Honolulu before the cut-off order. Now that's out.

Since a man must take his leave or lose it at the end of the year, most Americans go to Hong Kong. Invariably they return to Viet Nam flat broke.

Bangkok runs Hong Kong a close second. Most exclusive of all are the handful of superior types who've gone to Manila, Okinawa or Tokyo.

FEB. 18, SOC TRANG

The night before, I kept having this same dream.

There was this room with an old iron bedstead.

The second time it happened, Maj. Joe Levinson of Enterprise, Ala., who commands the 121st Army Aviation Company (Air Mobile, Light), shook me awake.

"You all right, Jim?" he asked, and I replied "Sure, sure" with more conviction than I felt. I was sweating bad.

I lay there, trying to figure out what it was that had scared me, and then I knew.

There were no doors and no windows.

. . .No way out.

        ❉   ❉   ❉

I don't know for sure that everybody who has ridden an H-21 Shawnee helicopter into combat in Viet Nam has felt the way I did that night, but I suspect a lot of them have. I am told that some don't sleep at all the night before a big mission, and the one Joe Levinson outlined for us after dinner was a big one.

There's something about riding one of those old birds into Viet Cong country that borders on the nonsensical. . .

If the odds weren't so great. . .

If what we're trying to do weren't so important. . .

        ❉   ❉   ❉

In this Shawne, you start to descend at 60 mph, and you coast in at 40, and you hover at 20 and come down at 10.

The ground beneath is friendly, but nothing else around is, and that's the reason you're there in the first place. There's a machine gunner in the rear door—wholly exposed—and one up front—equally exposed—and you feel for all the world like a sitting duck.

They shoot at us and we shoot back.

When they hit us, you know it. It sounds like a hatchet loose in an oil drum. The Shawnees out here have been stripped of their doors and insulation and noise-proofing to make them easier to fly.

Don't get me wrong. You don't get shot at every time. Not even, I'm told, often.

"The thing that really burns me," Lt. Fred Ross of Ashland, Ky., said one night, eyeing this particular reporter, "is when some reporter goes ahead and writes a story that scares my wife ach the road between Gia Rei and Kien Tien before refueling. He made it, and stopped, exhausted. Now he was ready for hat vital transfusion.

Lindsey helped goad Boneyard Special into a dust-churning hover. Prisoners slung nets beneath the fuselage. Into each net went three 100 gallon drums. Boneyard groaned, then heaved skyward. Behind her three more H-21s picked up their loads.

The M-113s waited in a wide circle. Rice fields on either side were in flames. But the Viet Cong—as they usually do—had disappeared; like chameleons, they had taken on the protective coloration of the countryside.

Lindsey led the way in. One by one, the Shawnees cut their nets, hovered, zoomed away. The drums would be left behind and destroyed.

All afternoon the chase continued. It was dusk when the Eagle party returned. With them, they brought two prisoners. Behind in the paddies they left 17 dead.

FEB. 29, THOI BINH

Bill Johnson's "neighbors" have marked him for assassination.

The Viet Cong, who are learning all they can about him, have just six months to accomplish it. That's how long he'll be here.

Johnson, of Stow, Ohio, is a major in the U.S. Army. He is also senior U.S. adviser to the 32nd Vietnamese Regiment, based in Thoi Binh and commanded by Major Le Van Tu. Major Tu's name also is on the Viet Cong assassination list. So is that of Sgt. Bob Kenniburgh of Kalispell, Mont., the other American here.

Bill Johnson knows this for a fact because the Viet Cong have publicly announced it. The government controls one-tenth of the Thoi Binh district, on the edge of a huge forest. The Communists hold the rest. Two and a half miles from here there's a rest camp where they take their troops after battle. In this "rest camp," the Viet Cong have a stage where they put on plays and give political instruction. It was there they identified Major Johnson, Sergeant Kenniburgh and Major Tu by name and discussed plans to kill them.

into thinking that we get shot at every time we go up."

But this much I know:

There is no finer bunch of fighting men in the world than those of the 121st Company, and none with whom I'd rather go into combat. Some of them are:

Dutch, with a disposition like sour apples, until you get to know him; and Ralph, who ought to be a United States Senator, he's that solid; and Bert, whose judicious calm reminds you of an old Federal judge back home; and little Ed, who simply grins and pours on the coals when they shoot at him.

Also Joe, who dreams of the day he saves enough to buy a cabin cruiser; and Norm, who pretends it's all a huge joke and punctures your fears and illusions; and Monte, who wheeled around his chopper about three days ago when they shot down Hank Farris and fought off the Viet Cong until his friends were safe; and Hank, who grinned and asked what kept him so long.

❖   ❖   ❖

"Heroism is routine out here," Joe Levinson, their boss, told his wife on a tape that night.

❖   ❖   ❖

They fly a ship that went out of production in 1956 and was outmoded before that. They have trouble getting parts, and the old girls ache in every joint, but their maintenance man, Capt. Bill Maling of Bangor, Me., is a wizard who manages to keep most of them flying.

Their mouths water when they reckon what, with all their experience, they could do to the Viet Cong with six—or even one—of the late-model choppers they read about in Aviation Week. They hate—and love—their ships. They volunteer for nothing but take any assignment that comes their way with the cheerful acceptance of proud men who know their trade. They often log 90 to 100 hours in the air in a single month.

❖   ❖   ❖

There is no way out when you take off.

In three days this week I made 29 touchdowns deep in the Delta country with these men.

I was with Jerry Cornell (Hatboro, Pa.) and Ed Porterfield

(Murfreesboro, Tenn.) when we took a hit; and with Monte Veal (Atlanta, Ga.) and Bob Broughton (Somerset, Mass.) with a load of Vietnamese Marines aboard when we had a fire and hustled back to Ca Mau where Pfc. Kelly Lookingbill (Twin Falls, Ida.) was on the ground with his extinguisher before we'd fully stopped.

I was with Bert Nye (Pollacksville, N.C.) and Gene Beyer (Abilene, Tex.) when our generator failed in a rice paddy deep in enemy land with a full-scale war going on all around us.

I flew with Ralph Hamner (Tuscaloosa, Ala.) and Fred Ross directly over Viet Cong lines to deliver a load of TNT and hand grenades to an embattled Vietnamese battalion.

* * *

There are some whose fears are greater than others.

"Sure, I was scared," one of them confessed last night after a couple of drinks, "I was scared as hell. Gets harder every time."

He looked around him at the bar.

"What's the matter with me?" he demanded. "Am I yellow?"

"Shut up," someone said. "We all are."

FEB. 26, BAC LIEU

Over the radio, high above the Mekong Delta in an H-21 Shawnee helicopter dubbed Boneyard Special, the air was filled with compulsive chatter.

As usual, the voice of "Bronco" from an accompanying chopper crackled with that special quality it took on when he was frustrated and angry.

"Lobo" in a sister whirlybird was the butt of Bronco's impatience and his voice was overlaid with strain. "Suzy's" voice was melancholy. "Eagle" spoke in staccato bursts. "Pickle" seemed at times almost to shrug. "Greyhound" barked genially.

Then, three miles away and 3000 feet straight down, "Eagle" found what the chopper band had been looking for—Viet Cong.

Bronco was no longer angry. Lobo's strained voice exulted. Suzy forgot to be melancholy and Greyhound's bark became a hunting cry.

The enemy had popped up almost in fron[t] party, and the chase was on.

It was a rare moment in a war in which t[hey] always to be somewhere else. The M-113 armored riers had forded the canals and were in the cle[ar] unlimbered. From Bac Lieu's "International Airpor[t] dry seas, 2 feet), we could see the smoke. Eagle's de[scription of] the chase was graphic, and Bronco's orders from the s[ky] overhead terse and to the point.

It is an operation peculiar to Viet Nam. No other known its like. It is a war plan conceived in deta[il] depending on chance for its execution. Helicopters are se[nt] loaded with friendly troops. They scour the countryside w[here] they have been told the enemy will be found. Sometimes t[hey] are found—more often not. When they're found, we land troop[s and] wait until they kill as many as they can, then come back an[d] pick them up.

We had started out at dawn. For Warrant Officer Billy Lindsey of Covington, Tenn., there was an added strain. This was his introduction to the Vietnamese war. He was learning the ropes with the 121st Army Aviation Company's "old man," Warrant Officer Barney Vanderkilk of Lafayette, Ind., in the cockpit with him. Barney looks like the movie version of a colonel and has 5000 hours in a chopper; senior officers defer to him and willingly go along as his co-pilot. And Barney is a patient, but demanding, task master.

We picked up a command post party at Gia Rei, where it had spent the night under siege. The three Americans, Capt. Howard Crowell of New Bedford, Mass., Lt. Gaylord Kershaw of San Francisco and Sgt. John Quaranta of Phoenix, Ariz., seemed relieved to be going back to comparative security.

Back in Bac Lieu, a group of black-jacketed Viet Cong prisoners in the process of rehabilitation through honest labor watched impassively. The air was still fresh, not yet spongy with humidity as it would become as the sun rose higher. An hour passed, and the armored personnel carriers would be running low on fuel. Their guns were blazing, and their commander hoped to

Bill was surprised how much they already knew about him; he has been here less than a month. He says they got it from the teenagers who go in and out of his post. Most of them are Viet Cong, though there's no way to prove it.

As a marked man, Major Johnson's plight is hardly different from that of hundreds of other Americans serving as battalion advisers in the field. Thoi Binh is a district of 35 square miles. Thoi Phuoc, its largest town, has 3000 people. Kai Quang, four miles away, has 2000.

The government controls the two towns, after a fashion, and a few supply routes. Outside the government's lines—which are marked by rolls of barbed wire—the enemy runs the schools and collects the taxes, which reportedly are five times higher than elsewhere.

Major Johnson's command post is the district police station in this town we hold. He and Bob Kenniburgh sleep on cots and air mattresses. For a while, they found it difficult to eat fish and rice three times a day; now they almost like it. But Johnson has lost 15 pounds, and Kenniburgh eight.

Johnson used to go into Thoi Phuoc's Chinese cafe in the morning for breakfast; occasionally they'd have hen eggs, but more often they were duck eggs. He no longer does that, now that he has been "sentenced to death." There are Viet Cong in Thoi Phuoc, too.

The 32nd Regiment has 240 soldiers here. Opposing them are at least four Viet Cong battalions of 300 men each, 200 men in their "rest camp" at all times, and four special squads, trained for sabotage and assassination.

Those aren't comfortable odds.

But Johnson takes all this philosophically. He recently got a radio and doesn't feel so cut off from the rest of the world. And he has a job to do. With the tools at hand, he's trying to do it.

MARCH 2, THOI PHUOC

Nguyen Huu Ngon was a brave man. I'd like to have known him.

The other day I paid my last respects to Nguyen Huu Ngon. I attended his Buddhist funeral. The Vietnamese grieve over their dead as we do.

Americans should know about Nguyen Huu Ngon, because many of us are likely to forget that the Vietnamese, too, can be brave and dedicated and willing to die for what they believe. Ngon was such a Vietnamese.

At 38 he was chief of police for the Thoi Binh District, which includes Thoi Phuoc where he lived with his wife and five children. His job paid him 1800 piastres ($18) a month. Americans in Can Tho and Soc Trang pay that much to their house boys.

Ngon took the police job, even though his parents live in enemy-controlled country on the little plot of land which has always belonged to the Ngon family.

They have since been taken hostage. They are still alive, but they have been abused. The Viet Cong used to slip photographs under Chief Ngon's door. They were not pretty pictures. Not when the old woman with the bloody face was his mother, and the old man tied to a tree was his father.

A few days ago Maj. Le Van Tu, commander of Viet Nam's 32nd regiment, launched an operation against the Viet Cong in his area. But Major Tu is from My Tho, elsewhere in the Delta, and the Thoi Binh area was pretty much unknown to him. He needed a civilian guide. Chief Ngon volunteered.

Major Tu's forces killed eight Viet Cong, which was more than he had hoped. He lost one man. That one man was Nguyen Huu Ngon. The Viet Cong, of course, were waiting for him. They were more than willing to swap eight corpses for one, when that one was Chief Ngon.

His body lay there almost 24 hours before a Vietnamese helicopter came in and brought it back to Thoi Phuoc. They stretched a canopy over the main street and the neighbors came and drank hot tea and expressed their sympathy to the widow. A Bonze came and invoked Buddha's blessings. Then they buried him.

The lot of a government man in Thoi Binh District is not an enviable one. Ngon was not its only brave man. Two weeks ago the Viet Cong kidnaped the village chief (mayor) of Kai Quang. He probably is dead by now, probably tortured to death.

Once a man throws in with the government here, he is marked. If his family is not already in Viet Cong hands, it soon will be. They cannot even go into the fields to work their crops. The Viet Cong will grab them if they do and carry them away for "re-education." Re-education is sometimes a brutal process.

Chief Ngon took hostages, too. That was part of his work. When he died, he had 11 suspects in the district jail. That was one reason the Viet Cong hated him so.

Even lowly soldiers, drawing $12 a month, are not spared. If they live here, their families also are taken hostage. Almost nightly the Viet Cong leave individually addressed envelopes outside their fence.

They contain printed pamphlets denouncing the government and the Americans—"you face death because the Americans have invaded our country." Most of the soldiers discount that. What does impress them is that the Viet Cong know their names and know they are here in Thoi Binh.

Nguyen Huu Ngon was a brave man. There are many brave men and women among the Vietnamese. It will help if we remember that.

MARCH 3, HOA TAY

They'd already pulled what was left of him out of what remained of his plane when we arrived.

Who was it, you asked, and when they told you and showed you his dog tags, there was that sickness inside, just like it had been before.

You knew from the moment you saw his plane go in that it had to be someone you knew—there aren't that many Air Force Commandos out here—and you told yourself all over again it is a mistake to get to know people in a war. It's much easier when they are simply names and faces, not friends.

He wasn't one of the bunch that played poker; he'd spent his off-duty hours at the pool table. His voice had been a booming one, and when he pocketed a ball, his yells filled the room. The poker players called to him for Pete's sake to shut up, and he'd sometimes yell back that anyone who played poker never had a mother or father.

They liked him, because he was the kind of man who bought more drinks than were bought for him, and Ralph Hamner, of Tuscaloosa, Ala., remembered later that he'd helped out the big Shawnee helicopters more than any one man in Viet Nam, which is a lot for an Army man to say about one who wears the Air Force blue.

He'd flown a T-28, an ancient single-engined trainer. The Air Commandos at Soc Trang had only four of them to start with—bravely painted up with tiger teeth in their noses—and they lost one the day before, so this cut their strength in half.

Just before he went in, the radio reported the T-28's were drawing heavy automatic-weapons fire. You figured it was a particularly big bomb or rocket, but then Lt. Col. John Roberts of New Orleans came on and said a T-Bird had crashed and exploded on impact.

We had to wait 30 minutes for Lt. Ronald Hines' M-113 armored personnel carriers to secure the area, which was heavily infested with Reds. Hines and his men shot a few snipers and chased out the rest, and with Lt. Col. Leon Byrd of Alexandria, Va., you'd taken a Huey over to the canal where he'd hit. Capt. Ronald Emery of New York City and Lt. Jim Herbener of Wilmette, Ill., had been piloting, and Kenneth Workman and Dave Donaldson were the gunners.

It was enemy country, all right. There were signs saying Americans should go home, or a lot worse, and a few booby traps you managed to avoid. The worst feature were the narrow log bridges over the canals. You got out in the middle of one and froze, and an old woman came running out and handed you a pole to balance yourself with—which was nice of her, considering she probably was a Viet Cong.

The name of the dead American pilot can not be disclosed from here because there is no certainty yet that his survivors have been notified.

They found his Vietnamese observer under the engine, which was wedged in a small irrigation ditch, and floated him to the surface. His name was Chau To Hoang, his ID card said, and he was 33. He wasn't badly messed up at all. He was just very dead.

In his wallet there were the usual family snapshots. Apparently he had had Thanksgiving dinner with the Americans because he had the menu with him when he died. It had been autographed, but the signatures were blurred now. There was a Thanksgiving Day message from Brig. Gen. Joe Stilwell, Jr., and a Thanksgiving Prayer.

"Dear God," it said, "we humbly bow ourselves before Thee . . ."

MARCH 4, HAI YEN

This is Father Hoa's domain.

We came in from the east, because a posted notice to U.S. airmen at Soc Trang says:

"Make all approaches to Father Hoa's at Hai Yen from east to west or west to east. Viet Cong activity has increased north and south of landing area."

Father Hoa is a man of God who says Mass twice a day. He is also a professional soldier. A colonel in the Chinese Nationalist Army, he escaped to North Viet Nam after Chiang Kai-shek was driven from the mainland. He fled to Central Viet Nam when the Communists took over in the north. He arrived in Hai Yen four years ago, when there were only three thatched-roof mudhuts at this southernmost outpost deep in the Ca Mau sector of the Mekong Delta.

After Mass each day, Father Hoa (pronounced Wah) sends out patrols. There are Viet Cong Communists all around him. Father Hoa loves them—as a priest. As a military commander, he can show them no mercy. His 1200 men, women and children live under their constant attack. His soldiers are among the best in Viet Nam.

Occasionally Father Hoa's men will take a Viet Cong prisoner. The Father takes personal charge. He tries hard to convert him, to show him the errors of his way and the fatal flaws of Communism. But what does he do if the conversion doesn't take?

"Naturally," Father Hoa says with a smile, "we shoot him."

You're not sure whether or not he's joking. Somehow, you suspect he's not.

Only about 20 per cent of Father Hoa's men are Catholic. The rest are Buddhist with a smattering of Cao Dai, an off-shoot religious sect suppressed by the late Diem regime. Father Hoa was a personal friend of the slain ex-President, who urged him to go to Hai Yen and establish a government post. He has, however, remained in good favor with the generals who now rule Viet Nam. And his Cao Dai soldiers give him their complete loyalty.

There are five Americans with Father Hoa. They are only slightly less ardent in their admiration of the man. Maj. John D. Bethea of Indianola, Miss., is Father's senior American adviser. Capt. Richard Brown of College Park, Ga., is his civil guard detachment advice-giver. Capt. Richard Rushton of Montgomery, Ala., and Lt. Quentin Garcia of Ridgewood, N.J., work under Major Bethea. Sgt. James Bard of Orange, Calif., is his intelligence sergeant-adviser and Pfc. Richard Graham of Boston runs the radio which is their contact with the outside world.

There are helicopter runs three times a week out of Ca Mau.

Father Hoa's fortified town is much larger now. There are at least 40 new houses. The Americans live in the second one the Father built. It also has a thatched roof.

Father Hoa strives to be impartial to the godly and military sides of his nature. The two newest, and biggest, structures in Hai Yen, built with U.S. funds, are a maternity hospital—it is still awaiting assignment of a doctor—and a fire direction control center. Father Hoa uses artillery to enforce the will of God.

MARCH 6, CAN THO

To understand anything at all about this strange little war, it helps to examine some of the organization problems.

For one thing, the command structure—ours and the Vietnamese—is grotesque. Like Topsy, it just growed.

On our part, we have MACV (Military Assistance Command, Viet Nam) headed by Gen. Paul Harkins. Harkins also is MACT (Military Assistance Command, Thailand).

Then we have MAAG (Military Advisory Assistance Group) headed by Maj. Gen. Charles Timmes. MAAG has been here since the early 1950's. It controls the advisory teams.

Then there is a Support Command, headed by Brig. Gen. Joe Stilwell, Jr. It controls the operating troops, such as the helicopter crews. Theoretically they are here to support the Vietnamese. In practice they are fighting a war.

On top of all this, we have a "country team" headed by Ambassador Henry Cabot Lodge, who is a major general in the Army Reserve.

Men in the field often work for all three commands. They must submit reports to all three. The paper work is horrendous. There are rumors that Lt. Gen. William C. Westmoreland will abolish MACV or MAAG when he succeeds Harkins. The troops devoutly hope this is true. Westmoreland is now Harkins' deputy.

The Vietnamese have four categories of troops in the field, some working for the Ministry of Defense, others for the Ministry of Interior.

At the lowest level there is the hamlet militia. They work in squads. They have, at most, one automatic weapon. If they are paid at all, it is by the people they protect. Usually it is in rice.

Next there is the Self Defense Corps. It is organized in platoons, and slightly better armed. Its men are paid $9 a month.

Third echelon is the Civil Guard. Roughly it compares with our National Guard. It is organized into companies. Its men draw $12 a month.

Finally there is the ARVIN (Army of the Republic of Viet Nam). It is organized into regiments, divisions and corps. Its men are much better paid. They have fairly modern weapons.

On top of this there is the Vietnamese JGS (Joint General Staff), comparable to our Joint Chiefs of Staff. And to add to the

41

confusion, the province chiefs (governors) are majors, and the district chiefs under them captains and first lieutenants. Each has his own troops. Each province chief has a U.S. Army major as his adviser.

Though the ARVIN is better paid and better armed, it is the Civil Guard that bears the brunt of the war. The average ARVIN battalion goes two weeks without making contact with the Viet Cong. An average Civil Guard company is fighting two days out of three.

There are reasons for this contrast. The Civil Guard is smaller (company-size units). It has less fire power; no artillery. Its men are sketchily trained. It does not have enough good officers, consequently it is not so well led.

But the big reason the Guard sees more action is psychological, and the Viet Cong are canny enough to exploit that. A Civil Guard company is a local unit. These boys grew up in the province where they're stationed. Everybody knows them.

If the Viet Cong can chew up a Civil Guard company, they effectively assert their rule over that area. A man joins the Civil Guard one week, and they bring his body home the next. That night the Viet Cong slip in and tell his widow, "We killed your man because he opposed us."

The message soon gets home. It makes no difference if an ARVIN battalion sweeps through the next week and kills 20 Communists while taking no losses—the villagers remember the local boys who died. The ARVIN soldiers are strangers.

It's a curious war, with all sorts of interlocking factors.

MARCH 9, CAN THO

The 15,500 U.S. military personnel in Viet Nam are divided into two camps—the "Hawks" and the "Doves."

The Hawks believe this war should be fought as a war. Their solution to South Viet Nam's problem is to kill the Viet Cong.

The Doves believe this war is different. They say it can be won only by winning the people. They believe in something called "civic action."

The Doves call the Hawks "military minds."

The Hawks call the Doves "Peace Corps types," or "State Department boys."

The dividing line is hard to define. Often, West Point classmates of the same rank are in opposite camps. It depends largely on their assignment and their experience.

Those who work most intimately with the Vietnamese are inclined to be Doves. Those with the least contact are more often Hawks.

They do have a common goal: to win the war. They agree on some points; for instance, that we must win the people. They agree we are not doing that now.

To win the people, the Hawks say, you eliminate the Viet Cong. The average Vietnamese gives his allegiance to whoever controls his hamlet. He isn't concerned with ideology; he wants security. Kill the Viet Cong, replace him, and you have the people. It's that simple.

The Doves say we first must convince the people, by our deeds, that ours is the right side—that democracy works, that we are genuinely interested in them. This is "civic action." That's why we send unarmed medical teams into enemy country to give cholera shots.

We sometimes get bogged down in details. Recently I sat in on a meeting in which AID and MAAG (military advisory) people argued all morning whether to pay members of teams sent out to teach democracy 30 or 45 cents a day. (AID held out for 30 cents.) The issue still has not been resolved, and the program is stalemated.

Because we send our best officers and men to Viet Nam, how to win this war is debated endlessly. Many young lieutenants and captains have written monographs on the subject. I have read a half-dozen.

One captain recently was duty officer from midnight until dawn. Barring an attack (which did not materialize), he had nothing to do but keep awake. He used this time to put his thoughts on paper. Later he sent the paper up through channels.

Among other things, he said we are going to be involved here

43

for at least 20 years, and the American people should be so informed. He (a Dove) also proposed gradually replacing our advisers with Nationalist Chinese. He pointed out we have trained their army well, but it has nothing to do so it can't remain good indefinitely. Send it to South Viet Nam, he said.

He suggested, too, that trading with the enemy be made a treasonable offense. Some foreign-owned companies, including American, operate with impunity in Viet Cong areas. They are widely believed to pay tribute.

One American officer says the enemy collects a tax on every gallon of aviation fuel. Two U.S. oil companies have filling stations in Viet Cong country. They have never been hit.

An article of faith with the Hawks is total mobilization. They say South Viet Nam is not mobilized, that it is still fighting a "part-time, peace-time, humanitarian war." They say you could raise another division from the boys walking the streets in Can Tho, or among the cab drivers in Saigon.

There are two Vietnamese divisions in the Mekong Delta; we need at least six, they contend.

The Doves say 100 divisions wouldn't do it.

The Hawks also want to deny the Viet Cong their privileged sanctuary in North Viet Nam. Bomb Hanoi, they say. Infiltrate North Viet Nam as the Commies have infiltrated the South.

Special Forces officers want to operate in the U-Minh forest, where no one but Viet Cong ever goes. Sure, we'd have casualties, they say. We might even lose whole units. But taking risks is part of our job. So far, they are forbidden to go.

Nonsense, the Doves say. We've tried infiltrating the North. And 85 per cent of our infiltrators were rounded up and shot within 24 hours. To make that idea practical, we must be able to command the similar loyalty from the South Viet Nam people. That, they insist, calls for more "civic action."

MARCH 10, TAM BANG

This is the story of a town—and its people—who refused to be written off. . .

Who decided, quite simply, because that is the way they be-lieve, that the Communists were not going to win this war, nor were they to be Communist victims.

For three years they have made that decision stick. It has not been easy. Some of them are dead. Others have been wounded. But they are happy, because the people of Tam Bang are their own masters. They control their own destinies and the land around them. They have done it themselves.

Four years ago the people in Saigon who decide such things judged that Tam Bang could not be defended. It was too far away. There were too many Viet Cong around it. Money and arms could be used better elsewhere. Tam Bang was not even eligible for U.S. "self help" funds.

So Tam Bang helped itself.

Writing off Tam Bang was not an easy decision. Those who so decided need not be condemned. They had to consider the "whole picture." The people of Tam Bang were concerned only with their town.

This is the pineapple capital of South Viet Nam. The late President Ngo Dinh Diem was fond of Tam Bang pineapples. He used to send for them, to be served in the palace.

Tam Bang had its Civil Guard and its Self-Defense Force. Its defenses were inadequate. Three years ago the town was over-run, its defenses destroyed. Many were killed. A handful of wounded, led by Lieutenant Cuoi, their commander, escaped.

They came back. Cuoi rebuilt Tam Bang's defenses to his own specifications. He persuaded two landowners to let him cut an open area through their valuable pineapple groves to provide a field of fire. When the Viet Cong attacked again, he was ready.

Americans love the underdog, and the Americans in Rac Gia, 50 miles away, heard about Tam Bang. They figured Lieutenant Cuoi was their kind of guy. In July they flew in here with plas-tic mines. They put on a demonstration. There were 4000 people —many of them Viet Cong—in the crowd. It was an impressive demonstration. Then they planted the mines around Tam Bang.

Since then the Viet Cong have retired. Rather, they are con-tent to fire across the canal.

45

The Americans have adopted Cuoi. When his wife was having a baby three months ago, they sent in a chopper to take her to Soc Trang. They brought her and the baby back.

When the Americans arrived, the people in the nearby town were hostile. Or afraid. They stayed in their houses. Now an American is a hero in Tam Bang. They teach democracy in the school.

Village Chief Chin Von Hoang sleeps in the Civil Guard fort every night. He has been sentenced to death by the Viet Cong for cooperating with the American invaders. He goes on every patrol.

This little fiefdom of 2.5 square miles is pro-government and pro-American. Outside its borders everything is Viet Cong. There are 65,000 people out there, and only 400 in Tam Bang, counting the babies. But they are happy. They are free.

The Viet Cong control the canal. Recently they said they had closed it for 10 days. Cuoi opened it on the sixth day. He says he "owed" that to the Americans in Saigon. They want his pineapples.

"Love us," Lieutenant Cuoi told us, and his wife smiled at his side. "Love us, because we are free."

MARCH 13, VINH LONG

Hovering 50 feet above them, you could read the terror in their eyes. They didn't want to die.

They were Viet Cong. And they were paddling, desperately, to get away. They hadn't counted on this. They hadn't counted on dying. No one ever does.

Lt. Lowell Helderbrand of Camden, Ark., swung his machine gun around and started to fire. Then he halted. An armed Huey, loaded with rockets, was whirling in. It could handle the job.

Funny, you thought. You'd sat in church with this red-headed Arkansas boy a few days ago. And now he was dealing in death.

In military parlance, they were a "target of opportunity." The call had come in late. You'd returned at 4:30 p.m. from an eight-hour chopper run of outposts along the Cambodian border and the Gulf of Siam to find everybody dashing to their parked aircraft.

You didn't wait to ask what was up. You ran to the nearest chopper and jumped aboard.

Maj. Joe Levinson of Enterprise, Ala., was at the controls. Capt. Joe Bruer of Springfield, Mo., and Daleville, Ala., was his co-pilot. Helderbrand and Crew Chief Odin Seaholm of Stratford, Conn., were the gunners. Capt. Dick Geis of Houston and Pvt. Ronnie Spradlin of Dallas were the medics aboard.

They were scrambling every ship flyable, not even waiting to change crews. Helderbrand, for instance, had just finished a seven-hour flight.

We didn't even know what the target was. We only knew it was a good one.

Quickly they briefed us. A dozen or more sampans, in military formation, had been spotted on a small canal, five miles away. They undoubtedly were Viet Cong.

Vietnamese troops were waiting along the runway, but their officers at first refused to go. Darkness was coming on. They needed an order. Someone produced a Vietnamese lieutenant colonel. He barked an order, and they came aboard.

They were scared. Shake, pal. You grinned at one. He was too scared to grin back.

A small plane over the canal reported it was drawing fire.

Our ship was off the ground, but its nose was still down. We had 16 people aboard.

"We're having difficulty getting airborne," Levinson announced. You prayed. Then the ship soared.

"We'll make one circle and hit," Lt. Col. John Roberts of New Orleans called over radio. Robbie has the room next to yours at Can Tho.

"Roger," Joe Levinson called back. "This is Bravo (his call sign) and we are ready."

Like quarterbacks, they plotted their strategy.

"See that stream up ahead?" someone called. "Put troops on either side."

Levinson exploded

47

"You've changed the damned plans again," he yelled. "First you said don't land on the other side."

"Our plans stand," Robbie called to Joe.

The radio was talking, and it was impossible to distinguish voices.

"I see people, with weapons."

"We can cut them off . . . Only thing is . . . well . . . No sweat!" That had to be Joe Levinson.

Now we were down. "Get them off, Crew Chief," Joe yelled. "They're off, sir!" Seaholm yelled back.

And they were. They were out in the mud, struggling forward. You lurched skyward, and that's when you saw the Viet Cong. In a score or more small boats, paddling like mad, looking frantically over their shoulders—not wanting to die.

The Huey came in, and they died.

MARCH 16, ABOARD AN AIR FORCE FIGHTER-BOMBER ABOVE THE MEKONG DELTA

It takes a while for a town to die.

Lang Chu Trung and Phong Lac have been sentenced to death. From the air, they look like any other hamlets on the highway leading out of Ca Mau. But these are Viet Cong hamlets. An American Air Force major, in a plane like ours, already has been hit. There are women and children in Lang Chu Trung and Phong Lac. There's also a company of Viet Cong Communist soldiers. And the hamlets are less than five miles from our big base at Ca Mau.

It had been a quiet Sunday morning, before the door burst open and Air Force Capt. Jim Tally of Los Angeles all but tumbled in.

"Want to go on a fast scramble?" he asked, and you quickly jumped into your flight suit.

Capt. John Rutledge of Fairland, Okla., helped you adjust your parachute.

"If you have to, go over the right side," he explained. "It's no sweat."

We were off at 9:05, and at 4500 feet by 9:10. The lead ship, with Tally at the controls, was 500 feet overhead. Capt. Jerry Shank of Winamac, Ind., was in No. 2, a ship called Rita Louise. Capt. Dean Hunter of Coronado, Calif., was in Sandy, No. 3. We were in No. 4, with Capt. Floyd Sweet of Laurinburg, N.C.

Each of the other three had a Vietnamese "student observer" in the rear seat. If *Stars and Stripes*, or any other government publication, writes the story, they'll say the raid was conducted by Vietnamese pilots with their American instructors aboard. That's a lot of stuff.

The Vietnamese are window dressing. They make it legal. If a plane is shot down, there'll be a Vietnamese body in the wreckage. That's all it amounts to.

Vietnamese troops surrounded the two hamlets and a spotter plane was in the air when we arrived. It already had dropped smoke grenades on Lang Chu Trung. The spotter briefed us over the air.

Viet Cong had arrived in sampans, and had been chased into the two towns. "Friendlies" (our troops) were 300 yards away, waiting to go in. The enemy troops had run into two large huts near the smoke bomb.

Having dropped his marker smoke, the spotter pulled away and circled to watch.

Tally went in and dropped a 100-pounder. A house caught fire. Shank followed, but didn't drop his. Hunter's 100-pounder— a white phosphorous bomb—landed on the roof of the hut where the enemy had sought refuge. A half dozen houses caught fire.

Soon Lang Chu Trung burned briskly. Now it was Phong Lac's turn.

Five minutes later it was on fire. But it takes time for a town to burn.

"Now we start our strafing pattern," Sweet said.

The first three ships went in, machine guns blazing. The Viet Cong fired back with .30-caliber machine guns. Miraculously, they didn't hit. At least, in no vital spot.

Our ship went into a nose dive. The altimeter spun crazily.

Sweet's machine guns blazed. You strained to see the ground, and he suddenly pulled out.

You blacked out. First it was all brown before your eyes, then total black. Whiteness returned, and you were sick in your stomach.

Sweet circled and dived again. This time you laid your head back and relaxed. It wasn't so bad. But the ship's soft underbelly was dangerously exposed for what seemed a long time and you almost wished you could black out again. They shot at you —you saw that—but they missed.

You swung down a third time, and fired your last rounds. That awful moment, when they have you in their sights, passed. Again they fired. But someone higher up likes us today.

The radio blared, and they were talking about the major who had been hit. Once they referred to him as "the body." It scared you. But he'd only been hit in the hand. You were grateful. He was a good guy.

Lang Chu Trung and Phong Lac were on fire. The smoke rose to 3000 feet, and still they burned. You circled, then went home.

It takes a while for a town to die.

On the ground, our troops move in, guns blazing.

MARCH 17, RAC GIA

They are government outposts, and they have been under siege for two weeks.

They are running low on just about everything.

We had taken off from Soc Trang, across the Delta, at dawn. Lt. Bernie Young of San Antonio, Tex., our intelligence officer, had briefed us. He warned of a Communist area with .50-caliber machine guns along our route. He didn't need to say we should be "extremely cautious."

We came to Rac Gia at 4000 feet.

The outposts we were to supply were Thu Ba and Dong Tai. If they sent up smoke signals, we would pull off and return. That meant the Viet Cong were still on the attack.

It wouldn't be safe for a chopper to land, even with Air Force fighter escort. But Capt. Tom Jones of Lawton, Okla., said he could almost promise there'd be no enemy.

It's good to fly with a guy like Capt. Ralph Hamner of Tuscaloosa, Ala. Ralph never turns back, but he demands everything due him. That way, he returns. Warrant Officer Wayne Lavender of Akron is his co-pilot. Corp. Louis Carrazzone of Millbrook, N.Y., is our crew chief and Pfc. Bill Cook of Maybrook, N.Y., our gunner.

Corp. Roy Leone of Manhattan Beach, Calif., is along for on-the-job training. Leone's father is superintendent of operations in Los Angeles' big new airport. Roy is proud of that.

The things an outpost under siege needs are varied. Ammunition, of course, has first priority. But there are batteries from Freeport, Ill., medicines from Nutley, N.J., and oil-coated nylon ponchos from Centerville, Tenn.

At Kien-An, the district headquarters, we drop magazines. Then we head for Thu Ba.

"You gunners briefed?" Ralph Hamner calls.

"Real good," they call back.

At 8:30 the fighters are overhead, and we head out. They travel in threes now. They lost a ship here two weeks ago. We had expected armed helicopters. This is better.

"They'll drop smoke," Jones says. "We may not be able to land."

We have Vietnamese aboard. Rac Gia's Chief of Police Lam Ngoc Thu and his assistant, Nguyen Van Phien. Also a paymaster, a battalion commander and his assistant.

We fly at 4000 feet, and it's cold.

We land at Thu Ba. Buddhist bonzes in saffron robes stroll from their pagodas to watch. There are barges in the canal. But Viet Cong guns along the Gia Song (river) are suppressed by Air Force fire.

Norm Laumeyer of Seattle, in the first plane, had gone in first. Warrant Officer Clarence Powell of Kansas City is his co-pilot. Pfc. Norman Hancock of Rockville, Md., is crew chief. Capt. Pete Kaley of New York City is riding with them.

The Viet Cong open fire. We shoot back. At one outpost

Chief Thu wants us to wait while he interrogates prisoners. Jones tells him we cannot leave the helicopters on the ground. Thu climbs aboard. Interrogation can wait.

It takes all day. But the outposts are resupplied.

MARCH 20, LONG KHANH

Our Town lives a life all its own.

It has but one reason for existence: war. Its men are concerned only with destroying the enemy and their own survival. They are confident they can accomplish both. If need be, on their own.

There are 12 Americans and as many Vietnamese in Our Town. They are Special Forces, each country's elite. With them are one to three companies of strikers (trainees). Their job is to teach these men guerrilla warfare. Their classrooms are the nearby Viet Cong-infested mangrove swamps.

Until Long Khanh was built 11 months ago, the Reds had ruled this part of the Delta. They still consider Our Town's people as interlopers. But their control is no longer complete, so the Viet Cong have vowed Our Town's destruction.

Long Khanh is not big, no more than a good-sized city block. Its city limits are an encircling mud wall. Beyond that are acres of barbed wire and deadly mines. At each corner, and in between, there are gun towers.

Our Town is provincial. Its citizens seldom see a paper, and Radio Saigon is so erratic they have all but given it up. The citizens war constantly with that nebulous entity known as "the rear." They are convinced that their friends back there deliberately hold up their mail, and conspire to send them things they do not need while denying them the things they want, on the thrice-weekly helicopter runs.

They have, for instance, an over-supply of flashlight batteries, yet they are down to three knives in their thatched-roof mess hall, and their single pinochle deck is tissue-paper thin.

Because of their isolation, Our Town's Americans cherish little things. When an Army plane swooped low last week and dropped a tow-sack of fresh-baked bread, it was Christmas all over again. Until then, they had made do with something baked out of rice flour.

They guarded their genuine American bread like gold, limiting each man to a single slice per meal and locking it up at night. Even after it went stale, they hoarded it, chewing it lovingly and pronouncing it unbelievably good.

Also because of their isolation, they improvise. Each corner tower has a searchlight used at night to sweep the minefields. But those searchlights are the headlamps of the town's single jeep and one truck, and powered by their batteries. They are used sparingly. At dawn they are returned to their vehicles.

Our Town has two mayors. The American is Capt. Edmond Fricke of Paris, Ill. The Vietnamese is Capt. Nguyen Hoa Tho of Pleiku. Fricke is backed up by Lt. Joe Maio of Chicago and Sgt. Marvin Pelfrey of Crossland, Tenn.

The Vietnamese and the Americans are close; they depend on each other to survive. Each knows a smattering of the other's language. Each has his own Vietnamese and American nickname. If the Americans are lucky enough to buy and slaughter a small cow, they share it with their friends. When the Vietnamese have chicken, they entertain.

The Americans in Our Town come from places like Jasper, Ala., Walled Lake, Mich., Whittier, Calif., Fries, Va., and East Gulf, W. Va. But because they are an elite force, and trained as a team, some of their families also form a close-knit community back in Fayetteville, N.C., outside Fort Bragg. Thus, a letter from Sgt. Billy Greenwood's wife like as not has news of Mrs. Pelfrey, and a picture of Sgt. Howard Mason's kids in Jasper, Ala., may include a couple of small fry from Captain Fricke's brood.

There are but two men in Our Town below the rank of sergeant—S4C. Martin J. McLaughlin III of St. Petersburg, Fla., (until recently of Glen Burnie, Md.), and S5C. George Johnson of Detroit. But Johnnie is up for the Soldier's Medal, the Army's highest peace-time award for bravery. He also is Our Town's only Negro. Sgt. Eugene Shepherd of Grand Rapids, Mich., the team medic, is up for the Silver Star.

Our Town is brave, important—and dirty. Showers are a luxury. You may take your clothes off during the day, but never at night. You carry your weapon with you.

Long Khanh holds its head high with a gamecock sort of perkiness, and it has a rakish pride. It is here to stay.

MARCH 26, LONG KHANH

According to a UPI dispatch in Stars and Stripes out of Tokyo, Sen. Edward V. Long (D., Mo.) says he has heard of the use of a portable "field-type lie detector" in Viet Nam and that it has proved successful.

Senator Long is quoted as saying this undoubtedly is "designed to instruct them (the Vietnamese) in the ways of free men."

I can assure Senator Long that his information is correct. Portable field-type lie detectors *are* being used in Viet Nam. They have proved successful. Because of this, a number of us, including the 12 American Special Forces men at Long Khanh, are grateful.

Without the detectors these men might not be alive.

The day I arrived in Long Khanh several weeks ago an Intelligence sergeant came in with one of those portable field-type lie detectors. He emphasized that it was not infallible. He said he was not qualified to evaluate his findings; he could only tell us what those findings were.

He came because Long Khanh's defenders were deeply concerned about the loyalty of 50 or more trainees from this area. Many of them had brothers and cousins fighting with the Viet Cong.

The Viet Cong have ruled this province uncontested for six years. The Viet Cong consider themselves legitimate rulers; we are the "rebels." Capt. Nguyen Hoa Tho estimates that, in the village outside our walls, 60 per cent of the people are Viet Cong, 30 per cent are neutralist and only 10 per cent are pro-Saigon and pro-American.

We did not tell the trainees that the little box was not fully reliable. We sought, instead, to endow it with almost magical qualities. We told them it could unfailingly assure us whether or not a man was telling the truth. They believed that. We wanted them to; our lives depended on it.

One of the men who took that test was Tran Van Co, 26. The polygraph indicated that Co was upset about something. He was not arrested. But he was put under surveillance. Captain Tho decided he could not be fully trusted.

This was, it turned out, a wise decision. Tran Van Co was the leader of a nine-man Viet Cong cell inside our ranks. Their mission was to spike our guns, neutralize our mines, kill all Americans in this camp.

Co was arrested in the act of spiking a gun. He was caught because we were watching him as a result of the lie-detector test.

Senator Long also was quoted as saying he hoped "that the punishment for failure to pass the test is not too severe, considering the unreliability of the instrument." I suspect Co's punishment will be severe. He probably will be shot. But not for failure to pass a lie detector test. Because he actually was a traitor.

And because this is war—a civil war—orderly procedures cannot always apply. The enemy is everywhere; he may even be the soldier beside you. Two days ago a patrol from this camp clashed with the Viet Cong three miles away. One enemy medical corpsman was killed. Later we learned he was the brother-in-law of a Vietnamese Civil Guardsman. We learned this when the Guardsman asked permission to bury him.

Tran Van Co has an older brother who is also a trainee here. He also took a lie detector test. Nothing has been turned up to incriminate him. He is still here, saddened of course by what has happened, but a loyal soldier of the Republic of Viet Nam.

MARCH 27, LONG KHANH

Except for their leader, Tran Van Co, they looked and acted like a bunch of frightened kids.

But each of the nine was a traitor, each of the Viet Cong—wearing the uniform of our side, manning our guns—and secretly plotting to turn those guns against us and open our gates to the Communist regiment waiting outside for the signal that, luckily, the traitors were never able to give.

The Airborne Rangers, flown in the day before, had surrounded the Long Khanh strikers (trainees) at morning formation. They probably knew then the game was over.

They had these things in common: They were young—17 and 18 years old. They lived with their families in the village a half mile away. They were all Catholic, products of Father To's school. And all were fanatic Viet Cong.

We'd known since the first of the month that the Viet Cong planned to attack Long Khanh. They wanted us to know. They had brought in 150 coffins and held memorial rites for that many suicidal victims to be sacrificed in breaching our mine fields.

Nor had we discounted the possibility of an inside job. The enemy used striker-agents when they overran Tan Fu last fall and took four American prisoners. The Long Khanh strikers were judged unreliable, if for no other reason than that their families were subject to blackmail.

The attack was to have come Wednesday at 11 p.m. At that moment the enemy's 1000-man Cuu Long Regiment would be waiting in the mangrove swamps less than a mile away. We learned this two hours before it was to have happened, at 9 p.m, when a sentry caught Tran Van Co red-handed in a bunker disabling a machine gun.

Taken before Capt. Nguyen Hoa Tho, he confessed. He was a Viet Cong agent. On his signal, the enemy would have attacked.

At dawn Co was flown to Can Tho. There, free from fear of reprisal by his co-conspirators, Co told all. He said there were three three-man Viet Cong cells in Long Khanh. (We have reason to suspect one is still operating; two men are under surveillance). He was in charge. He was also a cell leader. He dealt only with the two other cell chiefs.

Co is 26. He was born in Long Khanh; his parents, brother and sister still live there. He is married and the father of three children. He joined the Viet Cong in 1961; before that, he said, he, "lived in ignorance." Last year the Viet Cong ordered him to volunteer as a striker and take command of their apparatus inside the camp.

At first he merely distributed propaganda. Then a few months ago the Viet Cong told him to start ambushing our ambushes. It was easy to insure that one of his men went along with us. Once the ambush was set, he'd slip away and toss grenades, then sneak back undetected. Of late, Long Khanh's defenders had remarked on the regularity with which their ambushes had been foiled.

Early this month Co and a cell leader named Quang got a letter from the Viet Cong at Co's home in Long Khanh. They read and burned it. That letter set the hour for the attack on Long Khanh and gave each man his mission. It also contained 4000 piastres ($40).

Co's three-man squad was to spike our guns. Quang's was to wreck the power system. Nho, of Cau's squad, was to cut the wires that detonate our mines. One of Quang's men was to cut down the Americans as they ran from their huts.

Co was to signal the Cuu Long Regiment by blinking his flashlight. The Viet Cong, with our mines and guns spiked, would pour in. They would be stripped to the waist; Co and his men were told to wear only their shorts for identification. If the plan succeeded, they were promised another $260.

Co's fate is yet to be determined. He and his co-conspirators face court martial. A tip-off, however, is the written observation of his chief interrogator, Lt. Tran Khan Nghiem:

"Co agreed finally to speak the truth with the hope he might see his wife and children before he pays for his sin."

Meanwhile, the Cuu Long Regiment is still there.

MARCH 30, LONG KHANH

Sgt. Billy G. Greenwood of Olive Branch, Miss., was in tears.

"I guess I'm not much of a soldier," he said. "I get sick when someone's hurt."

57

One of our interpreters, a youth named Yi, had stepped on a mine. It had torn off his right leg above the ankle. We had called for a helicopter to take him to Saigon.

In the dispensary, Sgt. Eugene Shepherd of Grand Rapids and Jerome Burdick of Walled Lake, Mich., fought to keep him out of shock.

Interpreters invariably are shy, sensitive kids from Saigon, ill-suited for the brutalities of war.

Yi had been here less than a month, every hour of which he had lived in terror. When Capt. Ed Fricke of Paris, Ill., first talked with him, Yi's hands shook. They had never stopped shaking.

Yi had made the mistake of cutting through a mine field. Sgt. Benny Dunakoskie of Whittier, Calif., had yelled at him. It had been too late.

Sgt. Greenwood, a demolition expert, had placed those mines to defend this camp from the Communist Viet Cong. He had warned that some of our own probably would be hurt by them.

Now that it had happened, he blamed himself. Yi, he kept saying, was "such a damned nice kid."

The Americans share their food and quarters with their interpreters. Without meaning to, they have assumed the roles of father-away-from-home for these Vietnamese.

Yi's injury, the sight of the bloody stump that once was his leg, terrified the others. Capt. Fricke turned on them ruthlessly, barking orders, sending them back to their tasks.

Those who think of our Special Forces men as ruthless killers ought to spend some time at Long Khanh. Here I have met some of the truly good people I have known. Their relationship with the Vietnamese is a textbook story in how to get along with others.

Billy Greenwood, of course, is very much a soldier. When, the night before, word came that a Viet Cong platoon was within mortar range of Long Khanh, it was Greenwood who aimed and fired the rounds that dispersed them. He was with Capt. Fricke two months ago when Fricke was wounded. He helped get Fricke out.

Death and injury are never far away from the men at Long Khanh. The other day another Vietnamese stepped on a mine while on patrol. He also lost his leg. He was flown to Can Tho. His grieving wife went with him.

While this was going on, Lt. Joe Maio of Chicago and Specialist Martin McLaughlin of St. Petersburg, Fla., patroled a mile and a half in another direction. They killed a Viet Cong and brought his bullet-riddled sampan back to camp.

The day before that, our side killed a Viet Cong and took his body back to his widow in Donh Cuu. That same night the Viet Cong attacked a post five miles down the road and wounded 13 men. Our choppers took them out at dawn.

So it goes. Death and maiming injury occur daily. But somehow—Billy Greenwood can attest—you don't get used to it.

APRIL 3, LONG KHANH, AN OUTPOST UNDER SIEGE

"I've called you men together to give you the score," Capt. Ed Fricke of Paris, Ill., said the first day.

"The Viet Cong have announced they intend to overrun this camp. I say they won't. I'll let Sergeant Dillon fill in the details."

Jim Dillon of Fries, Va., took over.

"On March 1, at Ap Loi, the Viet Cong held a commanders' conference," he said. "They followed with a ceremony honoring the 150 men who'll die taking Long Khanh from us."

"Very dramatic," someone said from the back of the room.

"And very important to people who think the way they do," Dillon replied. "The next day they brought in 150 coffins. This is not rumor. It is confirmed." The men stared at each other.

Someone broke the spell. "So, let's send them 150 crosses."

Dillon went on. "As far as we know, they've set no date. We do know that they've brought in 1000 men. They're quartered in six or seven villages in from the coast. That's all I have, sir."

Fricke stood up.

"We're going to work night and day on our defenses," he said. "They are good. They're going to be better. Every day they wait, we get stronger. Remember this: They're not coming over those walls."

At dusk U.S. Air Force planes swooped low over the mangrove swamps and dropped their bombs. Behind their guns, Long Khanh's defenders cheered. After dark Dillon had more to report. Three hundred Viet Cong had assembled two miles away.

Long Khanh waited all night.

*   *   *

"These guys are Kamikazes," Fricke said when, bleary-eyed, his men met at the start of the second day. "This looks like a war of nerves, and a long one. They know we're ready now. They're not about to hit us while we're waiting for them. Not if they're smart. And they're smart. You guys are tense. You don't know it, but you are. Hell, I'm tense."

"Naaawww!"

Fricke grinned, and went on.

"You'll start snapping at each other. Little things will get you down. Don't let them. Anyone ever visit the Alamo? It's about this size. So let's think of this as the Alamo. Only we're coming out. Alive."

*   *   *

"I have a little more," Dillon said the third day. "Part of it's good. That air strike the other night got 61 Viet Cong. That'll hold them a while."

The night had been quiet, tense, watchful. No one had slept much. Someone had fired off a flare, and there had been sniping.

"I don't think they really want to take us on," Dillon continued. "But we hear that the people in their villages—there are about 4000 of them—have served an ultimatum: 'Either destroy Long Khanh or we're going inside government lines. We can't take this artillery and those air strikes any longer.'"

"In other words," Fricke said thoughtfully, "they may have no choice."

"Right, sir," Dillon said. "Lose their villagers and they starve. And we get the peninsula."

*   *   *

"The old man chewed me out good," Sgt. Benny Dunakoskie of Whittier, Calif., said on the fourth day. "I deserved it. Nothing like a good chewing to straighten a man out."

Benny had been getting edgy. He'd torn into a couple of his men unmercifully for things not their fault. To listen to him, nothing was going right. Everything was fouled up. Now, he said, he was happy again.

"You're still a dumb, mean Polack." Sgt. D. B. Brown of East Gulf, W.Va., grinned and slapped him on the back.

＊　＊　＊

"Sir," reported Sgt. Jerome Burdick of Walled Lake, Mich., one of the medics, after dark on the fifth day. "They're gone."

"Who's gone?"

"The civilian patients in the dispensary. An hour ago I gave them their medication. Now they're gone."

"This could be it," said Fricke. "If the Viet Cong got word to them this was the night, they'd leave, wouldn't they?"

"So," said Martin McLaughlin III of St. Petersburg, Fla., the team's youngest member, "we start playing that big game."

"What game's that, Mac?"

"The one called survival, sir."

＊　＊　＊

The patients straggled back the next morning. They had no explanation for their sudden exodus. We needed none.

"Don't get the idea we're alone," Fricke said after lunch. "We've got a lot of people and a lot of firepower back of us. The whole Corps knows we're in trouble. The Air Force is standing by. All we have to do is get one message out. But we've got to send that one message—and fast."

"It'll go out, sir," Brown and McLaughlin said with one voice.

APRIL 6, TAN THANH

The mother died five minutes after a helicopter-ambulance flew her out of Tan Thanh, and the little fellow on the bloodied stretcher beside her knew—with that sure instinct of a child—that she was gone.

61

He was about three, and tiny for that age, and he had been hurt. The back of his head was matted with dirt and dried blood, his nose was almost gone, and fresh blood seeped through bandages on his chest.

She had fretted about him up to the moment she died, crooning through blood-crusted lips, but now that familiar hand had gone limp and no sound came from her lips and he was frightened.

He slithered from the stretcher onto the chopper's throbbing deck. The first thing he saw was Carl Pickstone's leg and he fastened on to it like a little leech, digging his baby fingers into the firm flesh of the American soldier. The redhead from Perryopolis, Pa., put down his gun and reached down and cradled the little boy in the crook of his arm. The boy's sobs died out finally and Carl Pickstone held him that way until we landed at Cao Lanh 20 minutes later.

You glanced at Pickstone once and there were tears of rage and grief in the soldier's eyes.

How do you explain war to a three-year-old? What can you say to the little ones, in any language, when their own countrymen awaken them from their baby sleep with mortars and machine guns and grenades and tear the life from little bodies before they've had a chance to live it?

It's bad enough when men die and with women it's worse. But babies!

There are eight little ones in Tan Thanh we won't have to explain a thing to. They're dead. We flew out five tiny bodies in one chopper.

Capt. Jim Quinlan of Wichita Falls, Tex., turned aside while they dug three little bodies from the fort's wreckage.

"My God," he whispered, "I've got two little girls about the same age."

A dead baby's face isn't something you're apt to forget.

Tan Khanh was a civil guard fort along the Cai Cai Canal on the Plain of Reeds six miles from the Cambodian border and 30 miles from the nearest big settlement, Cao Lanh. Tan Thanh had 40 defenders who lived with their families inside the mud walls. It had one mortar and one machine gun.

The Viet Cong hit it at 3:40 a.m. Tan Thanh got out a single SOS and then the radio went dead.

At dawn Lt. Dave Wentworth of Orange, Calif., flew over the fort in a small plane and reported he saw no sign of life.

Slowly the Mekong Delta awakened and slowly it learned what had happened while it slept. They heard about Tan Thanh in Sa Dec at dawn and in Cantho at nine. They got word in Soc Trang at 10. Six helicopters on other missions were diverted to Cao Lanh and four on the ground were scrambled.

Meanwhile, Dave Wentworth had spotted an armada of 80 sampans moving away from Tan Thanh on the Cai Cai Canal. But they had already reached their privileged sanctuary, a safety zone extending one mile into Viet Nam from Cambodia. There we are not allowed to shoot at them.

Wentworth raged. "They're not soldiers," he said over the radio. "They're murderers."

Inside the fort the stench of human blood and cordite was overpowering. But its men had fought and died like soldiers. Quinlan flew in the first party—Lt. Cols. John Roberts of New Orleans, Leon Byrd and Charles Crain of Alexandria, Va., and Majors George Butler of Oxford, Miss., and Walter Zarnowski of Wilkes-Barre, Pa. They pushed through the burning fort to find Tan Thanh's defenders still at their posts, frozen grotesquely in postures of sudden, violent death.

From the fields, as more choppers came now, the wounded and other survivors waved weakly or fired weapons they took with them when they fled. From a village across the canal others brought back wounded and children. In all there were eight children and seven women dead.

The choppers were coming in relays. And down the Cai Cai Canal, only six miles away, the Viet Cong beached their sampans and took their ease in a friendly village. Dave Wentworth circled them, daring them to fire so that he could fire back. But they were too smart for that.

Tan Thanh was dead. As the day ended, a flight of 16 sleek Hueys zeroed in from Cao Lanh and the villagers stumbled aboard. Some carried a few possessions in their hands and on their backs; others took nothing out. In Cantho a decision had been made: Tan Thanh would be destroyed. Pets and livestock stayed behind to be brought out later by boat. One little boy clung to his dog to the very last.

In Cao Lanh they were put on buses, simple village folk who never before had been this far away from their homes. Their faces were blank. Only their eyes mirrored their terror and disbelief.

Dusk had come to the Delta when, with Dave Wentworth, we circled Tan Thanh for the last time. Down there, 1000 feet below, it burned briskly. A grenade exploded.

Now we flew toward the border.

The last of the Viet Cong — murderers, not soldiers — had crossed back into Cambodia.

APRIL 7, MEKONG DELTA

Lt. Fred Ross swore: "Damn it, they're sending us in again at the same place. And that ain't good."

Nothing about it was good. On an earlier flight with Capt. Jerry Cornell of Hatboro, Pa., and Lt. Ed Porterfield of Murfreesboro, Tenn., we had taken a hit just above the rear engine. We'd landed at Ca Mau, and Crew Chief Elmer Kennedy of Bradshaw, W. Va., pointed out the clean hole the 30 caliber slug had left. A few feet to the left and we might not have been so lucky.

Ross, of Ashland, Ky., and Lt. Henry Farris of Bedford, Va., were making their seventh run of the day, hauling in Vietnamese Army troops for an assault on the enemy's U-Minh battalion between Tan Fu and Thoi Binh. Three days earlier, Farris' Shawnee had been shot down in another sector of the Delta where it had gone to pick up a wounded American Special Forces captain. And now he was flying again.

We'd picked up our troops, run after run, in a dry rice paddy where they'd rested after a bone-wearying, all-night march from somewhere in the north. They waited patiently in single file as the choppers set down among them. The whirling rotors threw dust and dried rice straw in their faces, and they grimaced and some covered their mouths and noses with their hands.

They clamored aboard with their weapons and heavy mortars, and those who hesitated or had trouble making it were yanked into the helicopter by Crew Chief David Sands of Gassoway, W. Va. There was no time to be wasted on formalities.

There was something pathetic and almost childlike about these teenie-weenies, as Americans affectionately call them. They grinned, uncertain where to sit, awed by their surroundings. Some carried smoked cooking pots on the backs. Every man had his cheap wrist watch — his status symbol — looped through a buttonhole in his jacket. Some of the more affluent had brought their transistors.

It's a rough life these little fellows lead. Danger is their bunkmate, and death is always just around the corner. They live on what they can carry with them, and sleep on whatever ground they can control. But they are invariably uncomplaining, and find delight in little things. And they are brave. Even the mortally wounded bite their tongues and few Americans remember ever hearing one cry out in pain.

As the ship rises, one Vietnamese inches toward the open doorway. He looks down and trembles in an ecstasy of fear and excitement. Chattering his triumph, he comes back to tell his less venturesome mates what he has seen. It must have been a graphic account.

Now we're going in, and they fall silent. You wonder if they know what's really down there, and hope they don't. The battle was joined hours ago, and they'll be set down in the midst of it.

They see the smoke and the burning hamlets, and their faces cloud over. No one speaks now. Their eyes are big with wonder. One speaks softly to himself.

We put down behind a line of trees, within sight of the battle, and they're on their feet, moving toward the rear door. David Sands pushes at them, urging speed. In less than a minute they're off and no longer our concern.

They're on their own.

But maybe that's the way it should be. This is their country, and they're the ones who must save it.

FEB. 9, SOC TRANG

"Let's face it, sir," the captain spoke for the group, "that old girl just can't keep up with the flock."

The mission was tough enough as the Major had outlined it, but his disclosure that helicopter zero zero two nine would be the fourth ship in formation was too much.

They looked at each other and grinned wryly, and then Capt. Bert Nye, the group's exec, had taken the bull by the horns and voiced their concern.

They call her "Sweet Nothings" and, in their fashion, they like her. But they don't trust her. They know her too well.

"One time or another," Nye said later on, "she has almost got every one of us killed."

Maj. Joe Levinson waited, knowing the protest would come, ready to give way and never intending to use her in the first place. This sort of thing, he'd learned a long time ago, helps relieve tensions.

"Okay, out she goes," he said.

But the Major was exacting a price for his concession: "You've got the ships you say you want, so let's fly a tight formation. Last time, you got a little ragged."

There's a strange bond between these chopper men and their aircraft. They sometimes even think of them as people. Each Shawnee, they tell you, has a personality of its own. Geisha Girl often behaves like one, and Sweet Nothings amounts to just that.

The ships they fly are old. The last ones came off the assembly line eight years ago and none has been turned out since. They require constant nursing. Big, bald Bill Maling of Bangor, Me., is head nurse. He's the maintenance officer, and for Maling and his crews, 18-hour days are often the rule.

They swear some helicopters become hypochondriacs and if they aren't sick, they eventually get that way. Such a chopper is called a "hangar queen." The 121st has its share of those.

We were throwing 10 Shawnees against the Viet Cong—though we'd hoped to have as many as 15—with four more on standby for medical evacuations and administrative runs. That meant six were in the hangar, nursing their hangovers and doctoring their ills, as old ladies will.

Before we'd get through, 5 of the 10 would fall out, though only one would have to be left behind, and it would limp back the next day. I was on three of the five casualties.

Some call Sweet Nothings a hangar queen, but that's not fair. She has her defenders. It wasn't exactly Sweet Nothings' fault, they'll tell you, that she was disabled when a Viet Cong round hit her rear rotor a few days ago, though it might not have happened, either, if she'd had more power and could have moved out faster.

"I've flown her and she's all right," Capt. Ralph Hamner of Tuscaloosa, Ala., says. "It's just that she can't keep up and she can't maintain altitude. We'll start falling back and dropping down and about the only time I see the others is when we take off and land."

And it was Sweet Nothings they had to call on later when they needed emergency ammunition run to the embattled Arvin above Tan Fu. She made it, though she couldn't carry the load they'd have liked, and it took an agonizingly long time for her to get airborne again in country where it's best to get airborne quickly.

After we got back, I found myself eyeing her with something bordering on tenderness.

"I guess," I suggested tentatively, "old Sweet Nothings redeemed herself today."

Lt. Art Bein (Miami, Fla.) eyed her sorrowfully.

"This," he said flatly, "is a mighty sick girl."

APRIL 13, TAN HIEP

It's 11:23 a.m. and one of our helicopters is down.

Capt. John Britton of Soldier, Ia., and Warrant Officer Clem

67

Womack of Camden, Ark., were at 250 feet. We were below them at less than 100.

Our nose wheel had been skimming the grass all day.

Britton's sleek Huey took a direct hit in its engine from a .30-caliber machine gun. His ship shook, quivered and died.

Womack, at the controls, took it down. The landing was rough but everybody scrambled out.

Now they were down in the hostile paddies, and the Communist Viet Cong were shooting at them. The immediate problem was to get our men out. We'd worry about that $250,000 helicopter later.

It had been a rough run. It was our fourth into the landing zone, where we had deposited South Vietnamese troops to tangle with a hard-core, professional Viet Cong battalion.

The first three runs had been uneventful. But this time everything seemed to happen.

Hoy Miller, a Georgia boy in a big Shawnee chopper, took three hits and barely made it back here.

First Lt. Robert Cox of Memphis, Tenn., and Warrant Officer Ronald Garrison, Bethesda, Md., in the ship behind us, wrapped the top of a palm tree around their landing gear and spattered a low-flying paddy gull across their windshield.

Lt. Monte Veal of Atlanta also tangled with a tree.

Then Britton and Womack went down, and the flag went up.

The Viet Cong had automatic weapons. Britton had a carbine; Womack, a rifle; Cpt. Louis Del Rio of Carlisle, Pa., and Pfc. William Sobieski of Beacon Falls, Conn., the crew chief, had machine guns.

Del Rio and Sobieski are only 18. It was their first time under hostile fire, but you'd have to be told that. They exchanged round for round with the Viet Cong and enjoyed it.

The enemy was dug in, 50 yards away, along the banks of a canal. Our fellows were out in the open.

It had begun as a routine operation.

We had flown to Tan Hiep at dawn. This is what is known as an "unsecured airfield." Troops had been sent in to chase out the Viet Cong and search for mines just before we landed.

Maj. Joseph Levinson of Enterprise, Ala., and Capt. Joseph Laseau of Killeen, Tex., were my pilots. Specialist Pepe Mathey of Clinton, N.Y., was the crew chief, and Pfc. Ottavio Cruz of Realitos, Tex., the gunner.

"We got reports last night," Maj. Pat Delavan of Hawthorne, Nev., said at the 7 a.m. briefing, "that a hard-core battalion moved into this area last week. If that's so, they'll have anti-aircraft weapons."

He indicated the area around the town of Nha Binh. The landing zone was at My Hanh Dong, across a canal. The Viet Cong were five miles out of Tan Hiep.

Ground crews fueled the choppers, testing every barrel. If the fuel turned pink or blue—and often it did—they dumped the lot. It took time. A lot of fuel was dumped.

On an average strike, you fly between 2500 and 4000 feet. This time we hardly got off the ground. Our top en route was 12 feet; often we were down to two.

For one thing, the Viet Cong had anti-aircraft. For another, our target was only five miles away. To go up, and then come down, would alert the enemy. So we zoomed in low.

It took your breath. Villages whipped past. You could see the people up close. Water buffalo stampeded. Chickens squawked.

Often you passed trees beneath their branches. If you couldn't get past, you hedge-hopped. Or, like Cox, you decapitated them.

Up high, you seem to crawl. Down here, the speed made you dizzy.

Maj. Michael Baldasare of Dayton, Ohio, whirled around and landed his Huey beside the downed craft. Britton and Womack were on the ground, still firing. They jumped in.

"Jesus!" gasped Womack.

"Take off" yelled Britton.

Maj. Charles Kelly of Sylvania, Ga., followed. Then Sobieski and Del Rio hopped in with their machine guns.

"Everybody out of the paddy?" Kelly asked.

"Everybody," they said. "Take off!"

Back in Tan Hiep, Capt. William Monahan of Burlingame, Calif., and a battalion of South Vietnamese Marines were waiting. We flew them in. They fanned out to protect the downed ship.

The Viet Cong were using mortars. Monahan mortared them back.

There was $250,000 worth of helicopter down there, and both sides wanted it. All afternoon we fought for it.

Dusk came, and the Viet Cong withdrew—taking their dead and wounded with them.

We had won. The chopper was still ours.

Over coffee, Britton grinned feebly.

"No more," he said. "Ten days and I go home."

APRIL 14, THE MEKONG DELTA

It's only six miles from Cai Nuoc to Nam Tam, but it's the longest six in the world.

They're outposts—friendlies, we call them—and everything outside that fence is hostile.

The people have made their choice but the bitterness runs deep. They live behind their barbed wire, venturing into their fields only under the protection of the government's armed troops, and wait for the weekly helicopter run from Ca Mau for the things they need from the outside.

Almost nightly they're under attack from the Communist Viet Cong, just as the people are at nearby Dom Doi, and they fire back in a war that must seem to them to have no end.

We are on a re-supply mission, intended primarily to shift a couple of heavy mortars and their crewmen from one post to another and bring in fresh mortar rounds. But we don't fly south of Ca Mau in a chopper without a fighter escort.

We pick up our escort on schedule and start out. They're vintage F-28s, of an age long forgotten by most airmen.

We fly high and come down fast, giving those outside the fence no opportunity to shoot. We take care, too, never to leave the same way we came in, because they'll be waiting.

School lets out when our rotors stir the dust at Cai Nuoc. The kids love it. They particularly like having it blow in their faces.

They squeal and squirm and some roll in the grass, like street urchins under a fire hydrant on a hot summer afternoon.

The elders stroll from their huts, feigning disinterest but missing nothing—for helicopter day is the big event of the week.

It's war all right, because Cai Nuoc's mortars are firing. Cai Nuoc is a "strategic hamlet" protected by its own Self Defense Force, and Nam Tam is a river base for the South Vietnamese navy.

Many of the navy crewmen manning the junks are said to be juvenile delinquents from the streets of Saigon. But they've built their own Catholic Church at Nam Tam, and the streets of the town are full of shops and traders.

Back and forth we shuttle, each time picking a new flight pattern even though our fighters are with us and come in almost at roof level. That does the job. The Viet Cong are afraid of the fighter planes and take cover when they're here.

"I've never had any trouble when we have an escort," said Capt. Ralph Hamner of Tuscaloosa, Ala. "And I've never been able to get in without one."

* * *

Inevitably there are villagers and farmers who want to be taken away to greater safety. Some have waited as long as three weeks, camping out with their families, their bales and packages and their cooking pots. They'll be there the next time.

We can't take them, of course, and they should know that by now. Sometimes they climb aboard and have to be shoved off. They stare unblinkingly, without comprehension. Occasionally they'll cry and plead their case.

Sgt. Juan Marerro Ortiz of Puerto Rico, their friend and adviser, moves among them, helping them shift their supplies and listening to their woes.

Capt. Pat O'Meara of Council Bluffs, Iowa, makes a final check of his outpost and finds it good. We've made 18 trips over the six miles of hostile country that separate these two friendly outposts, and the day is shot.

Now it's time to go. Now they're on their own. Unless, of course, they're overrun and we have to come back to pick up the dead and wounded as we did at Dom Doi the other day.

The rotors start, and still the natives are around—begging, pleading, that they be taken along. Then, as our ship lifts, they squat down to wait some more.

APRIL 15, NAM CAN

The silence was eerie. South Vietnamese army engineers had just finished mining a Communist Viet Cong canal block. Our boats had pulled back, and now we were waiting for it to blow.

It came—with a rush and a roar. Black canal water pelted skyward, and hundreds of uprooted logs tumbled about like match sticks. Some fell in the water nearby. Others dropped into the paddies and disappeared.

A canal block is an evil thing. It is a body blow to the people. The canals are the Mekong Delta's highways. When one is blocked thousands of men and women are denied free movement between their homes and markets.

A canal block can also be a reminder of the enemy's sovereignty over the Delta's rich rice bowl. Failure to remove it is testimony to the government's impotence.

This one was two months old. It should have come out weeks ago.

An intricate maze of logs and wire interspersed with mines, it could be transited only by cutting a barge's engines and poling it through. Viet Cong assessors waited to levy their "taxes." They checked passenger lists and arrested those without passes.

Rounding the bend, barges from Ca Mau, ferries from Cai Nuoc and sampans from the villages instinctively slowed down and pulled to the shore. The people waited now as impassively for the block to be destroyed as they had waited, on other occasions, to be taxed.

After it was gone, they edged through, their faces betraying nothing. There'd soon be another. This is Viet Cong country.

It had been an impressive show of force, and a costly one.

Before we could venture into the canals, Vietnamese army troops had set out before dawn to drive the Viet Cong from the banks. But the enemy had mined the levees, and two men had been hurt.

We sailed from Ca Mau three days ago with the Vietnamese junk-boat navy for Nam Can. This remote Delta outpost was under attack. Helicopters could supply only part of its needs.

We sailed down the Song Bay Hop aboard a converted ICM, a landing craft dubbed the Monitor, with Vietnamese Navy Lt. Hao and Lt. Comdr. Frank Rhodes of Norfolk, Va., his American adviser.

We were, as usual, 30 minutes late getting under way.

"If these were Americans," Rhodes had said, "I'd have busted some heads. But they've got to learn to do things themselves."

Occasionally a red-and-yellow government flag flew from a farmhouse, a sign its people were friendly and working in the fields. Other farms were deserted.

Little goes down the Song Bay Hop without knowledge of the Viet Cong.

Our people recently broke one of their many codes. If a barge-master tipped his hat at a check point, his load was "clean." If he flew the flag, it meant he had government troops on board.

The Viet Cong has ambushed the Vietnamese navy in the past, with bloody results, but now they let us pass.

We were fired on once. Shortly before noon the tide went out and we were stranded on a mud bank within sight of a friendly fort at Cha La. Suddenly a mortar round hit with a muffled whoomp. We ducked for cover.

They had us, but—unaccountably—they failed to follow up.

The Viet Cong, apparently, can be stupid, too.

We were grateful for that.

APRIL 16, BAC LIEU

"John Hitti," a fellow officer says, "is not the least bit tough. Just brave."

He still looks like the Colorado schoolteacher he used to be.

Born in Durango, graduated from Colorado State College in 1961, he has been out here only two months. His commanding officer, Lt. Col. Jack Cushman of Bethesda, Md., has described these later arrivals as a "new kind of American officer . . . one trained to build, rather than destroy."

Shortly after noon on a Sunday of last month, Lieutenant Hitti was in the field near Gia Ria. It was his first Eagle flight on his own. An Eagle is an operation peculiar to Viet Nam. Employing helicopters, Vietnamese troops scour the countryside, looking for the Viet Cong. If they find them, they land, wipe them out, and climb back aboard.

This one was a success. Hitti's troops trapped the enemy in a hamlet. For a couple of hours they fought with hand grenades, eyeball to eyeball. They killed 12, and took only four casualties. The Viet Cong broke off and fled toward the mangrove swamps. Hitti called for helicopters to take up the chase.

Then disaster struck. One of the four armed Huey helicopters covering the operation was downed by enemy fire. It landed on its tail section, broke in two pieces, bounced along the ground and burst into flames.

Hitti was a quarter of a mile away. He raced that distance, over sun-baked rice paddies and over dikes. Other Americans nearer the scene had reached the wreckage. But exploding ammunition had driven them back.

Hitti did not hesitate. He had seen Lt. Kenneth Shannon of Lynchburg, Va., the co-pilot, rise from his seat and plunge forward. Ignoring exploding ammunition, Hitti unbuckled Shannon's seat belt and attempted to pull him from the flames.

A bigger explosion knocked Hitti down. He got up and went back. Miraculously, somehow, he got Shannon out. With his bare hands he beat out the flames.

(Shannon died later in another helicopter, en route to a military hospital in Saigon.)

Maj. Gen. Charles J. Timmes, head of the Military Assistance Advisory Group to Viet Nam, flew from Saigon to Bac Lieu the next day to present Lieutenant Hitti the Bronze Star with V (for valor). This is the highest award General Timmes can award in the field without referring the matter to Washington. That, of course, takes time. He wanted to honor Hitti on the spot. The award could be upgraded later.

Hitti was captain of the high-school football team in Durango, After graduating from Colorado State College, he taught a class of gifted sixth-grade students for six months in Colorado Springs before joining the Army. A Reserve, his application for a Regular commission recently was approved.

The citation which accompanied the award to Hitti concludes:

"By [his] act of heroism on the field of battle, Lieutenant Hitti demonstrated great courage in the presence of Allied soldiers and has brought great credit upon himself, the Military Assistance Advisory Group, and the United States Army."

APRIL 20, THE MEKONG DELTA

Wilbert Wong is 19 and he's three months out of New York City which—until he joined the Army—was the only world he had known.

Wong is a medic. He's 1500 feet above the Mekong Delta, 10,-000 miles from home, in an unarmed Huey helicopter. The call came that a man had been hurt. He'd stepped on a mine. He couldn't last until dawn.

It's pitch dark. And someone's shooting from down there. They're shooting at the Huey with a BAR and a machine gun. Wong has a dinky little carbine.

So what does he do?

He shoots back. So does his crew chief, Pfc. Armon Bender of Augusta, Mont. It seems almost absurd. The BAR's growl is that of a bulldog; the carbine's yip is that of a Pekinese.

But Wong shoots back because—medic or no—that's all a man can do. He's got a wounded man aboard, and his job is to get him out.

Wong and Bender are members of the 57th Medical Detachment, Helicopter Ambulance.

Their boss is Maj. Charles Kelly, a soft-spoken, hard-driving

75

man from Sylvania, Ga. Kelly was a World War II medical corpsman. Now he's a medical service officer. He's also a helicopter pilot.

And he's a man with a mission.

Kelly has been here three months, but already all over the Delta they talk about him. They call him "Crazy Kelly." Sometimes it's "Mad Man Kelly."

They admire him.

But they want no part of him.

Mad Man Kelly flies his helicopter at night. No one else does. Not in Viet Nam. Once a man goes down, they say, the Viet Cong have him.

In daylight, he has a chance.

At night, he's a goner.

But Kelly actually prefers to fly at night.

So he takes Wong and Bender and Lt. Jerry Shaw, Eureka, Mont., and goes off into the night. If it's not Shaw, it's Lt. Ernest Sylvester of Gulfport, Miss., or Brian Conway of Summit, N.J., or Armond Simmons of Meridian, Miss.

South of Ca Mau the other night, a ground-force captain, adviser to a Vietnamese battalion, tuned in his radio and heard Kelly up there. The Mad Major was on his way to visit Father Hao at Hai Yen. One of Father Hao's boys had been hurt. It was past midnight.

The captain also had a casualty. He asked if Kelly would stop by on his way back and pick him up. An American adviser with a Vietnamese casualty on his hands is on trial. Every eye is on him. Kelly said he would, but it'd be around 1 a.m.

Sure enough, at one he showed up.

They lit a bonfire and Kelly flew in. He flew out with the hurt Vietnamese soldier.

One night Kelly went after some wounded in Vinh Binh Province. He couldn't raise anyone. But he saw lights and landed near them. It was, it turned out, Capt. Ed Fricke's Special Forces camp at Long Khanh.

Kelly told Fricke his problem.

No sweat, Fricke said. His artillery fired an illuminating shell.

76

It scared half the countryside, but it was also a signal for the Vietnamese in district headquarters, five miles up the canal, to turn on their radio. They did. Fricke talked with them.

District headquarters then fired an illuminating mortar shell. The peasants, who by this time had come out of their foxholes, dived back in. Kelly swooped in, picked up three wounded and flew them to Saigon. It was, he insisted, "routine."

Statistics are impersonal things, but Kelly's are impressive. In March he airlifted 448 wounded or sick men. Of those, 103 were picked up at night, as late as 3 a.m. Thirty-two were Americans.

That's not supposed to be done. Kelly does it, however.

"I'm trying to show these guys," he insists, "the safest way to fly is at night—alone. I've been hit seven times. Always in daylight. Anyhow, these boys couldn't get to a hospital unless we hauled them."

APRIL 23, KAI QUANG

There was no hint of the horror to come when the operation began.

A Vietnamese regiment had tangled with a Communist Viet Cong regiment out of the dank U-Minh forest. The Americans were pleased. The same outfit that had done badly two months ago now was holding its own.

The choppers were called on for suppressing fire and to move troops about the battlefield quickly.

But tragedy struck with its usual suddenness when a flight of six Hueys idled down at midafternoon to pick up fresh troops. Without warning, one craft keeled over and started down.

Instinctively, Maj. Albert A. Johnson, Jr., of New Orleans, commanding the choppers, glanced at his instruments. He had been at 2200 feet; the doomed craft, piloted by Lt. Joe Galambos of Sonora, Calif., had been at 2100.

There had been no radio chatter; there had been no reason for it. But in that awesome minute, someone had tried to call out. Then there was nothing but the rush of air against a hot mike.

77

Galambos had been a good chopper man, due to return home soon. Now his craft had lost its tail assembly and was out of control.

Johnson followed the stricken ship, finally circling at 200 feet to spot survivors. They saw one man in a field near the wreckage. He had been thrown clear. It was Warrant Officer (co-pilot) David Miller of Onley, Ill. There was a big brush fire nearby.

Johnson took his machine down. The whirling motors sucked the hungry flames toward them, filling the cabin and cockpit. He had put down so near a clump of small trees that he had badly damaged his blades.

Gunner Harry L. Smith of Wadesboro, N.C., and Crew Chief Lane R. Ramsdell of Albuquerque, were out and rushing toward Miller. Through the flames surrounding the wreckage came three Vietnamese with another body. It was, they were to learn later from his dog tags, the gunner, Pfc. Albert Shimek of Thompson, Ohio.

The Vietnamese had Shimek half in the helicopter when they turned and fled the flames. Ramsdell dragged him the rest of the way. He died minutes later.

Smith reached the horribly burned Miller, who screamed at his touch and fell back.

"What will I do, sir?" the young man asked Major Johnson.

"Get him in!" Johnson ordered, and it was the voice of competent authority so necessary in any crisis.

The charred man no longer screamed. But he moaned. He touched Smith on the ankle.

"Water," he pleaded.

"Sir," Smith replied, and it was an instinctive reversion to training camp, "I can't. I've got to fire (at the Viet Cong)."

The desperately burned Miller grabbed for the ankle of Ramsdell.

"Water," he pleaded piteously. "Please. I'm on fire."

"Shall I give him some, sir?" Ramsdell asked.

Johnson, in the cockpit, set his jaw. It was no easy decision.

"No," he said. "Water might kill him."

Seeing him the first time, Johnson is the last man in the world you'd expect this from. He'd be more easily mistaken for the vice president of a suburban bank and a Kiwanis Club head. In a crowd he smiles easily, but with a shyness which plainly says he doesn't deserve to be there.

But he has nerves of steel and the guts of a burglar and he is beloved of his men.

They took Miller to Ca Mau, and from there, with Dr. (Capt.) Edward Cole of Orlando, Fla., at his side, he was flown to Saigon. At last reports he was still alive, but with 35 per cent of his body covered with third-degree burns.

Galambos' body was found the next day. The only identification of the missing crew chief, William Cavanaugh, Glendale, Calif., was his wedding ring.

Johnson was back to direct these searches, too. Much of the area is a bog. The dead reeds burn with the consistency of charcoal. Twice Johnson climbed trees because the smoldering fires were melting his rubber soles.

He was back at his desk the next morning, ready for the next task.

"To me," one of Johnson's men said, "this guy is nine feet tall."

APRIL 30, TAN CHAU

Everybody on our side—at least for the time being—is going out of his way to be nice to the Hao Hoa (pronounced Wah Hah), an off-shoot Buddhist sect.

Ever since the Hao Hoa made their peace with Saigon after the overthrow of the late Ngo Dinh Diem, nothing has been too good for them.

Defense Secretary McNamara flew to a Hao Hoa village to present a hearing aid to the sect-founder's mother during his last visit to Viet Nam.

Some Americans in the Delta also had planned to give her a hearing aid. Unlike McNamara, however, they'd had to test the idea through channels; they suspect the Secretary's aide stole their idea. Now they keep her in batteries.

Recently we sailed up the Bassac River in LST's with a cow and a calf for another Hao Hoa, a skinny, 41-year-old river diver named Tran Van Tham. Tham located the wreckage of a helicopter which crashed into the Bassac with two crewmen during the McNamara visit.

From our viewpoint, the Hao Hoa have one distinction: They are quite anti-Communist. The Reds once ambushed and wiped out a party of Hao Hoa leaders.

The Hao Hoa detested Diem because he once called a peace parley and locked up Hao Hoa delegates when they refused his terms. Under Premier Nguyen Khanh, a peace of sorts has been arranged.

It's difficult to say precisely what Hao Hoa are. Their villages look like any others. And so do their people.

The Hao Hoa say they practice pure democracy. In their religion, all are equal; there are no temples and no priesthood. It is a comparatively youthful movement, established in 1945 by a sickly youth, Hyugh Phy So, who was born in 1919 and died a few years ago.

Still, there are many who consider the Hao Hoa little more than bandits. They have sub-sects and factions, and they fight each other. Certainly the Hao Hoa are aggressive, which distinguishes them from other Vietnamese.

Everything the Hao Hoa do, apparently, is spectacular. After the helicopter crash, the U.S. Navy brought in diving teams with the most advanced equipment. The wreckage lay in 60 feet of water. Navy divers went down twice without reaching it.

Little Tham put a tube in his mouth, dived, and came up to say he'd found it. Nonsense, the Scuba men said. Tham dived again. This time he came up with a machine gun weighing almost as much as he did. The Navy men went home, red-faced. Tham attached a line to the wreckage and it was salvaged.

The U.S. and Vietnamese navies have offered Tham a job.

Giving him a cow and calf also seemed like a good idea. Men of the 114th Army Aviation Company raised the money and the purchase was made. Only later was it learned that An Giang Province, where Tham lives, is cattle country. It was carrying coals to Newcastle.

Actually no one yet completely trusts the Hao Hoa.

"If and when they chase out the Viet Cong," Lt. Col. Jack Cushmann of Bethesda, Md., recent senior adviser to the 21st Division, said, "the government may have to contend with the Hao Hoa. But one thing at a time."

The government obviously is thinking along the same lines. Hao Hoa men have been volunteering for army duty in droves. This also distinguishes them from other Vietnamese. They've completely filled An Giang's provincial civil guard—which had existed only on paper—and they're volunteering to serve elsewhere in Viet Nam.

In one Delta province, three Guard companies of Hao Hoa have been installed. American advisers there say they make good fighters and are "good with the people."

MAY 4, KIEN LONG

The death of a friend is always hard to take.

His name was Ron Hines, and he came from Amarillo, Tex., but we called him Pickle. That was his radio call sign, and somehow it seemed to fit. He was a thin, dried-up little guy, peering at you nearsightedly through thick-lensed glasses, but a live wire who was always on the go and with more courage than most. He was Pickle all over the Delta, and a lot of people didn't know him by any other name.

Looking now at his strangely composed face, you wondered what Pickle felt when got it. He died as you somehow knew he would, in a sudden, rash act of bravery, trying to save another man. The other guy lived, and Lt. Ronald Hines died.

Ron Hines died at 11 a.m. on a bright Sunday near a hamlet called Vinh Binh, six miles north of Kien Long where his M-113 personnel carriers had been based for the last two weeks. It was Viet Cong country, on the rim of the dank U-Minh forest, and he had chased them there. The Viet Cong don't like us to intrude in their territory, and they were waiting with automatic weapons.

The action that triggered his death started around 1 a.m., when the Commies launched an attack on a Civil Guard outpost. Around 2 o'clock we suddenly lost radio contact with the outpost and we took it for granted they had been overrun. Funny how you learn to take these things in stride. It was only a few miles away and men were dying, but there was nothing we could do, so we went back to bed.

Ron Hines, we learned later, took off after them at 5, and finally cornered them near Vinh Binh. Government troops don't ordinarily go there. The Viet Cong use it as a training base, they keep most of their supplies there, and it's a safe bet it's a regional headquarters. Escaped POW's say they've posted it, even against their own people, and call it their "Zone of Mortal Death."

We had hopped aboard the first transportation to show up, a lumbering H-21 Shawnee with Capt. Gary Heffner of San Angelo, Tex., and First Lt. Kennard Hill of Petrolia, Tex., at the controls.

"Here's the story," Gary had said after checking in. "There's a hell of a battle going on 10 clicks (kilometers) north of Kien Long, and an American adviser, a Lieutenant Hines, has already been killed."

The pain and shock must have shown on your face.

"Know him?"

"Know him?" Know Pickle? He was one of the first I met when I came to Viet Nam, and somehow his name crept into many of the stories I wrote.

Mostly he was in the field. Pickle's thin-skinned 113's roamed the Delta from the South China Sea to the Cambodian border, from Can Tho to Nam Can, hunting down the Viet Cong. He lived and slept in his mount. A lesser man would have broken long ago under the strain of constant peril. To Pickle, it was normal routine, worthy of no comment. He lived in constant peril because he was a West Pointer, steeled in the tradition of the Corps, and this was his life's work.

Another two weeks, we learned later, and Ron Hines would have been transferred back to the comparative safety of Corps headquarters. He wouldn't have liked that, of course, but they were merely waiting for his replacement to arrive. Near Vinh Binh, however, Ron's Vietnamese counterpart dismounted and was hit in the legs by machine-gun fire. Pickle should have stayed under cover. But that wouldn't have been **Hines. He** went after his friend, and got it in the chest. He died **on the** spot.

We tried three times before we got in by chopper, **and by** that time a medical evacuation ship had come in and Ron Hines started on his final trip home.

Death is always hard to take. But, here in the Delta, it is always close at hand.

MAY 11, SOC TRANG

The Communist Viet Cong didn't kill Jerry Shank.
His plane did.
Nor did they kill Bob Brumett.
His plane killed him.
Here we are, the most powerful nation on earth, boasting every day of our superiority in modern arms, and we send our young men out to fight a ruthless, determined foe with equipment long past its prime.

Jerry Shank and Bob Brumett died because they were ordered to fly planes that might better have been consigned to the scrap heap.

They were T-28's. "T" stands for "Trainer," and that's all it was intended to be. It was outmoded in 1953. It is practically the last two-seated propeller-driven craft in the Air Force inventory.

Yet out here we've loaded this antiquated trainer's wings with 500-pound bombs and napalm so that if one is flown long enough, it's inevitable that its wings will drop off. The men who fly them know that.

Politically, of course, the T-28 has its points. For no one, including the Reds, could seriously object to it. By using it we're respecting the armistice terms of the 1954 Geneva Convention, in that we're not introducing new equipment into Viet Nam.

Also, we can put a Vietnamese in the rear seat, contending he's a student pilot. Actually, few of them even speak English and instruction is non-existent. But if a T-28 crashes, there will be a Vietnamese body in the wreckage, and apparently that's important in this game of hide-and-seek we're playing here.

I'm glad I don't have it on my conscience.

As for Jerry Shank and Bob Brumett—every time they put their planes into a dive, they must have wondered if they would come out.

On April 9, Capt. Robert Brumett, 36, put his craft into a dive and it didn't come out. His buddies, flying nearby, saw the wings fall off and watched in horror as the plane plowed into the paddies.

They called over their radios for the choppers to come in and pick up what was left. The choppers didn't get there soon enough. The Viet Cong got there first.

I hope Bob was dead when they found him, because these are the same people who ceremoniously broke the arms and legs of a district leader's wife at Kien Long recently and then killed her. That's the kind of enemy we face.

We need equipment we can count on to keep us out of their hands.

Brumett was from Bethesda, Md. He was full of the love of living and as fine a fighter pilot and a man as you could want.

On March 24, Jerry Shank put his ship into a dive between Soc Trang and Bac Lieu and its wings separated from the fuselage.

Jerry was Capt. Edwin G. Shank, 27, from Winamac, Ind. When they shipped his body back, every shop and office in his home town closed for the day. Jerry was that kind of person. He liked everybody, and most everybody felt the same way about him. He left a wife and four children.

Before he came to Viet Nam, he was a MATS transport pilot.

He graduated from Notre Dame in 1959 with a degree in architectural engineering. He did his stint in the Air Force Reserve, liked it and decided to make flying his career.

Jerry had one consuming ambition: He dreamed of being the first American to land on the moon. Maybe he could have done it. He had all the qualifications.

It makes you wonder what kind of official thinking justifies taking the lives of two such young men—and there have been at least two others—and you make up your mind you will find out when you get home.

Such decisions may be easy to come by in Washington, where men are statistics and casualty rates are a wavering line on a weekly chart. But they're harder to take when you know the brave men who honestly fear their planes—because they can't trust the craft to do the job they're asked to do in their country's name.

The Pentagon says it's replacing the T-28 with a Navy carrier plane, the AD-6, more adaptable to dive bombing. And that's good. But why wait until now?

Moreover, the Pentagon didn't say when this would be done. And every day brave fighting men take off from Soc Trang in their T-28's, hoping the wings will stay glued until those new jobs get here.

MAY 15, TAM BANG

This was the town that refused to be written off.

I told about it in a dispatch of last March 10, and said it was a town the Americans had "adopted."

But now the Communist Viet Cong have burned Tam Bang, leaving only skeletons of its few buildings.

They fire-bombed it one night and the next morning there wasn't a house inside the mud-walled fort still standing.

Tam Bang wasn't much to begin with. Thatch-roofed, one-room huts with mud floors and tin sidings. But 400 people lived here.

The next morning, 72 of these 400 were dead. Among them,

24 women and children. But Tam Bang's defenders are here, led by gallant Lieutenant Cuoi, and they intend to stay.

Tam Bang will be rebuilt.

The attack began at midnight. A defense squad, on ambush, first ran into the Viet Cong. The squad was wiped out; every man died. But in dying they gave the alarm.

Then the fire raid began. The bombs came from across the Song Trem canal. The Viet Cong mixed sugar and rice husks with gasoline. They used matches for their fuses. Their shell casings were old cannisters or sections of bamboo. They are fired out of log troughs or with man-sized sling shots.

Two minutes later, Tam Bang was on fire. There was no place to run. Tam Bang is 100 yards long and not quite that wide, and the Viet Cong were on all four sides. The fort became a flaming skillet. Some found safety in shallow recesses dug into the parapets. But others died in the flames.

And the Communists scream the loudest if we use napalm.

They attacked, in battalion strength, when the fires started. The battle raged all night. The enemy reached the walls, but they didn't get in. Cuoi and his men are proudest of that. They held them off.

When the Viet Cong pulled out at dawn, Capt. Tom Jones of Lawton, Okla., flew in from Rac Gia and counted 21 dead Viet Cong outside the walls. When the enemy leaves that many bodies behind, he has been all but decimated.

Captain Jones loved Tam Bang. More than any other man in Viet Nam, he was its patron. He helped Cuoi build his defenses. He scrounged weapons and ammunition when higher headquarters said no. In July he brought Cuoi his first mines and helped plant them. Tom Jones knew—no matter what Saigon said— Tam Bang was the best, and most worthy, Delta outpost.

Lieutenant Cuoi's wife is gone, and so is his child, but he is still Tam Bang's commander. Word of the fire raid on Tam Bang spread. U.S. Maj. Gen. Charles Timmes, chief of MAAG, flew in from Saigon. So did the Australian military attache, Lt. Col Peter Oxley. Cuoi's province chief—who had never visited Tam Bang before—came from Rac Gia.

Capt. Robert Anspaugh of Fountain, Colo., came up to help Cuoi reorganize his defenses.

The Navy has arrived with ships, guns and supplies. Cuoi and his men know they are no longer alone.

Tam Bang still refuses to be written off.

MAY 19, CAU LAUN

Dragon Flight, with its six armed Huey choppers, loosed its rockets and the big sampan disintegrated.

So did the desperate men aboard it.

It was a quiet, sunlit morning, and this was a grudge fight. The men down there, or men like them, overran Tan Thanh three weeks before, killing defenseless women and children. Then they fled down this same Cai Cai Canal to their privileged Cambodian sanctuary.

Many who were at Tan Thanh that day—Lt. Col. John Roberts of New Orleans; Maj. Walt Zarnowski of Wilkes-Barre, Pa.; Lt. Col. Charles Crain of Alexandria, Va.; Maj. Charles Butler of Oxford, Miss.; Capt. Jim Quinlan of Wichita Falls, Tex. —had a score to settle. You don't soon forget the sight of maimed women and children.

Watching them die now, we feel no pity. Once they come within 2000 yards of the Cambodian border, they're safe. Until they do, they're targets. We caught them this time.

Since they overran Tan Thanh, Cambodian-based Viet Cong have all but ruled Kien Phong Province.

Our planning was thorough. So thorough that we had to abandon one proposed landing zone; it was too close to the border. A Vietnamese battalion, with Lt. Joe Zimmers of Harrisburg, Pa., as adviser, had been flown in, minutes after daybreak, between the Viet Cong and their Cambodian haven. It set up a blocking force. Other Vietnamese battalions had been put in front of them, and were even now pushing relentlessly against the enemy's dug-in positions. There was no way out but the Cai Cai Canal. And we were guarding that.

"With any luck," Crain had said, "we should get a few."

Capt. Bert Nye of Pollacksville, N.C., was less hopeful. He was flying in the blocking force.

"We'll have to overfly those guys four times," he said. "And they've got heavy weapons."

By our count, they had at least 34 machine guns. They also had recoilless rifles.

Capt. Ralph Floyd, Austin, Tex., leader of Dragon Flight, spotted them first.

"Five large sampans with numerous men aboard," he called over his radio. "We can't see any weapons, but they're paddling like mad. Will you give us permission to strike them?"

Colonel Crain wasted no time.

"Hit those sampans," he ordered. "You have instructions to shoot anything that moves."

From Colonel Roberts:

"Remember, the border's up there. That outpost is on the other side. Don't go past that little water pool on your right."

There was something unreal about it. The Hueys seemed to flutter in, like a swarm of dainty flies. But their rockets spoke with solid authority, and their machine guns barked like angry dogs. The lumbering sampans stopped dead, their oars dangling. They drifted toward shore.

Dragon Flight followed them—Ralph Floyd, Ralph Hamner of Tuscaloosa, Monte Veal of Atlanta, Fred Ross of Ashland, Ky., and Billy Lindsey of Covington, Tenn.—setting fires on the shore.

Viet Cong men scrambled onto the beach, and the Hueys chased them. Aboard the command chopper, Gunner Harold Ansai of Honolulu could hardly contain himself.

"Go ahead and shoot," Colonel Roberts told him.

Ansai's machine gun cut loose.

It was over in minutes. The five sampans were either afire or hopelessly adrift. They would never reach Cambodia.

On the ground, Joe Zimmers pushed ahead. He found empty foxholes and abandoned emplacements, but the Viet Cong had faded away. Later, however, he was to move south and pick up 36 prisoners.

We flew back over Tan Thanh. We abandoned and burned the post after it was overrun. At least 100 sampans were drawn up beside the village across the canal. But we saw no sign of life. Obviously, the Viet Cong were hiding.

It was over in midafternoon and we headed home.

MAY 30, MEKONG DELTA

The mortars still came, but not like they had during the night.

It had been rough. On our side, 11 Vietnamese were dead, 28 wounded. Maj. Charles Kelly of Sylvania, Ga., and his medical evacuation choppers were taking out the last loads. The wounded had gone first, back to Ca Mau. Now he was flying out the dead.

The Communist Viet Cong were across the Song Trem Canal, leading out of Rac Gia. Our troops had moved from Tam Bang, the town that wouldn't be written off, in pursuit of an enemy that had burned it two nights before.

They'd found them a dozen miles south. But the enemy was waiting with mortars and recoilless rifles.

They had suffered casualties, too. From here their dead can be seen along the banks. Capt. George Burnett had called in an air strike. U.S. Air Force T-28's and Vietnamese AD-6's had pounded the opposite bank with shell and rocket.

The Viet Cong, however, had stayed during the night. They usually pull out after dark. Their mortars had chewed into Burnett's ranks.

Capt. Ted Voorhees of Knoxville and his Vietnamese Rangers, moving up from the south, had run into an ambush at about the same time. They also had casualties. With this, any hope of trapping the Viet Cong vanished. They'd trapped us.

If the Viet Cong own any part of Viet Nam, it is here, just outside the U-Minh forest. They resent any intrusion. Talk of our side's abandoning the offensive in favor of a pacification campaign encourages them to hit at our isolated outposts, like Tam Bang, and district towns, like Kien Long. They'd like to drive us out altogether.

The sleek Huey chopper piloted by Capt. Ted Castle of Dallas and Lt. Robin Miller of North Manchester, Ind., came in high. Choppers don't coast in, here. They circle the landing zone at 3000 feet, then dive in. The descent is so rapid your ears pop. But this gives the enemy less target.

Below, armed Hueys, with Lt. Bob Finnerty of Bayonne, N.J., and Lt. Paul Young of Fayetteville, Ark., at the controls, flew cover. Almost arrogantly, they swept over the Viet Cong positions, daring them to fire.

We wished Kelly had got the dead out earlier. But he has only two hands and two choppers, and even a Kelly can't produce miracles.

This battalion had never had a fight like this. Its peasant soldiers, like any other, are awed by the indignity of death. A mortar doesn't leave much of a man. They stare at their dead as if they were some ugly mistake, preposterous rather than ghastly, the kind of thing a man doesn't quite believe.

"We did what we came to do," said Lt. Col. Jim Lee of Wilmington, N.C., adviser to the Ca Mau Brigade back in Thoi Binh where he had his command post. "We came looking for Viet Cong, and we found them. The enemy got hurt, too. Every time we hurt him here, we impress him there's no place south of the Bassac where he's completely safe."

But it's a seemingly endless business, and men tire. Every day somewhere in the Delta there are fire fights like this. Men die and men are maimed, and few ever know they lived. After a while you start asking yourself when it will end and what's the reason for it, and there's no ready answer.

A mortar whoomps in, and they duck for cover. But it's a reflex now. Without knowing it, overnight these men have been seasoned. They've grown up.

JUNE 1, CAN THO

Daily inspections since April 11 are turning up a high number of splits in the tail assemblies of UH-1B (Huey) helicopters being flown in Viet Nam.

90

On April 11, a Huey crashed near Kai Quang, on the edge of the U-Minh forest, when it lost a tail. Four men died, including Pfc. Albert L. Shimek of Unionville, O., a constituent of Rep. Oliver Bolton (R.).

Through Chairman Carl Vinson (D., Ga.) of the House Armed Services Committee, Bolton asked for and got a report on the safety and adequacy of U.S. Army combat helicopters in Viet Nam.

No official findings have been made public on causes of the April 11 tragedy. The doomed craft's tail assembly was shipped to an Army Aviation Materials Center at Corpus Christi, Tex., for tests.

But Army aviators here think it happened because an undetected split between the tail assembly and fuselage widened. A Huey's tail assembly is attached to the fuselage with four large bolts. The split occurs in the metal to which the bolts are attached.

(In Washington, Army Secretary Stephen Ailes recently said the "post-accident investigation revealed possible structural problems." The UH-1B was one of 32 choppers on which "local modifications to the tail boom structure" had been made to "strengthen the tail booms and eliminate problems of cracked longerons"—stiffeners in the fuselages.

(After the accident, said Ailes, all "field-modified" UH-1B's were grounded, as were all with more than 600 hours, and the manufacturer started work on a "longeron strengthening kit" to go to all users of the chopper.)

"The tragedy is that four men had to die before we became aware of the problem," said Lt. Col. John Roberts, New Orleans, commander of the Delta Aviation Battalion.

Since April 11, on Roberts' orders, all Hueys are checked for splits before they are permitted to take off. One or more are found daily. When that happens, the chopper is grounded.

Roberts' executive officer, Maj. Albert A. Johnson, Jr., of New Orleans, risked his life in an attempt to pick up survivors in the April 11 crash. Flying directly behind the doomed craft, Johnson put his own Huey down beside it. The co-pilot, Warrant Officer

91

David Miller of Olney, Ill., lived 11 days. The other three died on the spot.

Commanders of the 114th and 121st Army Aviation companies at Vinh Long and Soc Trang ask that their craft return early enough for routine maintenance. Often, however, they come back after dark and leave on other combat missions the next dawn.

Bolton also asked about phasing out CH-21 "Flying Bananas" still in Viet Nam.

Currently, 27 are in action, seven at Soc Trang and 20 at Saigon. By the end of next month the CH-21's are expected to be replaced by UH-1B's.

Until a few days ago, the 121st had eight CH-21's. But Warrant Officers Billy Lindsey of Covington, Tenn., and Victor Voisine of Bay City, Mich., lost one near Loung Tam trying to pull an artillery gun carriage out of the mud. They were under fire at the time. The lumbering Banana lost its balance and fell into a nearby canal. The crew suffered bruises and the helicopter was a total loss.

JUNE 3, DONG CAO

Long Toan is one of nine districts in Vinh Binh Province. It is the smallest and least populated. It is eight miles long and five miles wide. The district is heavily forested; most of it is mangrove swamp, the lair of snakes and Communist guerrillas.

For 20 years there has been no government authority in Long Toan. Once bandits ruled here. For eight years past it has been held by the Communist Viet Cong.

Back in Ap Chanh, a strategic hamlet where he had set up his command post, Lt. Col. Charles Crain of Alexandria, Va., was grim.

"We are going to make Long Toan uninhabitable for the Viet Cong," he promised.

It was not an easy decision for Colonel Crain; he is not a cruel man. Nor is his division commander, Col. Vinh Loc. Both

regard destruction of Long Toan as part of their paci
program.

"We are rooting out hard-core Viet Cong villages from ....
we can be attacked," said Crain. "We are destroying their eco-
nomic base."

A battalion of Vietnamese Marines, with Capt. Bill Monohan
of Burlingame, Calif., and Army Capt. Jim Anderson of New
Lexington, O., along as advisers, sailed down the Bassac River
and went ashore at Dong Cao. The Viet Cong resisted briefly,
then fled into the mangroves as we knew they would.

The center of Dong Cao was in flames.

Invariably when we show up in force, the men and boys
disappear. This was no exception. Only women, children and
old men were left. Their sons and husbands, the women
insisted, were fishing.

But the order was given: Dong Cao is to be burned. Its
people will go to Mac Bat. They will take everything, every pot
and pan, every duck, chicken and pig. They will take their
water buffaloes and fishing boats.

Some stare in disbelief. They were born here. They've never
been past the mangroves. But now they will be moved behind
our lines. If their men want to see them again, they must come
over, too.

Then it was Ap Long Binh's turn to be destroyed. It was a
propaganda center for the Viet Cong—a village of 200 families.
The center had been burned by the Vietnamese Marines, but
we found a typical poster, damaged by fire.

It depicted a giant octopus, its tentacles squeezing the life out
of the Vietnamese people. The face of the octopus was clearly
President Johnson's, emphasized by a 10-gallon hat. A heroic
Viet Cong had a dagger pointed at the octopus.

Ap Long Binh was also a Viet Cong arsenal. Here they manufactured mines, booby traps and grenades. Most huts have concrete bomb shelters.

For our planes and artillery this has long been a free-fire zone.
Here we shoot at will, here we can always drop our bombs.

The strain of war plainly shows on the faces of Ap Long

Binh's women. And now they are leaving. For many it is a relief. For others, it is heartbreak and there are tears.

The boats will come and take away the people of Ap Long Binh. Then the village will die. Their homes will be destroyed.

At Mac Bat, they will live among strangers. Each family will be given a new hut, or about $20 with which to build a home.

The government also will give them a living allowance and try to cleanse their minds. That will not be easy. They have lived with the Viet Cong for a long time. We are the first Americans they have seen.

It is cruel to uproot a people and move them against their will. But war is cruel, and this is war.

JUNE 4, SOC TRANG

The Army has pulled the last of its ancient CH-21 Flying Banana helicopters out of the Delta.

It still has a company of 20 of the craft in Saigon, however. They will be replaced this month with UH-1B's, or Hueys.

The last Banana to go was the first to arrive here, an ancient ship known as Old 639. It is the last of a contingent flown from Fort Devens, Mass., to the West Coast and put aboard ship for Viet Nam in 1961. They got here in December of that year. All the others have crashed, worn out or been replaced.

Old 639's other claim to fame was that she was used in search and rescue operations when two United Air Lines planes crashed over the Grand Canyon several years ago.

There was a brief plane-side ceremony, but no speeches. Most of the Army airmen stationed at Soc Trang took pictures. Now that the old ships are gone, many Army aviators nostalgically have decided they weren't so bad after all.

"If truth is told," said Lt. Tom Paasco of Stamford, Conn., "I prefer the CH-21. We're supposed to be a Light Mobile Aviation Company. Now we're—" He never finished his sentence.

"They're good ships," said Capt. Norm Laumeyer of Seattle. "Lots of good flying hours left in 'em."

Old 639 had 2200 hours of combat flying. In her better days

she could carry 2500 pounds of cargo. Recently that has been reduced. Even so, the big choppers could carry more than the Hueys, and the Special Forces, which depend on helicopters for supply, will miss the big birds.

Maj. Joe Levinson of Enterprise, Ala., commander of the 121st Aviation Company, shook hands with his boss, Lt. Col. John Roberts of New Orleans, and thanked him "for getting us the Hueys."

"Better take off," Roberts said. "The weather is supposed to turn bad this afternoon."

Levinson and his executive officer, Capt. Bert Nye of Pollacksville, N.C., took off in the first ship; Paasco and Lt. Tom Porterfield of Murfreesboro, Tenn., were in the second; and Capt. Joe Stevenson of Sumpter, S.C., and Lt. Kent Rudeen of St. Paul, Minn., flew out Old 639.

And what did Old 639 carry on her last mission?

A couple of slot machines to be repaired in Saigon.

JUNE 5, CAU NHEIM

Business was brisk in the Delta, and the Delta's business is war.

Capt. Mike Ilsemann's big 105 howitzers roared in angry protest. As they fired, Cau Nhiem's school children, ranged alongside, put their hands to their ears. There were two of the big hot tubes and they fired in unison. The roar was deafening.

Five miles down the canal, at a junction known as Check Point 16, the Communist Viet Cong had dug in. Ilsemann—of Cleveland—was firing air bursts. Twenty-five seconds after each round was fired, the muffled whoomp meant they'd hit.

"They're dug in," Mike said. "But that ought to get them."

Captains Ilsemann and Harry McFarland of Baden, Pa., had spent the night at Cau Nhiem. So had Maj. Tran Ba Di, Phong Dinh's Province Chief. Their forces had clashed the day before with the Viet Cong's C-20 guerrilla company. If the enemy got control of Khac Nhon District they would have a base from which to hit at Can Tho.

We had taken off at dawn from Can Tho in a Huey chopper with Capt. Bill Ward of San Angelo, Tex., and Lt. Joe Kliever of Streeter, Ill., at the controls. Sgt. David Hoffman of Manchester, N.H., and Pfc. Harold Ansai of Honolulu were the gunners.

"We don't know exactly where their command post is located," said Capt. John Nicholson of Struble, Iowa. "We'll ask them to put out smoke."

"They've got red smoke down there now," Ward reported.

"Check it first," Nicholson said.

The Viet Cong also have red smoke. They sometimes use it to lure our helicopters down.

We landed safely, and Capt. Jim Conley of Fremont, O., strode through the paddies to greet us.

"They've gone," he said, "but they're still around somewhere."

A dead Viet Cong lay alongside a dike. He'd been recently killed.

The radio chattered, and from somewhere up there came the voice of Maj. Charles Kelly of Sylvania, Ga. Kelly's call sign is Dust Off.

Dust Off was calling for an ambulance to meet him at Can Tho. He had a chopper-load of casualties.

Kliever was nervous as Nicholson and the Province Chief conferred with Conley. They came in here only the day before, Conley was saying, and started digging foxholes. That's when the people moved out. That's always a sure sign of trouble.

"We're in mortar range here," Kliever protested. "Keep a chopper on the ground too long and they're sure to creep up and have a go at it."

The big Huey took off, climbing to 3000 feet. It hovered there until Nicholson called it back.

Automatic-rifle fire barked from a tree line, and Hoffman and Ansai fired back, their automatic rifles yipping angrily at an unseen foe.

In the distance, Can Tho could be seen, peaceful, undisturbed. There, it was business as usual. Can Tho has grown accustomed to war. Not even Mike Ilsemann's big guns could disturb it.

Back at Cau Nhiem, the firing ceased and the children went elsewhere to play. The fun was over. Later, it would start again.

Ilsemann and McFarland began a game of cribbage. Jim Conley's battalion moved cautiously toward Check Point 16. It'd be hours before they got there, however.

Dusk came. Conley found what we'd expected. Nothing.

"They say they're gone," Kliever complained, "but nobody knows. Somebody shot at us. That I know."

The Delta's business is yet to be settled. The war goes on.

JUNE 16, RACH COUNG

Lts. Fred Ross and Monte Veal have drawn hostile fire. Five rounds, too close for comfort.

In a Huey chopper at 600 feet, Ross of Ashland, Ky., and Veal, of Atlanta, are over Ap Coung in an area around the big Soc Trang Air Base dominated by the Communist Viet Cong.

Ross and Veal are in the command ship above. Two other Hueys, including ours, are much lower. So much lower, in fact, that Warrant Officers Ron Garrison of Bethesda, Md., and Bill Kegelmeyer of Columbus, O., failed to clear a tree as they whipped over a village a few miles back. The Huey's nose knocked off the tree top.

We set out from Soc Trang after evening chow on the first snooper of the night. There will be others. The Viet Cong have stepped up their attacks on Soc Trang. They hit an outpost six miles away and wounded five men. A snooper led by Capt. Ralph Hamner of Tuscaloosa, Ala., caught them celebrating their "success." Rockets and machine guns unceremoniously put an end to that party.

We are whipping over towns and villages, snaking up canals and rivers. Fred Ross is calling signals . . . "hut on the right" . . . "town coming up on the left" . . . "check that sampan dead ahead" . . . "three men in the trees, keep an eye on them."

The noise below as the sleek Hueys roar overhead must be deafening. We come in out of nowhere and just as quickly are

97

gone. People pour from their huts, water buffalo stampede, ducks and chickens take off in feathered flurries.

If anything has saved Soc Trang from attack—it took 37 mortar rounds last month—it has been these night flights. The Viet Cong attacks on small outposts have been bloody and merciless. But the choppers have kept them off balance. They're afraid to concentrate in force.

Garrison and Kegelmeyer take their Huey over a small stream, and over the earphones Ross says:

"From now on we are in a free fire zone. Nothing here is friendly."

We sweep over a hamlet. Capt. Bernie Young of Antonio, Tex., in another low-flying Huey with Warrant Officer Victor Voisine of Bay City, Mich., spots three men in black pajama-like uniforms trying to hide. We swing back to check them out. Once, twice, three times we buzz the settlement. At our speed, however, we fail to pick them up again. A woman and three children are plodding the dikes outside the village. They don't look up.

We resume our search. Then Ross reports hostile fire at Rach Coung. He drops a smoke grenade. Red smoke curls from a grove of trees where it lands. Ross says the firing came from a spot 100 yards to the left.

Garrison and Kegelmeyer climb to 1000 feet and turn their Huey around. Specialists Billy D'Spain of Albuquerque, N.M., and Mark Gavorski of Cleveland open up. The noise is deafening. Spent shells whip through the cabin. We edge closer to target, then swing away, turning for another run.

Over the earphones, we hear Bernie Young and Vic Voisine open up. Their machine guns chatter, their rockets roar. The ground below churns as they dig into the wet earth.

We make a second run, then a third. Ross calls for a fourth, then reconsiders.

"Better save some ammunition for the trip home," he says.

We go back at 1500 feet. Darkness is coming on.

Maj. Joe Levinson of Enterprise, Ala., is waiting.

"Let's go hit 'em again," he suggests.

"Won't be necessary," we tell him. "We put 20 rockets and 4000 slugs in that hamlet. It'll be quiet for a while."

JULY 3, WASHINGTON, D.C.

The Viet Cong, as everybody in the Mekong Delta knew they would some day, finally got "Crazy" Kelly this week.

Maj. Charles Kelly of Sylvania, Ga., was a professional soldier, and a good one, who never hurt anybody in his life. He only wanted to help them. The conviction he should—and could —finally cost him his life.

News dispatches from Saigon say a Viet Cong sniper killed him as he landed his medical evacuation helicopter to pick up a wounded American. He had gone to Vinh Binh Province, 45 miles from his home base, when the Communists opened fire at close range. Kelly managed to get his chopper in the air but was hit as it began to lift. Statistically, he was the 149th American killed in combat.

Twenty-four hours after he set up shop in the Delta, Kelly had become a legend. We called him "Crazy," or sometimes it was "Mad Man," but we said it with affection. Kelly did things the bravest of the others wouldn't think of trying. So did the handful of youngsters who flew with him and gave him their full devotion. Knowing how much they loved the "Old Man," I'm glad I'm not in Soc Trang today.

Beginning in April, we heard about "Mad Man" Kelly at Ca Mau and Hai Yen, deep in the southern Delta, and we'd come across him a day or two later in the north. He was shy, almost diffident, with a half-smile which said there was a lot going on he refused to take at face value.

Kelly was a man with a mission. He was a Medical Service Officer who incidentally could fly helicopters. He was in on everything. He went anywhere, at any hour, if there were dead or wounded to pick up. At night he insisted on flying alone, without lights, because he said that was safest. Only Kelly and his boys ever tried to prove, or disprove, that.

He admitted frankly he was out to prove a point: that

wounded men can be evacuated as soon as they're hit. He had one ruling passion: to save as many lives as he could. The old-timers said sagely he'd burn out, that his enthusiasm would ebb, and he'd be like the rest, but somehow that never happened. Kelly had a hot-line phone by his bunk, and he answered personally. His call sign was Dust Off.

I must have flown with him a dozen times. I saw him in action even oftener. Nothing short of a bullet through the back of his head could have stopped him. In the end, that was what it took.

Even men who'd never met him knew about Kelly. At night, they'd hear his chopper overhead, his rotors churning the air, and it was a mighty comfortable feeling. There were some who said he was a fool to risk his neck picking up wounded Vietnamese, but Kelly's idea was that a wounded man needed help no matter what his race or color, and it was worth all the trouble he was put to.

The only time Kelly and I had words was when—after my third story—he complained I wrote about him too much and not enough about his boys. I told him his boys wanted it that way. He shouted back he was their commanding officer and he'd put a stop to that. I kept writing about Kelly, and no one but the man himself ever complained.

Kelly would fight for his rights. And it was his right, he felt, to do more than anyone expected. At one point, the brass decreed that no pilot could fly more than 90 hours a week. Kelly assumed that didn't apply to him. When he found it did, he spent a couple of hours with the generals and came out with a blanket exemption. Damned if he was going to sit on his duff while men died, simply because of some rule!

At Kien Long, he came in with a load of wounded just as a colonel was pinning medals on some of his troops. They waved him off.

"Colonel," he said acidly when they finally let him in, "there's too much medal-pinning going on around here."

That's the kind of man he was. We'll miss the likes of Mad Man Kelly.

Part Two

SEPTEMBER, 1964 – APRIL, 1965

The young Marine Captain spoke with emphasis, but without emotion—a tradesman discussing the vagaries of his trade.

"Everybody's been in there before," said Capt. Jim Gentry of Sacramento, Calif. "And everybody knows they've got the field bracketed with mortars. Go right in and get right out. Don't let anybody delay you. If we have to, we'll come back. But the trick is not to spend too much time on the ground."

His crewmen listened, nodded. They'd been to A-Ro before. Every day and every night—several times a day and night—it's under fire. Since June, U.S. Navy Seabees have been carving an airstrip out of the lush jungles five miles from the Laotian border.

Guerrillas of one stripe or another have ruled this land for generations; the French never tried to conquer it. The Viet Cong, who have used it as a supply route to their own base areas farther south, have watched us airdrop a 22,000-pound bulldozer and a 20,000-pound grader into a small landing zone where once there were trees more than 100 feet high. And they have thrown as much as they can muster into their fight to keep A-Ro from growing.

"I don't want two planes (helicopters) on the ground at the same time," Gentry concluded. "If you're fired on, or if you see anything, drop a smoke grenade on it so the armed Hueys will know where to fire."

They buckled on their armored flak vests and incongruous armored diapers and were off. Gentry and Marine Lt. James Lent, Jr., of Tiverton, R.I., with Rod Wood of Fitchburg, Mass., and Lawson Long of Lexington, N.C., as their gunners, in one chopper; Capt. Royall Geis of Greenwich, Conn., and Lt. George Minas of Pasadena, Calif., in the other. Cpls. Robert Yanchis of Brooklyn and Stan Carfield of Albuquerque would man the guns in the second ship.

Two armed Hueys fly escort, whipping low over the trees to

103

draw fire and smoke out the Viet Cong. Capt. Richard Daum of
Twin Falls, Ida., and Lt. Jim Deegan of Iowa City, Iowa, fly
one, with Cpls. Tom Blake of Newport News, Va., and Floyd
Turnage of Newton Grove, N.C., manning their guns. Lt. Darryl
Randolph of Washington and Warrant Officer Stan Bozek of
Detroit fly the other, with Pfc. Steve Clark of Evansville, Ind.,
and Jerry Dennis of Columbia, S.C., as gunners.

We fly through mountain passes, and the trees seem to reach
out at us. For anyone who has been in the flat Mekong Delta,
with its endless miles of paddy land, it is a startling experience.
The Viet Cong, old-timers say, often put mortars on the moun-
tainsides and actually fire down on you as you go past.

"After we pass the last of these three ridge lines we'll slow
down and let the Army move out ahead," Gentry called over the
intercom.

The country is breathtakingly beautiful from the air but
living hell for anyone who goes down in it. There are trails
down there, snaking up the mountain peaks, and you follow
them with your eye until you lose them, not knowing where
they start or end. But these are the highways of the jungle.
Hidden beneath the foliage are others—among them the Ho Chi
Minh trail—which the enemy uses to bring in supplies. These
are hand hewn, and no plane ever spots them.

Now A-Ro is below—a jagged, earthen scar—and we dive for
it. Gentry sets down first, and a quiet, orderly world becomes
bedlam. War is ever present in A-Ro, and war erupted here
minutes ago. Men rush helter-skelter, shouting incomprehensible
orders to each other.

An American sergeant appears out of nowhere, sweating,
shouting, cursing. A wounded Vietnamese is slung over his
shoulder. The wounded boy is tossed aboard. Other wounded
soldiers—their blood still fresh—are flung through the crowd.
Still others, claiming injuries, or just wanting out, fight their
way in and are wrestled off.

Gentry guns his rotors and we are off. He shoots skyward at
an alarming rate of climb, anxious to give the enemy mortars as
little target as he can. Even so, he barely clears the trees.

Now we are headed back, and rainstorms move in. The last few miles are touch and go. We clear the last ridge minutes before the clouds wrap it in their folds.

This is also the war in Viet Nam.

OCT. 1, A-RO

One by one during the day, and now late into the night, the guys would wander into the sandbagged command bunker, pretending maybe they had business there.

"Anything?" they'd ask with studied casualness, and whoever was on duty would shake his head no.

"Damn!" they'd whisper and go out again into the night, where someone else would ask, "Anything?"

It has been like this for 48 hours, and we've got another 24 hours to go. Four of our people—Capts. George McKenzie of San Antonio, Ken Skipper of Mobile, Sgts. Ron Collins of Detroit and Walter Meehan of Jersey City—are out there with 64 Vietnamese strike-force men and eight Nung (Chinese) mercenaries. They're looking for the Viet Cong. The Viet Cong are looking for them, too.

They'd kicked off before dawn the morning after a mortar barrage, and most of the camp got up to see them leave. Cookie served them steaks and eggs.

"What's this?" Captain McKenzie asked. "The condemned man's breakfast?"

The laughter this drew seemed forced.

Soon McKenzie looks at his watch and says it's time to go.

"Play it cool," someone says. "Don't try for no CMH's (Congressional Medals of Honor)."

"All I want," Meehan says, hitching on his 50-pound pack, "is to get me a VC (Viet Cong)."

They move toward the door, and you hear yourself saying: "Goodbye and God bless." Everybody looks embarrassed.

By pushing hard, old timers say, in nine hours you can make 1000 yards through the lush rain forests that all but engulf Camp A-Ro. That's a day's march. There are three layers of

105

vegetation out there. First there's the elephant grass, then the trees which rise to 70 feet. Above them are the giants of the jungle, rising to 120 feet. It's dark out there. It's hard to see three feet in any direction, including straight ahead. It's uphill and down, hacking your way through.

McKenzie has the radio, and there are two ways of maintaining contact on a patrol like this—report at agreed intervals, or come in whenever there's something to say. Each method has its advantages and disadvantages. McKenzie elects to report at his option. This makes it tougher on those back in camp. Hour after endless hour we sit by the radio and listen. It growls and crackles. Meehan's voice finally cuts through.

"Big Daddy, this is Ratfink," the radio says. "Got your log handy?"

Sgt. Bill Brown of Ashland, N.H., acknowledges.

"Two VC passing the outer perimeter this location taken under fire at 2:05 p.m. Negative casualties either side. That is all."

Brown puts down his book.

"I know they're going to step in it out there," he says to no one in particular, "and I don't want to miss a call. If they need a medical evacuation, we'll get it to them."

"If they saw the VC," someone asks, "how could they miss them?"

"You don't really see them" Brown says. "You just know they're there."

At 5 p.m., machine-gun fire is heard from the jungle and everybody gravitates toward the radio. It grunts and crackles maddeningly.

"Ratfink, this is Big Daddy," we say. The tension is too much. But Ratfink isn't answering.

"Could have been one of the other patrols," Brownie says. Before he left, Meehan sent out nine ambush and three six-day, five-man "snatch" patrols. They're routine. Their job is to camp on a known supply trail in hopes of getting a prisoner. So far, they haven't scored.

It's after midnight now, and for the second straight night no one is sleepy. The guys lie in their bunks and talk, mostly about women.

"I can't understand it," Dave Bowling, a Seabee from Knoxville, says from behind a glowing cigaret in the bunker's darkness. "I've never been wider awake."

I wandered outside and stared into the jungle. Brownie appears beside me.

"They're not about to admit they're worried," he says, "but no one's going to sleep until these guys are back. Hell, they're curled up in their hammocks out there sleeping. And we're back here stewing like a bunch of old women."

It's Sunday. They're due in at noon. At 10 a.m., there's a brisk fire fight at the end of the runway. Then McKenzie comes on the air.

"Request emergency medical evacuation," he says steadily. "Three casualties, two critical, one serious. That is all."

"The hell it is," Brownie says. "What happened?"

"Hit a mine on the trail," the Captain says. "Needless to say, we're coming in slower."

We call the Marines at Da Nang and ask for two choppers. Be there at 11:45, word comes back.

"They may have to wait," McKenzie answers. "We're still 100 meters out. These are stretcher cases."

We drive a jeep to the end of the runway, weapons at the ready, and wait. The advance elements then come out of the jungles. There are four casualties. Two are in shock, minutes away from death. We put them in the jeep and walk back. The choppers show up, and they're loaded aboard. A young Navy medic takes over.

"Welcome home," I say for want of anything better.

Ken Skipper grins.

"You know," he says, "damned if it isn't. Home, I mean."

OCT. 5, A-RO

It was a tense moment. Anything could happen.

Special Forces Capt. George McKenzie of San Antonio faced

the rebellious Nungs and ordered them back to work. They stared sullenly at him and sat on their heels.

Nungs are Chinese mercenaries. Their reputation as warriors is legendary. The French, when they ruled Indochina, maintained Nung divisions on which they relied for much of their dirty fighting. But Nungs fight only for money. For the Vietnamese they have nothing but contempt.

Their loyalty is to the Americans who pay them. Frequently they act as our bodyguards. The Vietnamese fear and resent them because they get the best arms. The average Nung draws more pay than the top-ranking Vietnamese army man in camp.

A Nung can quit when he wants. And the Nung payrolls here are a mess. Some claim they haven't been paid for two months. Others say they were promised leave back in Da Nang and haven't had it. In their view, Uncle Sam has breached his contract.

At dusk the other night, Nung leader Long Tan So announced he wouldn't post guards. His men were tired. Besides, he hadn't been paid himself.

Capt. Donnie Pearce of Cheyenne, Wyo., the senior American officer present, fired him on the spot. Next morning the Nungs refused to work. They also demanded to be paid and sent home.

McKenzie stood on a slight rise and stared into the sea of angry faces below him. Behind him, other Americans quietly trained their guns, including mortars, on the strikers. I stood beside McKenzie.

"Tell them," the young Captain told his interpreter, Ku, "that when they signed on, each man claimed he was a soldier." He spat in disgust.

"Tell them further," he continued, "they remind me of a bunch of old women crying because they don't get enough betel nut."

It was the ultimate in insults. I listened while Ku translated. The Nungs chattered shrilly among themselves. One shook his fist at the American. McKenzie's expression did not change.

"Tell them," he said, "that they have five minutes to decide what they will do. If they want to work, then let them go to work. If they want to quit and go home, have them bring me their arms. I also want their uniforms. I will take them to the end of the runway and start them walking back to Da Nang."

Da Nang is 80 miles away, through an almost impenetrable forest. "Come on," McKenzie said quietly. "Let them chew it over among themselves a while."

After five minutes, McKenzie came back. The Nungs broke into excited chatter.

"What did they decide?" the Captain asked.

"They go to work."

The camp sighed in relief. Minutes later most of the Nungs were back at work as if nothing had happened. But McKenzie picked out six ringleaders, paid them off, and sent them out in the next helicopter.

A-Ro is Viet Nam in miniature. The Americans, Vietnamese and Nungs who live here, frequently under Viet Cong attack, are barely on speaking terms. The Nungs despise the Vietnamese and tolerate the Americans. The Vietnamese fear and envy the Nungs and ardently dislike the Americans. The Americans have little use for either. The Nungs, they say, are overrated. The Vietnamese are unreliable.

It doesn't make for a happy camp. Recently, for instance, the Vietnamese commander refused to order his men to clear the runway so that American helicopters might land. The choppers, badly needed to bring in more men, returned to Da Nang.

Still later, the Vietnamese refused to refuel helicopters after they'd landed. The Vietnamese commander insisted his men were "too tired."

Some of the Vietnamese Special Forces here are mere babies. Some are only 14 years old. Few are over 20. They look even younger. Their training is non-existent. Under fire, they panic. The Americans fear to go on patrol with them.

OCT. 6, A-RO

Off the far end of the runway a machine gun barked in staccato rhythm and grenades exploded with muffled fury.

This was the second round of an unscheduled "battle for the sandbags." Twenty-four hours earlier, A-Ro's defenders had thrown up their hands in despair as a big Army Caribou swept low over the runway and then pulled out, dumping 40,000 empty sandbags—badly needed for our defenses—in the jungle 500 yards within Viet Cong territory.

We felt we had to make a try for them. Give them up without a fight, and the Communists would figure A-Ro defenders had gone soft.

"If you go after them now," Capt. Donnie Pearce of Cheyenne, Wyo., told the Vietnamese commander, "the most you will hit is two or three men. Wait a couple of hours, and you'll hit a squad or platoon. They saw them drop, too."

The Vietnamese waited a couple of hours. A 10-man patrol, sent to bring in the bags, came reeling back. It took two casualties.

Now, 24 hours later, a much larger patrol had been sent. The battle was joined as soon as it entered the forests.

Green smoke curled above the trees. Our people were marking their position and calling for mortar fire.

Inside Camp A-Ro, mortarmen elevated their guns and fired. The shells arched straight up, then tumbled down into what should be enemy positions. The salvos burst just inside the tree lines.

"The most we can hope for now," said Sgt. William Brown, "is to get to those bags and burn them before the VC do."

Eighty miles from the nearest friendly outpost, Da Nang, Camp A-Ro depends on airlifts for its supplies. Accidents of this kind are frequent. A couple of weeks ago, an Air Force cargo ship dumped several hundred sets of army fatigues at the other end of the field. We never did get those back. Presumably the Viet Cong are now running around in army uniforms in this part of the woods.

If this keeps up, Brown groused, the Viet Cong are going to establish permanent camps at each end of the runway to salvage our overdrops.

A-Ro is one of four Special Forces camps along the Laotian

border. Its mission is to harass Viet Cong supply lines out of North Viet Nam. The others are at Kha Sanh, Ta Ho and Khan Duc. Americans are based in each camp.

"We like to feel that we have interrupted some of their plans," says Maj. Gene Nance of Shelbyville, Tenn., senior Special Forces man in the First Corps area.

Obviously this has occurred. The Viet Cong have been striking at our camps with particular fury. In July they overran and all but wiped out an interior camp at Nam Dong. Two Americans and one Australian adviser were killed. Five Americans were wounded. Nam Dong was 95 per cent destroyed. It is now being rebuilt, however.

There are approximately 20 Americans, and two Australians, at A-Ro. They include Army, Air Force, Navy Seabees and a couple of Marines who—officially—aren't here at all. Inter-service cooperation is, of necessity, very real.

Almost daily A-Ro is under fire. Every day its men roam the jungles along its perimeter in search of the Viet Cong. They assume that anything outside the fences is hostile. If they find a hut or a settlement they burn it. Seldom, if ever, do they see people.

Simply to get to A-Ro is a risky business. We set out from Da Nang in a Marine helicopter at 8 a.m. At 8:15, Marine Cpl. Steve Smith of Anniston, Ala., the gunner, excitedly pointed toward the ground and beckoned. The Saigon-bound train which had whistled bravely past camp at breakfast was on its side, derailed by Viet Cong mines 10 miles out of town. The Viet Cong manage to untrack one train a week—just to show that they can.

On the edge of the jungle, machine guns continued to chatter and mortars whoomped. Meanwhile we still needed sandbags, and another 40,000 were on the way from Da Nang.

A big Air Force C-123 appeared on the horizon and announced itself.

"Get some men on those guns," Brown ordered, "in case they draw fire."

The big cargo plane swept low and crewmen kicked out the

first load. It missed the runway and fell among the bunkers. Miraculously it missed them all.

Capt. George McKenzie of San Antonio grabbed the radio.

"Ground to air!" he yelled. "Damn it, pull over a bit! We like our layout just as it is."

OCT. 7, A-RO

It's a good thing, everybody agreed later on, that Brownie is part jungle cat.

We were sitting around after evening chow when we heard Charlie drop his mortar in a tube a good 2500 yards away.

Brownie is Sgt. William E. Brown of Ashland, N.H., team sergeant for a handful of American Special Forcemen in this besieged outpost smack up against the Laotian border. Charlie is the Viet Cong enemy. Sometimes he's Joe, but most often Charlie.

I had heard nothing. Neither had anyone else. One of the Marines was spinning a war yarn. Brownie was listening but part of him was tuned to the rain forests outside Camp A-Ro. It couldn't have been much louder than the click of a cigaret lighter at that distance.

"Incoming!" he yelled.

You have 14 seconds after a mortar drops. You can do what you want with that time. You can stay where you are, or you can run for cover.

Brownie was the first man in the sandbagged command bunker. I was right behind him and lying flat when the first round dropped. It hit on the runway, a good 25 yards away, with a muffled whoomp. I listened for someone to yell he'd been hit, but it didn't come. Apparently everybody made it.

Now the clicks can be heard. One. Two. Three. Four. About two seconds apart. I hugged the bunker floor and rolled nearer the sandbagged wall.

"They're firing in salvos," said Capt. George McKenzie of San Antonio.

Whoomp! Whoomp! Whoomp! Whoomp!

Those were close. Too close. They went past the bunker, missing it by a scant 15 feet. The sandbagged walls shook. My ears rang. A shaving kit tumbled off someone's bunk. Dust was everywhere.

Now we were on the radio to Da Nang. A-Ro was under fire.

Hundreds of rifles and machine guns seemed to be firing at once. Much of it came from A-Ro's defenders. Some of it came from the outside. Inside the bunker, men fingered their weapons nervously.

"We'll be able to hold out unless one gets in here with us," Brownie said.

Clyde Stewart of Marysville, Ind., was posted at the door. Shoot anyone who tries to force his way in, Brownie told him.

Da Nang, 80 miles away, radioed that an air strike was on the way. Someone cheered. Brown handed the radio to Seabee Dave Bowling of Knoxville.

"You do the listening, I'll do the looking," he said.

More mortars. Whoomp Whoomp! Whoomp! Wounded were coming in.

The mortars kept digging into the earth, smacking around the fuel dump. Obviously that was Charlie's target, and he was hitting all around it. Seabee Lt. Bill Pitcher of Knoxville groaned. He had parked his bulldozer there.

There was a letup now, and we climbed cautiously out of our holes, keeping our heads down. Sgt. Johnny Cooper of Myrtle Beach, S.C., the weapons man, was talking.

"Five times," he said, "he has fired 81's at us. Why is he missing us?"

"Because," Brownie said, "he doesn't want to mess up the equipment. He couldn't care less about you and me. He doesn't want just to come in here and fight a battle. He's after guns, radios, food, ammo and medical supplies. And he figures this way he can get them."

It's 7 o'clock now and getting dark. Still no aircraft. Brownie's on the radio.

"We know where the guy is," he tells Da Nang. "Give us some planes to hit the area and we'll get him."

113

Da Nang is apologetic.

"Sorry," someone says on the other end. "No aircraft available."

"Or maybe," we yell back, "it's too near dinner time."

(These were Vietnamese planes that were supposed to come to our defense—not USAF.)

"It's been a rough day," I said.

"Every day's rough out here," Brownie answered.

OCT. 14, QUANG TRI

Don Bolner of Indianapolis is a tall, angular man in his late thirties. His manner is deceptively mild. His rimless glasses give him the appearance of a schoolteacher, which is what he'd like to be when he retires in a few years.

But Donald E. Bolner now is a major in the U.S. Army and a regimental adviser at Quang Tri, our last outpost before North Viet Nam. It is a harsh, demanding job and not one for which off hand, you'd pick such a man.

Yet a couple of Sundays ago you'd have found Don Bolner, rimless spectacles and all, atop a lumbering armored personnel carrier (APC) in the paddies around Linh An, shooting Viet Cong as they popped up around him.

One, a Viet Cong lieutenant later taken prisoner, lobbed a grenade into his armored mount. Fortunately it did not detonate. Maj. Bolner's men buried 82 Viet Cong after that encounter. They took 58 prisoners and captured 64 weapons of all types, 122 grenades and 5000 rounds of ammunition. They figure they all but destroyed two Communist companies. In all, not a bad Sunday's work.

Bolner and his Vietnamese counterpart, a Maj. Hanh, had planned well. The Viet Cong had set up a headquarters in Linh An, about six miles from Quang Tri. Vietnamese fighter bombers came in to hit them. One plane was lost, but the Viet Cong were routed. That was at 2:10 p.m.

The Communists found their way barred by two Vietnamese army companies with which Marine Gunnery Sgt. Edmund

Sewell of Jacksonville, Fla., and an Australian, Warrant Officer Bob Penman, were serving.

The Viet Cong fell back, taking heavy casualties. They fled back through the village into the paddies toward the China Sea. The water was waist deep. High winds had blown the rice flat.

The Red guerrillas stopped dead in their tracks when an armada of amphibious armored cavalry suddenly appeared ahead. Don Bolner was astride one vehicle. First Lt. Bobby Cowling of Texarkana, Ark., was on another. Major Hanh was on a third.

"Obviously," Bolner recalls with the air of a businessman telling of a successful deal, "they knew nothing about amphibious carriers. They were confident we couldn't come at them from that direction. That was our trump card. From that point on, it was a matter of tracking them down."

The armored halftracks swarmed through the rice fields, guns blazing. One by one the Viet Cong popped up. Some tried to run. Others chose to stand and fight. It didn't matter, really. They all died.

"They'd jump up right beside you," Bolner recalls. "They'd be three feet away. It was ridiculously easy."

It was also dangerous. The Viet Cong had rifle grenades. And they were pros. Whatever the odds against them, they did not panic. A rifle grenade fired into the guts of an APC kills every man in it. Fortunately, that didn't happen. Our losses: seven wounded.

Don Bolner was interested in prisoners. He saw one man fall, shot through the stomach, but still alive and kicking. He and the regimental surgeon, a refugee from North Viet Nam, went after him. But a Vietnamese private got there first. He calmly dispatched the wounded man with a shot through the head.

"I could have cried," Maj. Bolner says.

Maj. Hanh was luckier. Or more resourceful. As a young Viet Cong popped up beside him—Hanh was standing in the rear door of an APC—he grabbed the boy and yanked him aboard. He turned out to be a 17-year-old high-school student from Nam Dinh, outside Hanoi, who'd arrived four days earlier from the

115

North. Communist organizers had persuaded 50 high-school boys to spend their vacation "liberating South Viet Nam from the Americans." Glad to be alive, the kid sang like a canary.

"He was the frosting on the cake," says Bolner.

It was over shortly before dark, one of the biggest kills of the war. Exhausted, Don Bolner came back to Quang Tri for a hot shower and a meal. The Vietnamese have recommended him for their highest award for valor. Bolner dismisses that as of no consequence. He's proudest of his three combat infantry badges, one each for World War II, Korea and Viet Nam.

Bolner joined the Army in 1944, then was out for five years before coming back as a sergeant in 1950, just in time for Korea. He was commissioned a second lieutenant in 1952. He and his wife are from Hartford City, Ind., and have two sons back in Indianapolis: Patrick, 12, and Dennis, 8.

OCT. 21, DA NANG

Capt. Harvey H. is one of 18,000 American military advisers in Viet Nam.

He is young, energetic and ambitious. His superiors rate him a comer, a man whose career lies ahead of him if he does not stub his toe.

Captain H. is stationed at a remote outpost on the Laotian border. He is pretty much on his own.

"Dear Major McM.," he wrote his superior recently. "A few lines to let you know how we are getting along. I am making some headway with Tho. He seems to trust me now and is accepting advice. I scratch his back quite a bit and am careful to give advice in small doses."

H. is also a frequently bewildered man. He sees his job as a challenge. There is remarkably little grousing among American advisers. This may be because they are so carefully chosen. But Captain H. has been steeped in the American tradition that soldiering and politics do not mix. Americans frequently are shocked to learn that their Vietnamese counterparts are members of clashing political parties, aligned with the "ins" or the "outs" in the military hierarchy and reluctant to accept orders from officers with whom they disagree.

But Capt. H. likes to stick to business. He wrote:

"In addition to improving our own living facilities, I am providing Tho with certain materials to improve his and to generally dress up the camp."

They say of American advisers that they go through three stages here. They arrive as "chargers," eager to tackle the job and help win the war. Soon they become bitter and discouraged, convinced the thing is hopeless. After that they level off and do the best they can.

Capt. H. likes the Vietnamese with whom he works. In this he is lucky. One young American captain, saddled with an incompetent Vietnamese commander, demanded his removal. He was bluntly told that even if he backed his man into a corner and forced his removal he (the American) would be relieved, too. It was all part of the process of "saving face."

Like most Americans, Captain H. takes it for granted that all men are willing to fight for their country. He has been shocked to find that many Vietnamese are not, that the woods are full of draft dodgers and deserters. He had always assumed that promotions were based on merit. Here again he has been upset. In one Vietnamese regiment, for instance, the commanding officer (a colonel) served as a second lieutenant under his executive officer (a major) when the major was a captain. The colonel is a political officer. He bet on the right team; the major backed a loser. The Americans consider the major the better officer. But he has little to do; no Vietnamese ever lets a subordinate do anything.

On this score, Capt. H. wrote to his superior officers:

"Our bunkers and fortifications need much work. I do not intend to make recommendations until I have studied the situation. Then I will ask Tho to approve my plan and allow my assistants to work directly with his subordinates. He may consider this outrageous, and I will have to handle it delicately."

Like all the advisers, Capt. H. wants to win the war. He is distressed to find South Vietnamese fighting each other. He has his sights on one enemy—the Viet Cong. He is convinced the Communists can be defeated if we buckle down to the job at hand.

But to his dismay, he often finds that he has not escaped Saigon's inexorable demands for reports in triplicate. No matter how deep in the jungle he has gone, they catch up with him.

Then he can only express his frustration as he did in his letter:

"Sir, attached you will find the most ridiculous request for a report I have ever encountered. I would be interested in learning whose brainchild this is. Sir, we are fighting a war out here!"

OCT. 22, QUANG TRI

You learn to hate the rains.

There is no land or sky. Only the rains. They lash at you, bite at you, drench you. They never let up. You've forgotten when it was they started, and you have no hope they'll ever stop. You've never been dry. In all of your life, you've never been dry. You've always been wet to the skin.

Rains should be gentle and kind. Men should enjoy rains. But here rain is your enemy. It is not gentle. It is brutal and cruel.

Rains like this do something to a man. He ceases to live; he merely exists. After a while, he gives up. There's no place the rains can't get at you.

"It's not so bad," the sergeant said miserably, "until your bedding gets wet."

You know he's right. Still, you sleep in it, wringing out the water before you lie down, shaking the wet into the wetness around you when you get up.

With the rains come the crawling, creeping, flying things. The mosquitoes, of course. The leeches—loathsome blobs that manage, somehow, to get into your boots and satiate themselves. The tiny flying things against which screens are no defense; your coffee is coated with them after the first sip. And the snakes. They hate the rains, too.

118

You ride down the Street Without Joy, Route 1 from Hue to Quang Tri, and the road is covered with them. Corp. Dennis Lane of Cincinnati points them out and Thanh, the interpreter, identifies them. That one's poisonous; that one's not. Your jeep totters as you try to get them. You recall hearing that a wheel can throw a snake in among you. You shudder.

They come into camp, too, seeking the high ground, so that even in the grayness of daylight, you take a flashlight with you when you go out, check your bedding before you turn in, imagine you hear them in the dead of night.

Dawn comes and paints a new day grey. Day follows day in a monotony of days, and still it rains. It seems it always has rained—it always will. You've never known anything but rain.

The rain cuts your roads, grounds your planes. Units in the fields are cut off from their supplies. The paddies become rivers, then lakes, then oceans. And still the rains come.

Your only solace is that the Viet Cong must endure it, too. And they also are its prisoners. They can't move, either.

It rains in the mountains, and pours down into the lowlands in a mad rush to the sea. So you stay off the roads lest you be carried along, too.

The winds stop, but the rains go on. There is nothing in life but the rains.

OCT. 23, HUE

There was machine-gun fire in the valley between An Beung and Sun Qua, 700 yards to the west and 400 feet straight down the hill.

The call had come at 2 a.m.—while most of us were asleep—and had been taken by Marine Capt. John Bolton, Alliance, O.

The Vietnamese had surrounded a Viet Cong battalion 10 miles west of Hue. They needed reinforcements. Only the Marines with their helicopters could get them there in time. Eight government soldiers had been killed and seven wounded in the night's action. Enemy losses were anywhere from four to 14.

Thus it was, shortly after dawn, that 18 Marine helicopters

119

churned the air between Da Nang and Hue, where they would pick up their troops and get their final instructions. John Bolton flew in the lead plane with his squadron C.O., Lt. Col. Joe Koler, Jr., of Tustin, Calif.

It was hard to believe, on such a cloudless, crisp morning, that Viet Nam was at war. Below, released from the night's curfew, a bus made its way toward Hue. On the ground, once we landed, attractive Vietnamese women in their flowing native dress bicycled past the parked aircraft without seeing them. They had learned to live with war. It was no business of theirs.

Grinning cheerfully, the Vietnamese soldiers came aboard and sat on the floor. Their heads had barely reached the chopper's floorboards, and they carried staggering loads on their backs, so that you had to reach down and help them. One had a live duck hanging from his pack. Another carried a loaf of French bread.

The boy with the duck sat next to me. The duck raised up and regarded me with suspicion. I debated the best way to make friends with a duck and decided, instead, to shift position.

Now we were in the landing zone at An Beung. It's a steep hill, blanketed with sharp elephant grass. Joe Koler had sent spotter planes—Lt. Ray Thompson of Portland, Ore., and Lt. Bill Abel, Chevy Chase, Md., at the controls—and weather planes—Capts. John Zellich of Louisville and George Pratt of Tulsa—on ahead. They had guided us in, though they were low on fuel and couldn't hang around to watch.

The only decent landing zone was the valley below. But that was where the battle was. So we'd settled for a hilltop. It was tricky. Capt. Tom Wheeler, Chicago, and First Lt. John Cronin, Fall River, Mass., put their ship down and felt it slide. They gunned it, hovering above the grass, and settled again, one wheel on the slope, the other suspended in air. The Vietnamese, wide-eyed and excited, piled out smartly. On command from their lieutenant, they formed a skirmish line and headed out toward the sounds of war.

The Marines liked these boys. Best we've seen, they said. Took them eight seconds to come aboard. No more than that to get off. Don't have to kick and shove these lads. They want to fight. And did you see that Vietnamese lieutenant? And the way his men reacted? Sharp, man, sharp.

The letdown came a few hours later. The "surrounded" Viet Cong melted away into the hills. After an initial contact, all was quiet. That is the story of this war. For want of something better to do we burned Sun Qua, a hamlet of three huts. It had been the enemy's command post. Now the Vietnamese troops returned.

They clambered aboard, grinning cheerfully, but quickly sensed the change in atmosphere. The Marines had expected much; their hopes were dashed. The Vietnamese looked at one another, puzzled, then subsided into silence.

You fancied you could read their minds as they stared glumly ahead. They felt let down.

"These Americans," they seemed to be thinking. "What is it they want of us?"

The Americans also felt let down.

"These Vietnamese!" they were grumbling. "Had the enemy surrounded, and he got away. At this rate, we'll be here 20 years from now."

This, too, is the story of the war in Viet Nam.

OCT. 24, KHAM DUC

It had happened near Marble Mountain.

The unarmed Huey was en route to Tam Ky, a remote outpost near the Laotian border.

Only four miles from the end of the runway it had developed engine trouble, and the pilot had set down.

As he stepped out of the cockpit Viet Cong fire got him through the chest. He was wearing a flak vest, but it was open in front.

An old-timer would never have done that. He'd have known that Marble Mountain was bad trouble. And Marble Mountain is near enough to our base at Da Nang to be part of it. It's just beyond the beach where we sometimes send swimming parties under guard.

121

The pilot was dead. His crewmen were uninjured but shaken up and drawing heavy fire.

We first heard about it in the air as we neared Kham Duc. At that distance the signal was weak and the message garbled, but there was no mistaking what it meant.

As it turned out later, many people heard it.

Maj. Irwin Cockett of Koloa, Kauai, Hawaii, heard it in his office shack off the runway at Da Nang. He was four miles from where the sleek Huey went in, and the message came through loud and clear. He knew at once that it was one of his men.

Army Lt. George T. Johnson of Wichita, Kan., heard it in a sister ship as he prepared to take off.

Marine Captains Mike Barkovich of McDonald, O., and Ken Keck of Seymour, Tex., heard it, too, and weren't surprised when their C.O.—Lt. Col. Joe Koler, Jr., Tustin, Calif.—ordered them to move out of a long column of Marine choppers headed for Kham Duc and A-Ro. They were at the tail end of the long procession and nearest to the downed aircraft.

Army Specialist Lewis J. Green, Watanga, Okla., a helicopter technical inspector, heard about it when his major, Irwin Cockett, raced toward Johnson's Huey and ordered him to follow. Green didn't wait for details.

Now over Kham Duc—where the Marines also were drawing fire—we listened to the radio, trying to salvage a word or two from the crackling static.

Johnson was the first in.

"We are drawing heavy fire. There are still wounded on the ground."

Col. Hardy Hay, Austin, Tex., flying with Capt. George Boemerman of Greenwood Lake, N.J., checked his flight to be sure it wasn't one of his birds. All came in on cue.

Johnson's ship was on the ground now, and Major Cockett and Specialist Green hopped out. Cockett and Green shoved the downed crewmen aboard, then fanned out with machine guns in an attempt to protect the downed ship.

Barkovich and Keck were just behind Johnson. They drew fire as they set down beside the Huey. Cockett and Green hopped aboard with their own guns and the machine guns they'd taken from the grounded chopper.

There were others now. A couple of bubble-topped Air Force choppers circled the scene, keeping the Viet Cong down. Two more Marine choppers edged out of the column working between Kham Duc and A-Ro. With Barkovich and Keck they brought in 60 Vietnamese soldiers to hold the enemy at bay while we tried to fly the downed Huey back to Da Nang.

Barkovich's gunners, Corp. Mike Layman of Portland, Ore., and Pfc. Harry Deschane of Minneapolis, kept up a steady stream of fire.

All this we heard, sketchily, over the radio as a few days earlier, we had listened to the World Series. But there is something terribly personal about a "little war" like this.

In other, bigger wars, we have numbered our dead in the thousands. Here, we still count them in the hundreds. Ours is a compact little family; the death of one member can shock and dismay the rest. This pilot had been here but two weeks, but as soon as we heard his name we knew him. We knew, for instance, he had only 18 months to go before he retired.

We move out of radio contact now, and we have work to do. Our ships, shifting troops between Kham Duc and A-Ro, are drawing sporadic fire. Ours is a SAR (Sea-Air Rescue) ship. It's our job to pull our boys out if they run into trouble.

Later we learned that back at Marble Mountain, efforts to get the downed Huey out had failed. The ship was stripped, then burned.

NOV. 2, SOC TRANG

"Tiger Six" goes home soon, having headed a combat unit longer than any other American in the Vietnamese war.

"Tiger Six" is Maj. Joseph Levinson, 41, of Enterprise, Ala., commander of the 121st Army Aviation company, the famed Sox Trang Tigers.

Other Americans may have served in Viet Nam longer than Levinson. But they have been purely advisers or held desk jobs.

On the books the 121st is a "Combat Support" unit, but that should fool no one. It has been—and is—a combat outfit.

Levinson came to Viet Nam in November, 1963, and leaves quite a record of accomplishment behind him.

Eight Americans have been awarded South Viet Nam's highest combat decoration, the Medal of Valor. One was Gen. Paul D. Harkins. Four of the remaining seven are Soc Trang Tigers. Levinson was the first. The others have been Capt. Bert Nye of Pollacksville, N.C., Capt. Ralph Hamner of Tuscaloosa, Ala., and Capt .Charles Gordon, Nye's successor.

Levinson neither looks nor acts like a combat veteran. He was once a printers' ink salesman in Chicago. A member of the Illinois National Guard, he became aide to Brig. Gen. Julius Klein. Mobilized in 1950, he flew light planes in the Korean War, then decided to make the fledgling Army Aviation Corps his career.

He has done well at it. In Viet Nam he has logged better than 300 hours of combat flying, and added 11 Oak Leaf clusters to his Air Medal—for a total of 13.

With Brig. Gen. Dang Van Quang, commander of the 21st Vietnamese Army Division, and Col. Jim Kiersey of Durant, Okla., Quang's American adviser, Levinson has worked out a degree of cooperation and teamwork remarkable in this war. They refer to themselves as a team.

General Quang recently wrote Levinson: "As a result of your efforts, our division has inflicted heavy losses on the Communist insurgents in spectacular fast-reaction operations, despite adverse weather and flooded paddy fields. This reflects the determination of your men under your outstanding leadership."

The General also praised the rear guard in Soc Trang which "worked day and night to preserve the machinery and weapons to have an adequate number of helicopters" in the air.

Joe Levinson is essentially a family man. Every night he cuts a tape and mails it back to Enterprise, where he recently built a new home. Luckily, he is being reassigned to Fort Rucker, just outside Enterprise.

In Viet Nam he has had another family of several hundred men. He has welded them into a close-knit unit.

When he took over, Soc Trang was a rat-infested dump. Today the rats are long gone. He had finagled money from somewhere to build three clubs, a post exchange, a modern air-conditioned library, a hobby shop and tennis courts. As he leaves, a gym is under construction.

These things are important. To all intents and purposes Soc Trang is a beleaguered island in a sea of hostile Viet Cong.

Highjinks delight Levinson. He has developed a ritual for welcoming visitors in which the entire company takes part. Recently he called a meeting of captains in his quarters. His lieutenants promptly staged a "coup" and "overthrew" all captains.

Five times Joe was relieved of his command—fired—by Lt. Col. Ace Phillips, his commanding officer. Each time, he reinstated Levinson at dawn.

The next time Joe suspected he was in trouble, he wrote out his resignation, flew 50 miles to Can Tho and laid it on Phillips' desk. The Colonel read it, endorsed and approved it, then tore it up.

"Now, damn it!" he shouted, "get back to work."

Joe Levinson did.

Somehow, it won't be the same war with Joe back in Alabama.

NOV. 4, SOC TRANG

The Major unfolds his field map and noisily clears his throat. It's the signal for his pilots to crowd around and get the word.

"This area is allegedly pacified"—he lays heavy, sarcastic emphasis on "allegedly." "The area we want to work is right here."

Neighboring, warring hamlets, parted by a narrow canal. And it will be dark.

It had begun 10 minutes earlier, at 7:05 p.m. You'd come back from a chopper flight, swapping your flak vest for a sports shirt, your heavy boots for slippers, and had sprawled on your sack.

"Don't undress," Maj. Joe Levinson had said. "There's a hard-core Viet Cong company three miles out, preparing to mortar this airfield."

Soc Trang, home of the 121st Army Aviation Company, has been mortared before. Levinson, its energetic commander, doesn't want it to happen again.

He picked up a field telephone and rang Corps, 50 miles away. To Maj. Arnold Carillo of Tucson, Ariz., he yelled:

"They're planning to mortar me. Do I have permission . . ."

Loud laughter at both ends.

That seems a long time ago—actually less than an hour. But it looks like the Fourth of July at the Washington Monument.

You'd whipped off the bunk, laced on your boots and headed for Operations. On most strikes, the pilots know who is flying. Now it's first come, first on the assignment board. Joe is taking a flare ship. Lt. Ken Hill of Petrolia, Tex., hustles in and wins the co-pilot's seat.

Capt. Bob Hackett of South Amboy, N.J., is leading a flight of five armed Hueys. They flutter out into the dark. The men with him are seasoned vets—Bert Nye of Pollacksville, N.C., Ron Garrison of El Paso, Billy Lindsey of Memphis, Bill Kegelmeyer of Columbus, O.

The city of Soc Trang is a neon-lighted triangle in the distance as we circle the Rach River. Hackett and his armed Vikings keep low, asking for hostile fire. It's that kind of war. Those are the Rules of Engagement, and they're strict. You fire only if you're fired on. Sometimes you've got to beg for it.

If they're disciplined, they won't oblige. If one panics, you get it.

You know they're down there. They were last night. Tonight, friendly villagers had slipped into town with word they were creeping up, hoping to get close enough to lob something in. If they're three miles out, they're close enough.

Hackett's voice—calm, unruffled—comes over the phones.

"Viking 26 has drawn fire." He's Viking 26. He's talking about himself.

Minutes later: "Viking 22 drawing fire." That will be Ron Garrison.

After that, the war is on. Everybody draws fire.

One by one the Vikings peel off and open up. On board, the noise is ear-splitting. At a distance, however, you hear nothing. You don't see the choppers. But their red tracers pour out in a steady stream, flowering at the end as they hit the ground. Like a garden hose.

Now the rockets come—white-hot projectiles to illuminate the night.

In the tree lines below, the Communists shoot back. You spot gun flashes until you can no longer count them. But there's no mistaking them. The farm huts doused their lights with the first salvo and the people went to cover. A hut light is steady and unblinking. A gun flash is abrupt and angry.

"I wondered why we were drawing so much fire." Levinson's voice has a grin in it. "Stupid of me. I forgot to turn off my lights."

It's war, but it's strangely beautiful. Vikings are everywhere at once. Their red landing lights blink lazily. One, however, has a white light. You wonder about that.

"The VC shot the red one out," Joe explains.

Sgt. Lester Blaxton of Vidalia, Ga., Joe's gunner and crew chief, has given you his earphones. If he's to fire, you're to tap him on the shoulder. Joe calls, you tap, Les Blaxton fires his machine gun. That brings the war closer.

It's 8:15. An hour and 10 minutes have passed. You're back on the ground at Soc Trang. Maj. Hartwin Peterson of Bryan, Tex., American adviser to the province chief, is waiting. Hit 'em again, he suggests. We hit 'em again for good measure. And for Peterson. He caught a bullet in the hand a few months back, flying with Joe.

It's over finally. Maybe we got them this time. We can't be sure. But they never got around to mortaring us.

NOV. 5, CA MAU

You listen carefully, not wanting to miss any of it, because if anybody knows the score, it's this guy.

You're heading for Rach Rang, a remote outpost on the South China Sea, and Captain Alton B. Parker, Fairmont, N.C., is filling you in.

"They stayed right here last night and moved out around twelve," he says, pointing to his plastic-encased map. "Evidently they're getting ready to hit Rach Rang."

He points again.

"They may be crossing here. We hear it's a Viet Cong company."

Your pilots, Capts. Terry Oliver of Indianapolis, and Curtis Dassonville, Frazer, Mont., scribble on their overlays.

"They have this valley on the far side," Parker continues. "It's bad. It's always bad. And don't come too damned close to that canal. We have reports there are built-up areas here . . . and here . . . and here . . ."

So how do we get in?

"So you whip right around to the north," he replies with a tight grin. "That may be your best bet."

❀   ❀   ❀

They call this the milk run. Without it these outposts couldn't survive. The Vietnamese at Rach Rang know about war. Two months ago they were overrun. Fifty men were killed. Others were wounded or taken prisoner. The post is still a shambles. But somehow they hold out.

"We can't supply them properly," Al Parker says. "The C.O. keeps crying for more men, but we can't sustain them. They're smoking cigarets made out of old newspapers as it is."

Now we're heading for Rach Rang. It's a 15-minute hop from Ca Mau. We fly at 4000 feet, dodging the rain clouds. It had been unbearably hot on the ground. Up here, it's unbearably cold.

There are troops aboard, men heading for Rach Rang. A couple are solemn, sad-faced. The others seem cheerful enough.

We're on the ground now. The men pile out, greeting old friends, slapping one another on the back. One of Rach Rang's shell-shocked defenders spots someone he once knew and kisses him on both cheeks. Somehow that affectionate buss doesn't seem out of place.

Vietnamese, their Rach Rang tours completed, rush toward the helicopter with their hand baggage. Obviously we can't carry them all. Some will have to stay behind. It's a tough decision, and it's up to Crew Chief Milton Frith of Fort Worth, and Gunner Ricardo Lopez, Santa Ana, Calif., to decide. They let on eight men, wave off the rest. It has happened before and they accept it stoically. There'll be another milk run another day. A couple rush forward to congratulate their buddies who made it.

The lucky eight chatter excitedly as the big Huey churns the dust and flutters aloft. They're heading for Ca Mau. They spot it in the distance and cheer.

To them it's civilization.

* * *

Milton Frith bothers you. A teen-ager with a lot of mischief in him, he hangs over the side at 4000 feet, leaning his weight against his machine gun mount, more out than inside the aircraft. You look away. If they get my ship, he says, they'll get me first. But he's competent. His tour ends Dec. 22, and they're sending him to Fort Rucker, Ala., as an instructor, though he's only a Specialist Fourth Class. "Shouldn't be hard," he says. "I'll teach the know-nothings—the privates." And he seems to have a rapport with the Vietnamese. He buckles them in, grins at them, lights genuine cigarets and passes them around. This is his Huey, and they're his guests.

Next it's Song Ong Doc, across from Rach Rang. It's also under fire. Then to Nam Can—where we bring out a naval family of four and a load of mortars—then Hai Yen. After Hai Yen, Nga Ba Dinh. Outposts all. A platoon or so of men. A mortar or two. Maybe a field artillery piece. And always the lurking danger. Always the Viet Cong.

"Tam Bang has been abandoned," Parker says at lunch. "Dom Doi will have to go."

He shakes his head.

"Dom Doi is bad news," he adds.

129

Why do we keep these little forts, someone asks. What good do they do?

"We're giving them up gradually," he replies. "They just draw fire. Get men killed."

In the late afternoon, it's Thoi Binh. Big Thoi Binh. Tam Bang was Little Thoi Binh, and it's gone. Big Thoi Binh is surrounded. We put down, hurriedly toss out mortar rounds, leave mail for the Americans, whirl away. Once airborne, we're all right.

They stay, waiting for the night and the Viet Cong.

And—if they're lucky—another milk run.

NOV. 9, CAN THO

American medics in the Mekong Delta have been issued 22-year-old first-aid kits containing, among other things, a tourniquet ordered destroyed in 1951 and iodine swabs banned by the Army surgeon general.

They were to have been used in medical work among Vietnamese villagers as a gesture of good-will.

"To use any of this would be murder," said one U.S. medical adviser who understandably does not want his name used.

It is impossible here in the field to establish responsibility for obsolete issue. Fifty large shoulder-sling packs arrived in Fourth Corps Headquarters last week from Saigon, for distribution to medical field teams in the Delta. American medical advisers here were told by their superiors in Saigon, to whom they complained, that the ancient packs were selected because "we're running low on money."

American doctors in the Delta say the packs are not worth shipping charges.

"All we can do," said one, "is keep the canvas container, throw out everything, and requisition more."

That will mean additional shipping expense.

In addition to the tourniquet ordered destroyed 13 years ago because it caused excessive tissue damage, and iodine no longer used by our Army doctors, the first-aid field packs contained:

—Rolls of adhesive tape with an issue date of March, 1942, unserviceable and badly water-stained.

—Gauze bandages, issued Sept. 10, 1942, mildewed.

—Mildewed first-aid dressings.

—Rusted safety pins.

Vietnamese medical teams are supplied late-issue kits which include a device for mouth-to-mouth resuscitation and surgical forceps. The vintage packs sent the Americans do not even have a pair of scissors.

The World War II packs were to have gone to newly authorized sub-sector teams which will operate in district towns. Each sub-sector team will be headed by an American Army major and will include an enlisted medical corpsman. This results from a recent decision to raise the number of U.S. advisers here from 16,-000 to 20,000.

Until now, no Americans have been based below province (state) capitals. The sub-sector teams will operate in the equivalent of county seats, with much more intimate contact with the villagers and farmers.

Recently Gen. William Westmoreland visited the Central Highlands and asked a young corpsman how things were going. The corpsman said everything was fine except he had no supplies. Westmoreland ordered that supplies be issued immediately from Saigon. Apparently someone located the World War II packs in a warehouse somewhere and—mindful of the fact "we're running low on money"—sent them to the field.

For all practical purposes, medics with the Delta's sub-sector teams have no first-aid packs.

NOV. 13, CAN THO

It happened to him on patrol. The little Vietnamese soldier stepped into a booby trap. That's all they can tell you about him, and he cannot speak. It must have been a powerful one, intended for many men. He was out front, and he took the full blast alone.

Now he's a triple amputee. Both arms and his right leg are gone. He is blind in both eyes. His face and body are horribly burned and scarred.

There isn't much they can do for him except ease the pain. Apparently they've done that. He lies there quietly, though they say he's awake.

"This one probably will live," a doctor says.

Live for what, you wonder.

A visit to a Vietnamese field hospital is a sobering experience.

Every other man among the 650 patients is an amputee. Some have lost legs. Others their arms. Ten to 15 per cent are tuberculous. All the others have combat wounds.

It isn't a pretty sight.

Day and night the helicopters come, bringing in wounded men. There seems to be no end of them. Nor will there be until this war is over.

The handful of doctors and nurses work hard. By now, most know their jobs. They should. They've had plenty of experience.

Sometimes Americans become exasperated with them. Their ideas of sanitation leave a lot to be desired. At least, we think so. But they're learning. And their survival rate is good. They lose only 35 out of every 1000 stretcher cases.

Their hospital here adjoins our compound. We see it every day. A lot of myths have grown up about it. Many of us believe them.

One myth is that a wounded man's family or friends must feed him. If he is a bachelor or friendless, so the story goes, he must shift for himself or starve.

Most patients are cared for by their wives, relatives or sweethearts. They come from all over South Viet Nam and live on the hospital grounds. Some patients with funds are fed from the outside by their families. But this is a matter of choice.

Wounded officers get about 40 cents a day ration allowance. Enlisted men get 18 cents.

Rice is free and plentiful. At meal time, trucks carrying huge vats of boiled rice make the rounds of the wards.

Walking patients, wives and children come with their trays, bowls and cups to help themselves. It is a mob scene. Americans long ago gave up efforts to get them to stand in line. That is not the Vietnamese way. It's everyone for himself. But no one goes without.

If a man is without friends or relatives, and bed-ridden, Red Cross girls see that he is fed. Often a wife of one patient will care for as many as six others. She is paid.

The Vietnamese still have much to learn. During the recent battle of Bac Lieu, Vietnamese pilots would not fly after dark to evacuate their own wounded. But on other occasions Vietnamese rescue pilots have distinguished themselves.

They have ample time to learn. The end of this war—and the suffering—is not yet in sight.

NOV. 16, MY THO

Pete Kendrick called from his armed Cobra helicopter. "Five men dug in off road on your left, short of the bridge ahead. Stay alert."

The big moustached Army Captain from Killeen, Tex., is one of a handful of Americans wearing the Vietnamese Medal of Valor. A good man to have around.

Capt. Don Masters of Austin, Tex., gunned his jeep. Three big gas tankers roared behind it. Jeep and tankers sped past the first foxhole.

A Vietnamese Self Defense Corpsman pointed frantically to trees across the paddies on the right and held up 10 fingers. That's the signal for Communist Viet Cong.

We'd plunged headfirst into a gun battle. But with the appearance of the armed choppers, the Viet Cong quit.

It was, we told each other, a good thing we had Pete with us.

Ours was the first all-American road convoy from Can Tho, on one bank of the Bassac, to My Tho, on the far bank of the Mekong 70 miles away.

133

Our cargo was vulnerable—three tank trucks each with 1200 gallons of volatile fuel. One was full of aviation gas; the other two carried jet fuel.

In addition, two trucks loaded with Vietnamese draftees bound for Saigon had attached themselves to us.

There were armored cars fore and aft. We hoped the lead car would detonate any mines. Unless, of course, the mines were electrically detonated. Then the Viet Cong could be selective.

"After we cross the Mekong," Maj. Charles Holbrook of San Antonio, Tex., the convoy commander, briefed us at the first ferry crossing after dawn, "keep your heads down. We've had five ambushes along this road in the last three weeks.

"If we're shot at, keep going. If we hit a mine, stop, get out, go for the ditches. Keep a good distance apart. That way we don't give them too much of a target, and we may save our own skins. Otherwise, drive no slower than 40 miles an hour.

"I don't need to tell you one of their favorite tricks is to stand up in the middle of a bunch of women and children and shoot at you. If that happens, we don't—repeat, don't—shoot back."

The drivers and shotgun riders around him grinned amiably. The oldest was 24, the youngest 18.

"They didn't tell us all this when we volunteered," said Specialist Roy White of Cincinnati. White is a supply clerk who revolted against routine and asked for this assignment.

The convoy roared down the road, tore through a half-dozen hamlets. Buses and trucks pulled aside to let us pass.

Traveling at high speed, the big tankers followed the jeeps, dodging broken places in the paving—where the Commies plant mines. The Commies also hide mines in the piles of rock which construction crews leave on the right-of-way. Flying rocks kill men and wreck vehicles.

"The Vietnamese must know something we don't," said White. "They brought along a chaplain."

The padre, bound for My Tho for services, passed out religious tracts at every stop.

Pfc. Dennis Caspelich of Biloxi, Miss., studied the armed choppers circling overhead, never out of sight.

134

"Beautiful!" he said. "If those guys run low on fuel, we'll take care of them."

The choppers were our security. Frequently they were only 100 feet overhead.

"I want you to know," boasted Pfc. Carlton Sylvester of Biddeford, Me., "we've got the 'Hog' up there."

The "Hog" is the biggest of the armed Cobras. It totes 48 deadly rockets, 24 on each side. The Viet Cong respect it.

Messages and alerts came in a steady stream from the whirlybirds overhead.

"Two men dug in just ahead."

We sped by and drew no fire.

"Two suspicious sampans on the right. Watch them."

The pace was brutal but there was no hanging back.

"This your first?" White asked me.

I nodded. "Me, too. We're all virgins," he said.

White was a construction worker before he joined the Army. He hopes to work for Proctor and Gamble when he goes home six months hence.

Truong Lung went past and My Tho was in sight. But there was no letdown.

"Heavy concentration on your left," Kendrick called from above.

His Cobra swooped in to investigate. The farmers—if that's what they were—didn't look up. That's always a suspicious sign.

We reached My Tho and stopped.

"Cobra to Blackbird," Kendrick made his final call. "Am I released?"

"You are," Holbrook acknowledged. "Well done."

The pressure was off. We'd made it.

Tomorrow Roy White will be back in his stockroom, checking inventories.

NOV. 17, CAI RANG

Capt. Joe Pollard of Newbern, Ala., was exultant.

"The Sheriff buys the beers!" he called over his radio.

135

The "Sheriff" in any military outfit is the provost marshal. And Sheriff (Capt.) Jim Sender of Seattle, military police adviser to the Vietnamese in the Mekong Delta, would buy the beers back in the compound because he'd been the first to tumble off a monkey bridge.

A monkey bridge, most Americans here will agree, is an invention of the devil. It's a single log, often narrow, usually damp and slick, across a murky, sluggish canal.

The Vietnamese negotiate them with ease. The Americans invariably have trouble. These men have a standing wager: The first to fall in buys.

But the beers would come later. Our objective of the day was the Communist Viet Cong's Chau Thanh District Company, a regional force which hangs around Cai Rang and usually operates in platoons. Cai Rang itself, a town of 4000, is officially pacified. The country around it isn't.

"We see this company often," said Maj. Ed Elledge of Coolidge, Ariz., "but it usually won't stop and fight."

The company has 120 men, two mortars, two machine guns and five automatic rifles. It often harasses remote outposts.

We heard the night before that it would be working around Cai Rang. We decided to work in here, too.

We were up and into the field before dawn. But the spot picked by Lt. Col. Tran Ba Di, province chief, for his command post couldn't be reached. A bridge was out.

Col. Di decided to set up shop just off the main highway. His two artillery pieces pointed across the roofs of nearby homes. The occupants were not favorably impressed with his choice.

At 7:45 a.m., Capt. Pollard and Lt. Billy Murphy of Portland, Me., reported triumphantly they had killed two Viet Cong and captured one Russian rifle. The dead men had been lookouts.

They could have hidden their weapons in the paddies and pretended to be farmers. But they knew their ages—they were in their 20's—made them suspects and they'd be picked up. So they chose to make a run for it.

They didn't make it.

Pollard and Murphy with one column, and Capt. Jack Park of

Dallas and Lt. Larry Nahlen of Little Rock with another, continued to flush the paddies and search the hamlets.

It was dirty work. It had rained the night before and the mud was often knee deep.

At 8:20 a.m., Pollar dreported one of his Vietnamese GI's had stepped into a spike trap and become a casualty.

The day grew hotter. In the paddies, the search continued. Along the highway from Can Tho through Cai Rang, traffic flowed. Beneath the muzzle of one of the big guns, a small boy whitewashed a fence. A pushcart vendor sold soda pop.

The radio crackled. Lt. Bob Thornton of Clinton, Miss., was overhead in a small plane. He was our relay. Elledge's messages went to him, then to the men in the paddies.

"Playboy (Capt. Park) reports one platoon near Checkpoint 21," Thornton called. Checkpoint 21 was a hamlet called Gia Xuan.

Troops were sent to search. They found nothing.

It's often that way. Vietnamese are notorious gossips. Frequently a lone guerrilla becomes a whole platoon before word reaches headquarters.

Well into the afternoon our troops searched the paddies. Park and Nahlen's unit picked up a woman cadre member. Pollard and Murphy arrested two suspects. The bag grew, until at dusk there were nine prisoners.

The operation dragged to a close. It would never make the communiques.

Yet—

"I'm beginning to think," said Col. George Barten of Fairfax, Va., senior adviser in the Delta, "that these are our bread and butter, our meat and potatoes. Kill two, pick up nine, in a half-dozen spots every day—and in the long run that could tip the scales."

NOV. 18, KHAI QUANG

Johnny Hingle would probably be the first to declare it a great day for our side.

137

We had flushed the Viet Cong within a stone's throw of this beleaguered outpost and driven them back to their lair in the U-Minh forest. They broke off after dark, glad to have it over with, but behind them they left 59 dead and more weapons than they could afford to part with. Our side had four dead and 20 wounded.

Johnny Hingle of Houston, Tex., was the only American casualty. The big gunner, here on 90-day assignment from Hawaii, caught a round in his arm as his Viking helicopter came in with its load of rockets. Hingle got a severed artery. The pilot, Lt. Max Summers of Groom, Tex., probably saved Hingle's life when he went aft to apply a tourniquet. But they had to pry Johnny loose from his gun to put it on him.

Now Hingle has been put up for the Silver Star. Every man in the 121st Army Aviation Company at Soc Trang is pulling for him to get it.

When a man has a severed artery in a helicopter flying between 95 and 100 miles an hour—and a chopper that has no doors, at that—it isn't a pretty sight. Blood covers everything. It soaks every man in the aircraft, makes the windshield useless.

The Viet Cong had crept down from the U-Minh the night before to assault an outpost just outside Khai Quang.

The assault lasted all night, and it was a wonder the small garrison held out. But it did, though it took casualties. The Viet Cong, we learned later, weren't really interested in Khai Quang. What they wanted—expected—was that reinforcements would come down a small supply canal from Thoi Binh. The Viet Cong dug in along the canal with their mortars and machine guns and waited for us.

We flew in our Rangers that afternoon. We put them down on top of the Viet Cong. It was fierce while it lasted. It was also one-sided; we had the helicopters. Most of the dead we found the next day obviously had been killed by airbursts. They died of head and shoulder wounds.

Hingle was back in Saigon by then, resting easy in the Naval hospital, and out of war for a while. Around Khai Quang, however, they were bringing in the dead Viet Cong by sampan, hauling them out of their holes or the canals into which they had jumped or fallen.

They were kids, most of them. Good-looking, healthy kids in their teens. They tell you not to feel sorry about them, but somehow you wonder how much these boys really understood about the conflict between two worlds.

Or were they simply in it for kicks? Did they fall for the Communists' promise that things would be ever so much better after they take over? Teen-aged boys, the old-timers say, are about as harmless as cobras in the Delta. Give them a rifle and no one asks their age before shooting them. But these boys won't ever be firing rifles again.

We leave them there overnight, in neat piles, hoping the Viet Cong will sneak back to get their bodies and we can ambush them. The Communists had taken some away in sampans when they fled.

They don't come back.

Inside the fort here, the defenders settle down to wait for the next time the Viet Cong come.

NOV. 23, BAC LIEU

There's one outfit in Viet Nam busily disproving the notion we can't fight the Viet Cong guerrillas on their own grounds.

For the past several months the 21st Vietnamese Division here in the Delta has been doing it successfully.

Brig. Gen. Dang Van Quang, division commander, and Col. Jim Keirsey of Durant, Okla., his American adviser, best friend and expert needler, insist they have no formula. After every 21st Division victory, however, an amazed Saigon sends staff officers from other divisions and corps to find out how it's done.

"We've got no secret," says Col. Keirsey. "We just go looking for them. Sometimes we don't find them; you've got to expect that. But sometimes we do. And then we're ready for them."

At least once every two weeks, or so it seems, the 21st flushes a Viet Cong concentration of company or battalion size and decimates it. In one month it has killed close to 250 enemy soldiers. These are counted dead. The Viet Cong customarily try to carry off casualties so they can't be counted.

The 21st also has taken automatic rifles—of which the Viet Cong have few—and has even captured intact mortars. The Viet Cong always try to sink mortars in the canals rather than have them fall into our hands. But dead men can't sink mortars.

Actually, General Quang's and Colonel Keirsey's "formula" may be no more than a combination of good hard intelligence and luck. They are able to learn where the Viet Cong are, and what they intend to do, with uncanny precision. How they do this is their secret.

Recently the Ca Mau brigade—a part of the 21st—on a routine operation found the enemy in numbers and killed 59, captured 27 weapons, including two automatic rifles and one mortar. General Nguyen Khanh, head of the armed forces, flew from Saigon to hand out 30 decorations and promote several men. By chance, exactly one month earlier, at the same spot, the 21st killed the same number, 59. Most of the dead were teen-aged boys—although trained cadre-men—from nearby farms and paddies.

General Quang and Colonel Keirsey go on every operation. They believe a commander's presence in battle is vital. They rely heavily on their Ranger battalions. A keen rivalry has grown up between these units. Each keeps close tabs on the other's "kills."

Quang scorns paper work. "I am a combat soldier," he says. "Paperwork is why I have a chief of staff." Ordinarily an amiable, party-loving man who once served in the French army, he becomes a bulldog in action.

He believes in exploiting victories. When he scores a good one, he brings the Saigon press to the Delta by the planeload. He makes sure the news gets on the radio. Loudspeakers blare it in every village and hamlet square. Pictures of dead Viet Cong are printed on pamphlets and given wide distribution. All this pays off.

"General Quang is a square shooter," says Keirsey. "When a

guy comes across, when he's honest with you, you've got to go along with him."

Come to think of it, that's probably their "formula."

NOV. 25, TRA VINH

Twenty-five hundred feet beneath our helicopter, Vinh Binh Province is a world of banana groves and sugar cane fields, of canals and rice paddies, white egrets, Buddhist shrines, Annamite temples and family altars. Its people are attractive and friendly.

There are few Americans here who have not, at one time or another, remarked what a beautiful country this would be if there were no war. Each man seems to think he was the first to make this discovery.

But there is war in Vinh Binh today, as there was yesterday and as there will be tomorrow. The people in the cluster of hamlets that make up Thieu Khanh village are hostile—for all their inherent attractiveness. Thieu Khanh is marked on our maps "free fire."

There are 300 Viet Cong in the neighborhood. Invariably we draw fire here. An armed helicopter has been hit; a single bullet shattered its windshield. We heard the excited chatter over the air.

Fourteen more helicopters, in groups of five-five-four, arch through the skies out of Tra Vinh, nose-down like angry hornets on the attack, skim the paddies and finally hover, their blades turning the paddy water into sprays. Vietnamese soldiers from the Ninth Division climb out and plop into waist-deep muck. From the sky they look like ants. They form up smartly and move toward the hamlets along the canals.

As if forewarned, the villagers have disappeared. Word probably came to them through the enemy's excellent grapevine soon after breakfast. Smoke swirls from a few chimneys. A few sampans have been hurriedly moored. In front of some huts, peppers have been spread to dry. But there is no sign of life, of people.

141

There never is. With the appearance of the first helicopter, everybody goes to cover.

Another flight of 14, then a final one of 12. Forty helicopter loads in all.

Armed Hueys circle warily. One draws fire from the third hamlet on the left. The others swarm in. Machine guns chatter. Rockets roar. Canal water erupts in geysers. A rocket scores a direct hit. A hut bursts into flames.

"We've got friendly troops all along here," someone warns.

"I know," comes the answer. "We had friendlies where we got shot before."

Maj. Albert Johnson of New Orleans takes over.

"Mark friendly troop positions with smoke," he orders.

Troops of the Ninth are in the hamlets now. Methodically, taking their time, they search each hut, each out-building. They find nothing, just as we had expected.

They'll come back after we've gone, to pick up the pieces and start rebuilding. And they'll fire on us the next time.

"We're going home," Major Johnson calls, and we head for Can Tho.

This could be such beautiful country if there were no war.

But there is war. So it isn't.

NOV. 27, CAN THO

The notice on the bulletin boards made it official:

"Thursday, 26 November, 1964, will as far as practical be observed as a holiday."

Thus, throughout the steaming Mekong Delta and, indeed, in all of war-torn Viet Nam, Americans gathered in their chapels and messes to celebrate Thanksgiving far away from home.

Each came with his own thoughts, fears and hopes. For some, the separation, the hardship and the danger are burdens almost too great to be borne. For others, the days ahead loom endless and filled with foreboding, for they have just arrived in this hostile land. And some came in gratitude that they had survived and would soon enough be home in America, God willing.

Some, of course, couldn't make it. For the war went on, from Ca Mau to Sadec, from Rach Gia to Soc Trang. The patrols were out, the skirmishes were being fought, the chopper blades churned the air.

First Lt. James Blundell, 25, of Far Rockaway, N.Y., had particular reason this year to be grateful. He's alive.

He and Capt. Dick Holbrook of Manitowoc, Wisc., and Sgt. Jerry Gruzewski (who has no address but lists his next of kin as Col. Coy Curtis, Headquarters, Fourth Corps, Birmingham), left camp the day before Thanksgiving up in Vinh Binh Province to protect villagers rebuilding an outpost overrun in Tra District.

The Viet Cong attacked and he was wounded when a bullet struck him in the jaw. But the bullet had spent its force and barely broke the skin. So he was able to get back for Thanksgiving dinner and, however painfully, eat his share.

For Capt. David Radike, of Port Huron, Mich., and Sgt. First Class Delbert Yocum, 36, of Columbia, Tenn., Thanksgiving meant another day of war and cold C-rations.

At 3 a.m., they went to Chaudoc near the Cambodian border with a Vietnamese battalion. Their mission: to protect a village in the Seven Mountains region from a large Communist force surrounding it.

Elsewhere, however, voices sometimes faltered as they were raised in hymns of thanksgiving.

In Can Tho, Chaplain Major Frank Deese, a North Carolina Baptist, preached his final sermon and left at mid-afternoon for home, his tour completed.

"Gratitude is an antidote for despair," he counseled.

Even the remotest outposts had turkey with all the trimmings. Sometimes it had to be parachuted in, but it got there.

And printed on the menu for each man was a Thanksgiving message from Gen. William Westmoreland in Saigon:

"We Americans should offer our grateful thanks for the abundant life we have been provided and for our ability to assist other peoples in the world to attain the rich treasure of freedom we ourselves enjoy."

If, as we ate our turkey in the turgid Mekong Delta, we had a reason for being here, that was it.

DEC. 4, CHAU NOI

Men shouldn't have to concern themselves with ambushes on a bright Sunday morning.

But the shots had come across the Occidental River soon after we'd cleared Chau Noi outpost. The boats slowed, then bolted ahead like scared deer to clear the tree line from which the snipers fired.

There had been eight shots in one volley. A brief pause. Then another salvo. It had come from the left bank. A Viet Cong squad had been reported a few meters back during the night. In all probability it had moved down to the river bank. The VC had spotted our first boat and, thinking it was alone, had taken it under fire. Then three more had roared around the bend from Chau Noi and they'd broken off.

At least, that's the way we figured it.

We were headed for Long Khat. There's a Special Forces base there. Also a district town. The Cambodian border is less than a mile from Long Khat.

Our boat was a Sears-Roebuck outboard designed for water-skiers. Sgt. Rosier Williamson of Austin, Minn., was at the wheel. Capts. Paul Virciglio of New York and George McElroy of Boston were in the back seat. Each carried a machine gun.

Capt. Dennis Greene of New York and Minneapolis was in another boat. Capt. Floyd McAfee of Chicago, a former Illinois University football star born in Houston, was in a third. Lt. Bill Brown, Newington, Conn., was the American in the fourth.

Leaving Moc Hoa, Airman Ronnie Ward of Fort Worth, a radio operator, had lent me his web belt and canteen.

"It's going to be a rough trip back," Captain Virciglio had said. "Going up, you catch them by surprise. But there's only one way back, and they know we've got to go back sometime."

The convoy swept past Binh Chau without drawing more fire. Friendly troops along the bank and in sampans waved in greeting. At a "Y" in the river, we turned right toward Long Khat.

"Okay, you can breathe easy now," Virciglio said. "That way goes to Vinh Loi. All the posts there are strongly held VC."

This is dangerous country. Cambodia backs up against Chau Phanh district, and Cambodians aren't our friends. Last night there had been a fierce fire fight near Xam Ay Quao. We'd heard it from Moc Hoa. As it turned out, the Cambodians were shooting up some Viet Cong trying to sneak back without advance notice.

The river edged closer to the border. Across it, you see the outline of Cambodian towns.

On our side there are Vietnamese towns. Once these people were friends. They may be again some day.

Long Khat is astir. This is election day and there are six candidates for village chief, a position not always so eagerly sought. The Viet Cong put a high price on a village chief's head. But Long Khat is a good town and a good district. Already, at noon, 500 have voted and the polls are crowded.

We head back to Moc Hoa at midafternoon. Long Khat's district chief, however, has been busy. The river bank has been searched. Every mile or so we pass sampans loaded with friendly troops. They're heavily armed. It's Sunday, and their day of rest, but they've come out from Chau Noi and Binh Chau to guard us. The Viet Cong and their guns remain silent.

We get home, tie up, and go in to dinner.

The steaks were mightly good that night.

DEC. 8, SAIGON

The 20,000 or more Americans in South Viet Nam are the last to be told what is happening.

They depend primarily on Armed Forces Radio Service (AFRS), which broadcasts from downtown Saigon. From AFRS, they hear a lot about the Congo, Sudan, Syria and Panama, but the average U.S. serviceman's concern is about disturbances in Saigon.

About this, he is told next to nothing. He must rely on his own grapevine sources and the rumor mill. It adds up to the crudest—and most indefensible—kind of censorship, because military security is not an issue. Officers and enlisted men alike resent it.

"This policy," a senior officer in the Delta said, "is based on the assumption we aren't mature enough to receive straight news."

Those responsible deny that.

"This is the last impression we want to get around," says Barry Zorthian, head of U.S. Information Service (USIS) here. "There are other considerations, however."

Censorship apparently is based on the idea we can't risk offending an eavesdropping audience of a million Vietnamese who understand some English.

Our answer to what Zorthian describes as the "delicate problem" of telling the truth and not provoking our hosts is to do nothing.

Capt. John H. Carr of Oak Ridge, Tenn., in charge of AFRS, concedes his station has said "damned little" about Viet Nam's current troubles. (Carr formerly was with Radio Station WATO, Oak Ridge.)

Zorthian admits AFRS "can be improved." He says a plan has been worked out whereby Lt. Col. Louis Breault, Gen. William Westmoreland's personal PIO, will rush to AFRS studios the moment trouble occurs. Breault is a veteran trouble-shooter who has seen service in Korea and Berlin. He will have the final say in what goes on the air.

Until now, Carr has not been able to say anything about Viet Nam without clearance from a committee composed of Col. B. L. Baker, information chief for American Forces, Zorthian and a representative of the Embassy's political section.

AFRS on occasion has mentioned Saigon's disturbances. But this usually consists of giving the location of the trouble and urging Americans to stay away. More often Americans learn of trouble when AFRS announces that "the Girl Scout cook-out, scheduled tonight, has been cancelled."

Baker concedes there was a foul-up recently when Buddhists

JIM G. LUCAS has been writing for the Scripps-Howard Newspapers since the close of World War II, in which, as a Marine Corps combat correspondent, he covered the battles of Guadalcanal, Iwo Jima and Tarawa—where for three days he was listed as "killed in action." For his brilliant reporting of the battle of Tarawa, Lucas received the 1943 National Headliners Award. In addition to the Pulitzer Prize in the field of International Reporting awarded to Lucas for his coverage of the Korean War, other honors held by Lucas include two Ernie Pyle Memorial Awards, (1953 for Korea, 1964 for Viet Nam); the National Medal of the Republic of Korea; the Omar N. Bradley Gold Medal of the Veterans of Foreign Wars; the Fourth Estate Award of the American Legion; The George Polk Memorial Award of Long Island University; the "Non Sibi Sed Patriae" medal of the Marine Corps Reserve Officers Association. Mr. Lucas has eight battle stars, has been decorated with the Bronze Star and holds the Presidential Unit Citation as combat correspondent with the U. S. Marines in World War II.

demonstrated during the funeral of a young riot victim.

"We couldn't reach agreement on what should be said," he said. "I argued we should tell the truth. The Embassy said to let them read it in their own newspapers."

Their discussion apparently never involved Americans' right to know.

Those down the chain of command throw the ball back to Zorthian who, they say, runs the information show here. Zorthian says only one item concerning Viet Nam has been submitted to him personally and he said, "Sure, go ahead."

The fact is, however, practically no information concerning Viet Nam reaches troops in the field for fear Vietnamese feelings will be hurt.

Baker was asked if he felt a straight news story from United Press International or Associated Press tickers about Viet Nam would upset the Vietnamese.

"I wouldn't say a story by UPI or AP would be straight," he replied. "As a matter of fact, we toyed with that idea recently and discarded it."

In what way aren't our news agency reports "straight"?

"They're often colored," Baker replied.

Zorthian says UPI and AP stories are played back to Viet Nam after the situation has materially changed.

It was pointed out that Stars and Stripes, printed in Tokyo, carries wire stories.

"The comparison isn't valid," Baker said. "Stars and Stripes is 48 hours late reaching Saigon. Besides, few Vietnamese ever read it."

Zorthian says the problem would solve itself if AFRS had a trained, "politically conscious" news staff. He says it doesn't.

"This is no reflection on them, but they're idealistic, enthusiastic kids with no concept of the impact they have," he said.

He cites a story by Voice of America in August reporting "religious disturbances" in Da Nang.

"The story was perfectly straight, but the Buddhists seized on it and we are still hearing about it," he said. "Can't you visualize what would happen if we indiscriminately used the wire services or let our boys broadcast what they thought they saw? We could be wiped out."

Zorthian said AFRS is the "Commander's and the Ambassador's link with the American community. It must be maintained. The answer to the problem is not silence. We know that. I hope the new system works. (This is the plan under which Breault rushes to the studio in emergencies and decides what goes on the air.) If it doesn't, we'll try something else."

DEC. 9, SOC TRANG

They handed Maj. George Vlisides some coffee and he warmed his hands on the cup while he drank it.

It had all happened so fast, he said, he still wasn't convinced it had happened to him because he'd never been shot down before. And though—like all fliers—he had thought about it and often wondered what it would be like, this wasn't exactly the way he had thought it would be.

Anyhow, he said with a grin, it was good being still alive, and he was mighty glad the others had been there when they were.

Vlisides, who hails from Ann Arbor, Mich., and his Vietnamese observer had been in a Skyraider over Vinh Binh Province.

Near Long Toan, on the South China Sea coast, they'd struck a wooded area with fragmentation and phosphorous bombs. That done, in their business-like way, they'd taken on a second target to the southeast.

Major Vlisides made one pass on the woods, and then strafed. The men on the ground called up that they were getting mortar fire, so he moved down and strafed twice more.

It was the sort of thing he often did, flying out of Bien Hoa in support of friendly forces in the Mekong Delta, and he was not even aware his plane had been hit and crippled. As he told it:

"Then plane No. 4—I was No. 3—called and said I was in trouble—that I had a big oil leak, with lots of smoke, and it looked bad. I asked if he thought I could make it back, and he said it would be too risky. I looked for the first place to set down, and Long Toan was there."

The abandoned airstrip at Long Toan is known to be mined—by both sides—but the Major had no choice.

No sooner had he braked to a halt than an Air Force light observation plane was down with him, ignoring the dangers.

"Get aboard!" shouted Capt. Lloyd Lewis of Lubbock, Tex., and Vlisides and his observer sprinted. An L-19 usually carries two people, but on the 10-minute hop back to Tra Vinh this one carried four, three in the back seat, which probably sets some sort of record. Lewis brought it home at tree-top level.

Vlisides and his observer were picked up at Tra Vinh by a medical evacuation helicopter flown by Capts. Vincent Cedola of Lyndhurst, N.J., and Charlie Clark of Elba, Ala. They flew the downed Air Force men here for a medical check.

As luck would have it, Cedola and Clark were escorting their boss, Col. William Hamrick, head of the Army Medical Service Corps, on his first tour of the Delta. Hamrick had wanted to witness a medical pickup, and wags were later to charge that Cedola and Clark staged it for his benefit, but Major Vlisides said, as far as he was concerned, there was nothing staged about it.

Colonel Hamrick later pinned Air Medals on both Cedola and Clark, but their awards had been won on a previous occasion.

Neither Captain Cedola, a graduate of St. Peter's State College of New Jersey, nor Captain Clark, who attended Jacksonville State College, are strangers to danger in the Delta war. Day and night they answer calls for help.

On Oct. 27, Captain Clark and Lt. Armond (Cy) Simmons of Meridian, Miss., took three direct hits while helping rescue wounded during an assault against the Viet Cong near Bac Lieu.

They say it's all in a day's work.

George Vlisides can be thankful it is.

DEC. 12, ABOARD SHIP IN THE GULF OF SIAM

A few miles ashore 14 men—including three Americans—are dead. Nine more South Vietnamese are wounded.

All this in an operation which achieved precisely nothing. Operation Dan Chi 855 was meticulously planned. From the start, however, nothing went right. What was lacking was direction; someone to insist that schedules be met, plans be executed, things be done right.

But no one did that—on the old excuse of lack of authority.

So the Viet Cong struck and got away. They wiped out the top command of a Vietnamese battalion and most of its American advisers.

The dead include Capt. Norman Heck of Ida, Mich., Lt. James G. Dunton of Melrose, Mass., and Sgt. Guy Freeland of Fort Smith, Ark. Twenty-four hours earlier I ate with these men. I slept in the same billet with the two officers. They left Rach Gia with one Vietnamese battalion, I left with another. Rach Gia is on the western side of the country's tip end, facing the Gulf of Siam.

Their battalion went ashore. Ours remained on this ship, the *Chi Linh*. We heard what happened at dawn.

After they went ashore their battalion strung out along a canal leading to a French-operated cement plant near Ha Tien.

They neglected to post guards between their bivouac and the Gulf. Any idea that the Viet Cong might hit from the sea apparently never occurred to them.

But the enemy did come in from the sea, without challenge, at 1 a.m. Our men were asleep by then. The Viet Cong proceeded to demolish their camp. The battalion commander, his executive officer and the three Americans never knew what hit them.

Dan Chi 855 was to have been a well-executed amphibious operation, the first ever attempted by the Vietnamese. On paper it resembled those we carried out in the Pacific in World War II.

Three battalions were to encircle 400 Viet Cong near the Quan Thui customs house while our battalion landed from the sea and pushed them inland. It was to be a perfect trap.

The Chi Linh—a former U.S. Navy ship turned over to the Vietnamese last January—waited at Turtle Island, 18 miles offshore, throughout the night.

At dawn we moved in.

By all rules of naval warfare, our troops aboard should have gone ashore at the first light of dawn. Without such a surprise element, amphibious assaults seldom succeed.

But Lt. Col. Hguyen Khac Tuan, in command, refused to let his men disembark without an air strike first. The Vietnamese air force commander reported he wouldn't be ready until 8 a.m.

Since we were in position at 5 a.m., this gave the Viet Cong a three-hour alert. And the Viet Cong are neither blind nor stupid.

Eight o'clock came and still there was no sign of Vietnamese planes. An hour and 50 minutes later two fighters circled overhead and then flew away. Colonel Tuan was unable to contact them by radio. At 10 o'clock he reluctantly decided to move ashore.

The naval bombardment preceding the landing was dramatic but succeeded only in tearing down several trees.

By 10:30 our troops were ashore. Aboard the Chi Linh we were congratulating each other over the apparent fact we had made an unopposed landing.

Our explanation for all that went wrong is the usual, "We only advise." But some are beginning to suspect that isn't explanation enough.

Too often "We only advise" is the equivalent of "I only work here." Heck, Dunton and Freeland undoubtedly advised the Vietnamese to post sentries. They might be alive now if they had insisted on it.

Similarly, Colonel Tuan might have caught the Viet Cong by surprise and avenged their deaths if he had risked landing his troops at dawn. But this was his first amphibious experience. Understandably he was nervous and uncertain. The Americans advised him what to do, but they didn't insist. They did not argue the point.

Actually, records in Tactical Operations Center at Can Tho will reveal that Tuan didn't ask for the air strike for which he waited in vain. He merely asked for air coverage. The records will show he got that, though it wasn't evident aboard ship and he couldn't establish radio contact.

Again our answers are a shrug and a pat "We only advise." So

14 good men including three Americans died, and Dan Chi 855 was a flop. It need not have happened.

Maybe it won't next time if we have learned anything these last heart-breaking 48 hours.

DEC. 14, AP XA BEN

Suddenly the Viet Cong were everywhere.

They poured out of the burning houses, into the village streets. Some tried to hide beneath thatched eaves and watched in horror as their comrades were shot down in front of them. Others jumped into the river and the canal.

"Get 'em!" yelled Lt. Col. Bill Hammack of Quannah, Tex., as he swung his helicopter to provide better aim for Pfc. Bennie Feltman of Lineville, Ala.

Feltman's machine gun poured it on the swirling ranks below. His tracers arched luridly as they covered the 2000 feet.

Throughout the day we had chased them, knowing where they were holed up in marshy land.

Once, at mid-morning, we had been close enough that they had left clothing and food behind in their holes. The Viet Cong sometimes live in their foxholes. It's hard to dislodge them when they choose to stay and fight. Now, however, they fired and fell back . . . fired and fell back.

"The C-74 Company (an enemy unit) moved to four successive positions in the last four days," Capt. Hayward Riley of Columbia, S.C., had briefed us. "As of 0730 today it was confirmed they were in the vicinity of Objective 41. They've got workshops and a dispensary there."

Riley's boss, Col. Jim Keirsey of Durant, Okla., explained:

"They've broken up into smaller groups to harvest rice and collect taxes. That's why our ambushes have been going so well. We had more small contact last night than we had last month. But it's tougher to catch big units out in the open and make them fight."

By mid-morning, the Rangers had killed two and captured three. They'd brought in three captured weapons.

We had flown over the area in the first hours of Operation Dan Chi 91, crisscrossing it in a propaganda helicopter while a Vietnamese major shouted into the loud speaker:

"Your comrades in the next hamlet have surrendered. Now it is your turn."

Aside from the fact this hadn't happened, it was doubtful that to say so did any good. Winds blew the words before they reached the men on the ground and garbled the message.

WO Ken Hessemer of Portland, Ore., spotted from a light observation plane.

"Lots of trails," he called back. "Now I see people running."

We were pushing them hard, driving them against the river banks. Armored personnel carriers cut weird patterns through the rice paddies. A unit of Rangers was slogging through the mire.

The payoff started when Kessemer radioed: "They're out in the open now. They're going west."

After that it was bedlam—a real turkey shoot.

Armed helicopters came in with their rockets and machine guns. That's what the Commies had been trying to avoid; why they were hiding. Now village after village caught fire, the flames leaping up in mushroom clouds of smoke. The sound was deafening as the rockets tore into the houses.

The Viet Cong were in panic. But there was no place to run, no place to hide. Helicopter after helicopter came in, guns blazing. Many died where they fell. Others dived into the water and died there.

Then it was over. Below, you could hear the sullen roar of flames, and overhead the whirl of the rotors. But all else was quiet. The running men were still. They lay where they had fallen, and the flames enveloped them until the whole of the scene was flames. Later we would try to count them.

DEC. 19, GIONG RIENG

When Lt. Nguyen Van Huynh came to Kien Binh 10 months ago as its District Chief, the area was in a shambles.

His predecessor had been driven out of his mind and still is confined; in his final operation, this man had lost 89 dead in a Communist Viet Cong ambush.

Their widows tried to lynch him. He fled into the paddies in his shorts. It took a company of Rangers to bring him out.

Then Huynh took command. Today his control of government areas is total.

Consider what this cherubic-looking officer—who once studied to become a Catholic priest—has done since last February:

Killed 214 Viet Cong; wounded 33; captured 24; persuaded 41 to surrender.

He also captured 38 weapons and 597 rounds of ammunition; destroyed five Viet Cong information centers and two medical stations; and wrecked three training camps and four prisoner camps.

But the government controls little more than a tenth of the area in Kien Binh. Even in supposedly pacified areas one cannot be certain of safety.

Huynh will not permit his three American advisers, Maj. Ralph Waara of East Lansing, Mich., Capt. Stuart Larson of Galesburg, Ill., and Sgt. Fred DeMarco of Rapid City, S.D., to go into Giong Rieng after dark without an armed guard.

A week ago a terrorist tried to shoot a South Vietnamese officer while he was getting a haircut. The intended victim was able to disarm his assailant. But Huynh is not sure the Americans would be as alert. Or as lucky.

Life in Kien Binh is a never-ending game of wits.

The other night, for instance, the Viet Cong slipped into a fort under construction along the road back to Rach Gia. They intended to booby-trap it. But Huynh had anticipated that. He left his own booby traps for the would-be booby-trappers.

About 9 p.m. he heard the explosion. It killed only one man, but Huynh had outguessed them again.

His problems are many. Right now, he says, an enemy battalion is only 10 miles away. But its camp is not in Huynh's province.

Political boundaries are a formidable barrier. For permission to fire on this unit he would have to apply through channels to another area and the answer would have to come back the same slow way. Meanwhile the battalion would probably have moved elsewhere.

"If I fired on them without permission," he says sadly, "I'd be put in jail."

Huynh has a pretty wife, a five-year-old son. Yet he has not been home in three years. He has not had leave in that time.

He brought his family here four months ago. The Viet Cong greeted their arrival with mortars, and Huynh sent them back to Saigon the next day.

The Viet Cong offer 500,000 piastres for his body. If his family remained in Kien Binh, he said, they'd have a price on their heads, too.

Huynh sleeps only in snatches. He drives his men as hard as he drives himself. If they foul up, punishment is swift and sure. His intelligence officer currently is serving 30 days in a chicken-wire coop.

He also knows the value of rewarding his men. When a man shoots a Viet Cong or captures a weapon he is given a cash reward on the spot. Huynh does this publicly to impress his people.

His prospects of getting away soon are remote. In 10 months he has been wounded three times without losing a day's work. The last time, his commander met him at the hospital.

"Get back to your district," he ordered.

Yet for all this, it is doubtful the people in Saigon—where life is easy—ever heard of Nguyen Van Huynh. When victory comes—if it does—he could easily be overlooked. The record of his achievements—and his sacrifices—will be left behind in Kien Binh.

His "reward" if the Communists win is more certain. They list him as a war criminal.

In a Communist Viet Nam he would die before a firing squad. If he were lucky.

If this bothers Huynh, there is no evidence of it.

"What's in this for you?" I asked him.

155

Huynh seemed surprised at the question.

"This is my country," he said. "And I am a soldier."

DEC. 22, CAN THO

"The next three miles," said Beverly Ann Fry, "are very much Viet Cong."

Ann, who hails from Pocatello, Ida., is as brave as any American in Viet Nam. An 80-mile trip by car was her idea. No American male of my acquaintance has ever attempted it. Most would be appalled at the idea. But what can you say when a young lady calls at 6 a.m., getting you out of bed, and says sweetly:

"Let's drive to Rach Gia today."

Ann is well on her way to becoming an American legend in Viet Nam. Head of AID's public health program in the Delta, she goes everywhere. At the start she carefully observed regulations and notified authorities where she was going. But she usually forgets that formality now.

"If we're captured," she said gleefully, "no one will know about it. How's your Vietnamese?"

We barreled down the highway in Ann's late-model American station wagon.

"My driver," Ann said, "knows where the Viet Cong are. If he guns it, he has a good reason."

In Can Tho everybody loves Ann Fry. Her house is our social center. Her cook can prepare crepes suzette. Her food is the best in Southeast Asia. An invitation to Ann's is something no man refuses and all men covet.

Recently the officers and men of the 13th Aviation Battalion—helicopter lads—presented her a plaque they had made in Hong Kong conferring honorary membership on Beverly Ann Fry. She earned it with countless evenings that resembled—as nearly as it can be achieved in Viet Nam—an evening at home.

A Veterans Administration nurse in Palo Alto, Calif., two years ago she joined AID and was sent here.

"I'm the luckiest girl alive," she says. "They send me 10,000 miles away to a place like this, among people like these, to a home like this, where I have the best friends in the world. What more can you ask?"

Ann figures she has advanced the cause of public health 75 years in Viet Nam. It has not been easy, for her or the Vietnamese. It has been possible only because the Vietnamese wanted to learn.

"I'm so proud of these people," she says. "They've learned so much in so little time."

Ann's job is also dangerous. She has been shot at, though she is still unconvinced they really meant it. Some time back at Ho Ngia she was watching a movie when the Viet Cong attacked. The men rushed to their posts. Ann was deeply impressed. "Everyone knew just where to go and what to do." She was ordered to get down on the floor.

"There was really no reason not to be comfortable," she says, "so I put a pillow under my head and I lay there eating popcorn."

Later a captain stuck his head in the door and assured her it would soon be over.

"About time," Ann said. "I'm running out of popcorn."

The next day she drove to Saigon. Seven minutes after she had passed, the Viet Cong ambushed and killed an American major.

"They wanted him," Ann says. "I'm not that important."

Of the 18 hospitals in South Viet Nam, Ann supervises eight here in the Delta. She worked her way through the wards at Rach Gia, and the people greeted her with warmth and affection. Dr. Nguyen Phoc An was at her side, glowing. The doctor, educated in France, is a roly-poly Vietnamese whose wife, Ann swears, "is the best cook in Viet Nam, that's why he is so fat." Dr. An would very much like for Ann to stay in Rach Gia permanently.

Ann, daughter of a retired Air Force colonel, goes home soon on leave. But she will come back to Can Tho.

"Otherwise," she says, "I'd resign. This is my home. I like being among my own things."

That's where Ann belongs. Americans and Vietnamese are agreed on that.

DEC. 29, VINH LONG

Getting to Minh Duc is comparatively easy.

It's getting back that requires planning.

Capt. John Laughinghouse of Jonesboro, Ark., flew us there from Vinh Long, about a 15-minute hop. The first time we couldn't make it, and we kidded him that he couldn't find the place, that maybe they had moved it. Actually, clouds were in the way.

But we got there, and in time we were ready to go out. Minh Duc isn't on the regular chopper runs; Capt. Hal Morgan of Chattanooga, Tenn., said that in the months he'd been in Minh Duc a chopper had stopped there only twice, and he didn't expect another any time soon.

"We'll drive out," he said.

Vinh Long is 20 "clicks" away. A click is a kilometer. A kilometer is six-tenths of a mile. That makes Vinh Long 12 miles distant. Not too far as crows fly. But quite a piece when the Viet Cong control most of the way.

"We'll start," Hal said, "sometime between 9 a.m. and 2 p.m." At dinner that evening, I tried to pin the time down a bit.

"When'll we start for Vinh Long?" I asked Maj. Vo Van Hoa, the district chief.

Everybody froze.

"We never talk about those things in front of the cook," Hal said later. "Tomorrow, sometime, Major Hoa will suddenly say, 'We're going to Vinh Long,' and we'll take off. It's safer that way."

The cook is the cousin of a province chief. She could poison everything we eat. But we don't discuss plans in front of her. Hal tells about a district chief who was assassinated recently by a man who had been his bodyguard for six years. But he was a Viet Cong, awaiting orders to strike.

It was 10 a.m. the next day when Major Hoa strapped on his pistol holster and said we were about to start.

Then we waited.

Would I like some coffee? The coffee came and was consumed.

How about a beer? No thanks. Too early.

In cases like these you don't push. The Vietnamese will never tell you the road is unsafe—that would be a reflection on them. They simply say that it's not a good time to go. So you wait until they decide the time is "good"—which means the road is relatively safe—and off you go.

Messengers and subordinates came and went, conferring earnestly. A commandeered bus drove up and soldiers piled aboard. A dump truck was produced from somewhere else and more soldiers piled aboard that.

Eventually we found ourselves in jeeps and off we went.

Now I could see why Major Hoa had waited so long. There were soldiers every quarter of a mile along the way. It was hot and some had made improvised pup tents out of ponchos. Some had walkie-talkie radio sets.

Every few miles, Hoa pointed out an ambush site. The road was narrow and rutted, but it was a through highway for this part of the Delta. Only two days ago the Viet Cong cut the road. It had been hastily repaired. The convoy slowed to a crawl while we went over it.

It wasn't the pressure-mines we worried about. They'd have gone when the first civilian buses passed over them in the morning. Besides, the Viet Cong don't use pressure-mines; they aren't after civilians. They're after us. We worried, instead, about the electrically detonated kind. They can be selective with those.

You wondered if those peasants—their hands concealed in the rice stalks—actually had hoes in their hands. Or could they be holding a couple of wire ends, ready to touch them together and blow you to kingdom come?

At Tan Lap, Hoa conferred with his village chief, and then we went on toward Vinh Long. We turned right onto a better

159

highway—the one that runs to Vinh Binh—but we didn't relax. Those groves on either side of the road offered too much cover for snipers.

Yet 30 minutes later we were back in Vinh Long, safe and sound and a little sheepish, now that it was over, about all the pains we had taken to get here.

But that's probably why we made it.

DEC. 30, DAI NGAI

Gunner Bobby Payne, trying to protect the wounded pilot of his downed helicopter, stopped a bullet with his chest and went down as though he had been pole-axed.

Seconds before, a call had come over the air, "Aircraft down," whereupon Maj. Ed Porter of Farwell, Tex., had spotted the downed ship and answered that his Huey chopper would go in to help. I was aboard.

It was the fiercest, bloodiest battle that has occurred so far in South Viet Nam.

In paddies and trees around Thu Bay, Nha Mac, Ngai Hoa and along the Han Thanh River, we had stumbled upon 1500 hard-core Viet Cong. We had been hunting them farther south all morning.

Now here they were in a horseshoe around a cluster of villages. There was at least a regiment of them. Before night we were to fly in 700 tough Vietnamese Rangers. We had planes and artillery. They had .50-caliber anti-aircraft guns, recoilless rifles and mortars.

Three of our choppers were involved in the action.

An anti-aircraft gun downed the first Huey chopper flown in by Lt. Paul Young III of Fayetteville, Ark., and Warrant Officer Dick Eskey of Virginia Beach, Va. They were 30 feet above the paddies when their ship spun to the ground.

Young was badly wounded. He had to be moved out before he bled to death.

In chopper No. 2, Young's wingman, Lt. Jerry Thiels of Alexandria, La., had followed him in. The two ships sat in wet paddies 50 yards from a strong gun position of the Viet Cong.

Thiels and his co-pilot, Warrant Officer Harold Simpson of Jacksonville, Fla., and Crew Chief Donald Airheart of Holly Springs, N.C., were struggling to get the wounded pilot Young out of his cockpit.

Eskey, Crew Chief Ed Bascovsky of Pittsburgh, and Gunners Payne of Swainsboro, Ga., and Paul Pires of New Bedford, Mass., had climbed out of the crippled ship and taken defensive positions around the aircraft.

Each had a machine gun, and each was firing into the trees to protect their wounded commander. Thiels and Simpson finally got Young free and carried him toward their aircraft.

Meanwhile, Major Porter and Capt. Terry Oliver of Indianapolis had put our Huey—the third of the trio—into a steep dive. In a matter of seconds it dropped from 2500 feet to 10 feet.

Porter and Oliver whipped our ship across the paddies and stopped in the zone of fire. Our crew chief, Charles Gagnon of Fall River, Mass., and Gunner Mike Rayne of Oakline, Mass., opened up with their guns. Then Gagnon's jammed.

"Keep firing!" Porter screamed.

Gagnon struggled with his balky weapon. He managed to clear it and started sobbing.

"Ammo! Ammo!" he yelled.

I scrambled about the aircraft searching for ammunition, all thumbs, and realized later I was sobbing, too.

It was then that Bobby Payne went down.

He did a double flip and landed on his back. I was convinced he had been killed. I was surprised to see him get up again, clutching his chest. He took a couple of steps toward me, then collapsed again.

Bascovsky, running slowly beside him, was gasping for breath and carrying two heavy machine guns.

The rice was waist-high and the water shin-deep. It was heavy going, a tableau in slow motion. Payne fell the second time.

With Gagnon I jumped out of our ship and went after him.

A flight of armed Hueys roared in at tree-top level and plas-

161

tered the enemy 50 yards away with rockets. Mud, water and debris filled the air.

Overhead, Lt. Col. Jim Lee of Wilmington, N.C., was watching. He told me later: "You'll never know how hard I was praying for you down there. Tracers were all around you. I counted at least 100 around your ship."

Young's ship was a shambles. It was between us and the Viet Cong. It rocked gently as bullets cut through it. But it masked and shielded our ship. Without that, we never would have made it.

Gagnon and I picked up Payne and half-dragged, half-carried him to our ship. All this takes longer to tell than it did to happen.

Bascovsky and Pires already were aboard. Pires was shouting, cursing and shaking his fist at the Viet Cong. I was afraid he would try to tackle them barehanded.

Payne's eyes were glazed and his body was limp.

We were all shouting wildly. I remember now as I write that I was screaming: "Never mind Never mind!" This was meant to be reassuring. I doubt now that it was.

Under conditions like these a man coolly calculates the odds and realizes they're no better than 50-50. Then another part of him reacts instinctively to demands of the moment. He feeds ammo to the gunner; goes after a wounded man without thinking, because that is what he has got to do.

Eskey and Pires tried to go back to their ship. They seemed in a state of shock. They are airmen and an airman's instinct told them not to go off and leave the ship, but it had to be done.

Porter had to get out and manhandle them back into our Huey.

Bobby Payne's life was saved by his flak vest. One round had flattened against his chest and burned him badly. He will have a bruised chest for a couple of weeks. But a big grin spread over his face as he realized he was still alive. He couldn't talk.

With the rescued men aboard, we took off. Tracers followed us as we rose. Ten minutes later we were safe in Soc Trang and the wounded men were in the hospital.

"Let's go back," Pires was yelling. "I want to kill the bastards!"

Then the reaction set in—always apparent when men start making feeble jokes.

"This," Terry Oliver said weakly when someone handed him a cup of coffee, "is the first time I have ever seen a .50-caliber gun from that end."

I took one swallow of hot coffee and gagged. I couldn't keep it down.

These guys I have known and worked with for 10 months crowded around me that night and congratulated me as if I actually had something to do with what happened out there. Now, truly, I felt like one of them.

"You've been writing about us," one of them said. "Now we want you to write about yourself."

So I did. And this is it. But it's mostly the story of Bobby Payne and Paul Young and Ed Bascovsky and Dick Eskey and Jerry Thiels and Ed Porter and Terry Oliver . . . the story of a brave bunch of young Americans we can be proud to call our own.

JAN. 11, SAIGON

The recent award of the Medal of Honor to an American hero in South Viet Nam has focused attention on the fact that decorations have become an important factor in this, as in every other, war.

But the inevitable emergence of a quota system on medals could cheapen many honestly won on the battlefield. Much more than pride and the human desire for recognition is involved. A military man's career can be furthered if his files show he has been decorated for bravery under fire.

In the last six months our Army has awarded 10,317 medals and citations to its men in Viet Nam. The other services have decorated many of their men, but their totals are not available.

In addition, South Viet Nam decorates 125 to 175 Americans a month. At the moment, Americans can only "receive the tender" of a Vietnamese medal. Congressional action is required before our personnel can formally accept a decoration from a foreign government.

Enabling legislation will be asked of this Congress, and it is expected to be granted. Until Congress acts, however, Vietnamese medals are retained by our military departments in a sort of escrow.

The U.S. Army decorations conferred in the last six months are those which can be approved locally.

Authorities here can confer medals up to the Distinguished Flying Cross. Included on the list are the Soldier's Medal, the two Bronze Stars (with V for Valor, or with M for Merit), the two Air Medals, the Army Commendation Ribbon, and the Purple Heart.

The Pacific Commander-in-Chief, headquartered in Hawaii, can approve award of the Joint Services Commendation Ribbon and the Legion of Merit.

All others must be approved in Washington.

The Medal of Honor is the oldest and the Joint Services Ribbon the newest of the awards. The latter has been awarded only since 1961—after the Korean War—so this is the first conflict in which it has figured.

This makes the ribbon a much-sought prize. It is the only Defense Department ribbon, and is given to men who have served with distinction on a joint staff such as MACV (Military Assistance Command, Viet Nam).

Those in command deny it, but many men in the field are convinced decorations have become such big business that quotas are set for particular engagements.

After a recent clash with the Communist Viet Cong near Ca Mau, in which armed helicopters distinguished themselves, Maj. Gen. Delk N. Oden, head of the Army Support Command, authorized on the spot the award of 32 Air Medals for Valor.

These were divided between two Army Aviation companies, 16 to each company, apparently without too much regard for who did what. The men of another Army aviation company, newly arrived in Viet Nam, understandably felt miffed.

After another battle, another helicopter pilot wrote me in obvious complaint:

"Our commanding officer was told to select 12 pilots for the (Vietnamese) Medal of Merit. He turned down the offer, saying he could not possibly single out any 12. But he and our executive officer had the medal forced on them in order to keep the Vietnamese from losing face."

The Army has salvaged the Bronze Star—awarded so freely in War II it became an object of derision—and upgraded it to the point where now it means considerable. The Bronze Star with "V" is given out only in exceptional cases. Some of the citations accompanying it would entitle the holder to at least a Silver Star in other conflicts.

The Vietnamese always decorate Americans who die here. If a man is killed in action he gets two Vietnamese awards—one for valor and the other for meritorious service.

JAN. 19, HAO HOA

Le Thi Nham, high priestess of the warlike Hao Hoa sect, today formally turned over her 400-man "palace guard" to the central government.

She watched it sail down the Bassac River to take up arms against the Communist Viet Cong in another province.

The high priestess' decision may have been partly influenced by the still-remembered visit here last year by Defense Secretary McNamara—who gave her a hearing aid. Le Thi Nham, now over 70, is quite deaf.

Negotiations for the transfer of the palace guard have been under way for several weeks. Final agreement required approval of Premier Tran Van Huong in Saigon. It was endorsed by Brig. Gen. Nguyen Van Thieu, Armed Forces commander in the Mekong Delta and one of the strongest men in the country.

I have been aware of these negotiations since before Christmas, but I was sworn to secrecy. I was one of three outsiders present in this village today.

The Hao Hoa is a Buddhist sect founded in 1939 by a young

165

intellectual who later was killed in a Communist ambush on the road to Can Tho. Actually the sect at that time was inclined to collaborate with the Reds and the founder was en route to negotiate with Red leaders. But apparently there had been a breakdown in communications.

Whatever happened, the Hao Hoa have never forgiven the Communists. For years they have maintained their own armies, at times fighting both sides. Some insist the Hao Hoa were little more than bandits.

After the overthrow of the late President Diem, most Hao Hoa under arms joined forces with Saigon. Le Thi Nham, however, retained control of local troops who were guarding a 20-square-mile area around the sect's central pagoda here. The actual commander is a tough 32-year-old, Huynh Trung Hieu. It was these troops the high priestess committed to government control today.

High Priestess Le Thi Nham is the mother of the sect's founder. Hao Hoas everywhere insist the founder is still alive and some day will return.

Following colorful rites in which Le Thi Nham blessed the departing troops, Hieu and the men went aboard Vietnamese navy craft for the 25-mile down-river trip to Lap Vo, the district town in Vinh Long Province.

Hao Hoa village is in Chau Doc Province, up against the Cambodian border. It is virtually the only part of South Viet Nam free of the Viet Cong, a place where one can go about freely.

Steamy local politics were considerably mixed into the decision to bring the Hao Hoa into the government. For one thing, Major Hieu was feuding bitterly with a militia lieutenant colonel, the Province Chief who previously had lined up with Saigon.

Rather than accept Hieu's "surrender" of the troops, this Province Chief would have preferred to wipe them out—particularly Hieu. So it took quite a bit of maneuvering to transform the "palace guard" into regulars, in face of the Provincial Chief's personal enmity.

But once they were safely aboard ship, the deed was accom-

plished and the troops' arrival in Lap Vo was jubilantly celebrated—with army bands, banquet tables and pretty girls gar-
landed with jungle flowers.

"It's better this way," said a resident American. "To have tried
to subdue the independent Hao Hoa would have cost untold
numbers of lives, and gained nothing. This way we have gained
400 first-rate fighting men."

JAN. 23, CAN THO

This is a story about one man. He is a proud man, a man of
talents and ability, wanting to do the job for which he was
trained, and denied that opportunity.

Sgt. Raymond M. Young, 42, of Oak Hill, W. Va., is an Army
photographer with 17 years of service and impressive credentials. A combat photographer in World War II, he did a three-
year stint as a civilian aerial photographer before returning to
the Army in 1951. He has since served as head of the First Division's Photo Lab in Germany where he helped train NATO
officers and, since 1955, as a medical research photographer.

At the Army Medical Research Lab at Fort Knox, Ky., Young
helped develop the art of colored X-ray photography. It took
him two years to produce one picture. He often was 15 to 18
hours on the job without realizing it. He is co-author of a number of impressive Army Medical Research reports and documents. His work has brought him one Army Commendation
Medal, of which he is justly proud, and many letters of praise.

Last year the Army sent him to Southeast Asia as part of a
medical photo team. Among other things, he worked in Saigon
during the plague epidemic. Again, he toiled 15 to 18 hours a
day, seven days a week, and was delighted.

Last Sept. 11 Young was back at Fort Knox when orders came
sending him again to Viet Nam. It was an "emergency requisition." He was to report Oct. 10 to San Francisco to take a jet to
Saigon.

Young asked 15 days' leave to arrange his affairs. He was
given 13.

167

"The unit dropped everything and helped me clear post in one day," he said. "That's almost unheard of. But we knew there was a war in Viet Nam. We figured I was badly needed to be pulled out of where I was, from the job I was doing."

Immediately on getting his orders, Young had to vacate his quarters at Fort Knox. This was particularly unfortunate, because Mrs. Young is not well. His orders came on a Monday. On Thursday the movers packed and loaded his household goods. That Sunday, he rented a house for his family in Oak Hill, his home town, where Mrs. Young would be near his folks. On Tuesday, his furniture arrived in Oak Hill. On Oct. 10, as ordered, Young was in San Francisco but it was Oct. 16 before he flew out for Saigon.

Young owns approximately $8000 worth of photographic equipment. He had called Washington and asked what he should take with him. Forget it, he was told, the boys in Viet Nam have the latest and best.

Young arrived in Viet Nam Oct. 17. They had no camera for him. Eventually he was assigned to the Public Information Office in Can Tho. He never had done Public Information work, doesn't like it. That was three months ago.

In those three months, Ray Young has not had an official camera in his hands. He occasionally has borrowed one to take a picture. No Government cameras are available. Every so often he dutifully calls Saigon, which is beginning to get touchy. Cameras, he is told, are "on order." No, they have no idea when they will arrive, etc.

The Army has invested $100,000 in training this man. Yet today, Sergeant Young is the man who drives the jeep that meets correspondents arriving in Can Tho. It's a job for a fuzzy-cheeked private. To keep from going stir-crazy, Young has taken to clerking in the post exchange. There he earns $1 an hour. He doesn't particularly need the money. He just needs something to do.

If Sergeant Young's story were not typical it would not be worth telling. Unfortunately, there is good reason to believe it is too typical.

Cryptography is one of the Army's most critical occupation specialties. Yet a trained cryptographer, with the highest possible security clearance, also clerks in the PX here. This man has 12 years' service and had intended to put in 20. Now he says he'll resign as soon as he gets home.

More than half the 23,000 Americans in South Viet Nam are concentrated in Saigon with no visible employment. I heard today of a Quartermaster Corps colonel for whom they made a job in Saigon. A week later he had a staff of seven to help him in his no-work.

The job from which Ray Young was yanked at Fort Knox has not been filled. They want him back. They are told they can't have him. Doesn't Fort Knox realize there's a war on in Viet Nam? And that Sergeant Young was ordered here on an emergency requisition?

As this is written, Ray Young has 270 days ahead of him in Viet Nam. Given a camera, given a job, they can be productive days.

Otherwise, they'll be ridiculous.

JAN. 26, PHUONG HIEP

The armed helicopters swooped down in a sort of slow hurry and plastered the village with their rockets.

House after house caught fire. Flame and smoke licked skyward. Even at 2000 feet we felt the blast and heard the muffled whoomp.

One chopper was hit. Its crew was Lt. Don Flohe of Suttons Bay, Mich., and Warrant Officer Ron Garrison of El Paso. One round had lodged beneath Flohe in the pilot's seat. Another had smacked into the engine. A third had knocked out the radio.

Flohe eased about and headed his ship for Soc Trang. Ten minutes later he was on the ground. Both he and Garrison were all right but their ship would be out of action for a while.

We had spent the day looking for the Viet Cong, hoping to resume a battle broken off at dusk the day before. They couldn't have gone far. But they had split up. And now, at mid-afternoon, we hadn't been able to locate them in enough force to justify sending in the Vietnamese Rangers waiting on the heat-baked runways back at Soc Trang.

"We'll send the Young Turks," Col. Jim Keirsey of Durant, Okla., told Brig. Gen. Don Van Quang, the 21st Division Commander. "They seem to think they know how to find the Viet Cong."

"Just give us a chance," said Maj. Ed Nix of Atlanta.

The Young Turks, in this division, are Nix and his counterpart, Maj. Do Duc Tam. They're Operations.

So the Young Turks had taken off in their own helicopter and, out over the canals that lace and interlace the Delta, they apparently had found some of them. Suddenly Major Tam saw an automatic weapon firing at us. We edged back. It fired again. And again. There was no doubt about it.

Nix called for the armed helicopters—the Vikings. Capt. Charles Teague of Oklahoma City brought them swarming in. They plastered the area.

Finally the Vikings exhausted their ammunition and headed home. Another fire team came on station. But try as it might, it got no ground reaction.

"They're getting too smart for us," Keirsey had said back on the ground. "Remember how it used to be? Remember how all we had to do was fly low and get shot at?

"We taught them better. They stopped that about two months ago."

Tam, always excitable, proposed calling in fighters. He illustrated his point with swooping gestures of expressive hands. Fourth Corps, back in Can Tho, wisely disapproved. Tam sank back in his chopper seat, dejected.

Pass after pass, each lower than the other, turned up no Viet Cong. No one would shoot at us. These boys know how to hide.

Suddenly Tam is jabbering into his radio. He's talking with a Viet Cong on the ground. The VC even know his call sign. They swap insults. I wished I understood what was being said.

The Viet Cong apparently think Major Tam is on the ground, too. His radio is so strong they think he's close by. They want him to fire a shot in the air so they can spot him. In expressive Vietnamese, Tam tells them where they can go.

Back on the ground in Soc Trang, Tam pleads for a troop strike using helicopters.

"We can put it down here," he says, pointing to the map. "There's got to be Viet Cong there. I talked to them." General Quang and Colonel Keirsey veto the idea and cancel everything.

"We don't gamble on probables," Keirsey said. "I don't like the looks of that landing zone. If they're there, and we don't know precisely where they are, they could cut us to pieces."

JAN. 29, BAC LIEU

Webster defines it: Harass (military)—to worry by repeated attacks.

A nightly briefing follows chow. It's pretty routine.

"The Vietnamese," Intelligence said, "picked up a small lad this afternoon. He had a one kilo (2.5 pound) mine on him. It was to have been thrown into our compound."

Mines have been found here before. One exploded outside our fence a few months ago. It broke all the windows in the main building of U.S. advisers. The only casualty was a six-year-old girl playing in her own front yard. Later they picked up a high-school boy perched in a tree, making a sketch of the American quarters. He seemed particularly interested in where the senior officers lived.

We remember all that as the Intelligence man comes up with his punch-line:

"There are supposed to be three more mines somewhere in town," he said.

This is harassment. In Viet Nam, the word takes on real meaning.

* * *

Maj. Vo Quoc Su, Province Chief, and his American adviser, Capt. David L. Wyatt of El Paso, stepped from the helicopter and strode toward the reviewing stand.

There was to be a change in command, swapping one district

171

chief for another. Major Su was due elsewhere within the hour. The ceremony was necessarily brief but nonetheless impressive. The honor guard looked sharp and the band played reasonably well.

"Incidentally, Captain," Su said on the way back. "They found two six-kilo mines under the stands just before we arrived. A medic is missing. We suspect him."

This, too, is harassment.

*　＊　＊*

Maj. John Crosby, Helena, Mont., and Lt. Bob Reid, whose parents live in Security, Colo., were at Vinh Trach. They'd made the trip to pay death money to the family of a dead combat youth. Suddenly their radio said a Vietnamese squad had been ambushed and was under fire at Khan.

They whipped back with their armed escort in time to break it up. The Viet Cong, firing from a tree line nearby, saw them coming and broke it off.

"Harassment," Bob Reid called it.

*　＊　＊*

In the thatch-roofed Officers' Club in Can Tho, artillery suddenly shakes the walls. A marathon bridge game temporarily suspends. The players tune professional ears in on the racket.

"Across the river," says North.

If it's across the river it's in another province. Not our problem. The game resumes.

Someone across the river is being harassed.

*　＊　＊*

At about the same time, in the American compound in Vinh Long two sergeants are sipping beer.

"They mined the Toonerville Trolley today," says one.

The Toonerville is the highway from Vinh Long to Sa Dec, with twice-daily courier runs. The Viet Cong know about them. Until now, however, we've had to cope with no more than sniper fire.

Anyone seriously hurt?

No, it was just harassment.

*　＊　＊*

At the early morning briefing in Bac Lieu they summarize what had happened while we slept.

Giong Bien harassed by 100 Viet Cong who fired briefly and broke off. Two wounded. Chau Ong harassed with small arms . . . a watchtower at Nham Dan overrun . . . an ambush and two roadblocks on the main highway to Soc Trang—they're being cleared now . . . Viet Cong stopped 145 sampans yesterday and collected taxes. . .

Harassment

* * *

Harassment never makes the communiques.

But it's the harassing, day after day, week after week, month after month, that wears men down.

We try to close our mind to it; dismiss it with a word: harassment.

But a man can be harassed to death.

Sometimes, in Viet Nam, men are.

FEB. 2, MY THOI

She squatted in the dusty road that meanders along the banks of the canal and cradled his head in her lap. She grieved for him —her wails muted, her body wracked with dry sobs.

To us, he was a dead Communist Viet Cong guerrilla who got what he deserved.

She knew only that he was her man. And that he was gone.

Yesterday he was alive. Today, before the morning had been fully born, he was dead.

She had seen him die, watching from the door of her hut, and she had rushed to him, dirty skirts billowing, calling his name, begging him to stand up again and tell her it was just a cruel trick her eyes were playing.

The men who had chased and killed him stood about, studiously ignoring her. So did her neighbors. They wanted nothing to do with this. With government troops about, who was to show sympathy for a slain Viet Cong?

She left him and wandered helplessly into one of the huts off the canal. They stared at her as if she were a stranger and turned their backs. She came back and squatted alone in that peculiar way of the Vietnamese and wept quietly to herself. Her man lay where he had fallen.

"He stopped," one of the government soldiers said. "He was running with the others and he stopped to throw a grenade. That's when we killed him."

The soldier said it accusingly—as much for her benefit as ours —as if to establish it was the slain man's fault, not theirs. After all, if he had kept on running—as plainly he should—he wouldn't have been killed. Didn't the others get away?

The man was in his late 20's or early 30's, a husky fellow. Papers on him showed he had been a Viet Cong for at least a year.

She insisted that he had been coerced, that his heart wasn't in it. But a reluctant Viet Cong doesn't stop running to throw a grenade.

He'd been part of a tax-collecting platoon operating with considerable success along the Bassac River out of Binh Minh. We set out before dawn with a Vietnamese Navy River Assault Group (RAG) hoping to trap them.

We had been trying to surprise these "tax collectors" since I came back to Viet Nam last fall, always without success. This time it was different: Before the day ended, six Viet Cong were killed and five wounded. But the bulk of the platoon got away, leaving a sack of mail and documents behind.

There had been the usual foul-ups. Captain My, the Binh Minh district chief, and his troops were late reaching the river for their rendezvous with RAG. And Lt. Cdr. Cho, the RAG commander, had trouble finding the spot and cruised up and down the river past dawn whereas the troops were to have gone ashore while it was still dark.

Aboard Cho's boat, Naval Lts. Bill Barschow of Cleveland, Clyde Smith of Sapulpa, Okla, and I drank hot coffee as protection against the early morning chill.

Somehow the Viet Cong got word we were coming and started to flee. Captain My's forces—with Maj. Charles (Bud)

174

Rainey of Guymon, Okla., Specialist Milton Lee Hollihugh of San Diego and Specialist Ralph Gilbert of Harlan, Ky.—took out after them.

RAG mortars—100 in all—marched inland from the Bassac, methodically tearing up the gardens the Viet Cong live off. Mortars from the river boat also whoomped into the carefully tended patches, hurling dirt, cabbages and radishes skyward.

It was over by 10 a.m.—we kicked off at three—and we headed home, picking up Captain My's straggling troops along the canal banks as we went. At My Thoi we came across the last batch.

And as we pulled away, we could still see her—sitting there in the dust, holding his head in her lap. He was another dead Viet Cong—and good riddance. He was also her man.

FEB. 5, SOC TRANG

One of the many jobs of Capt. Robert T. Hackett of South Amboy, N.J., is flying his helicopter so he will be shot at.

Under the rules of this strange war, our side can't shoot at the Viet Cong unless they first have fired at us.

For the past three months, this 28-year-old West Pointer has been leader of the 121st Army Aviation Company's armed helicopter platoon, deep in the Red-infested Mekong Delta. His call sign has been "Viking 26."

Over the weeks and months we have grown accustomed to hearing his voice come over the air as he skims over the rice paddies.

"Viking 26 drawing fire," he'll say—and then the war is on.

It's a difficult art, getting shot at, and no one has mastered it better than Bob Hackett.

"They don't make them any better," says Col. Jim Keirsey, senior U.S. adviser to the 21st Vietnamese Division. "Some men are brave but reckless. No one questions Captain Hackett's courage. But he's a professional. He is as cool and calculating a customer as you can find. You've got to admire him."

In his year in Viet Nam, Bob Hackett has flown more than

5000 hours, a lot of it under fire, all of it over hostile country. As head of the 121st's Vikings, he has commanded 15 helicopter pilots. They are among his biggest boosters. So are his commanding officers all up the line.

The Pentagon doesn't like the newspapers to announce in advance that a man has been recommended for specific decorations. So it wouldn't do to say that Bob Hackett is up for both the Silver Star and the Distinguished Flying Cross. If, however, this turns out to be the case, the recommendation will bear the enthusiastic endorsement of every colonel and general who has dealt with him.

Captain Hackett has no idea how many combat missions he has flown. He has one Purple Heart. Ironically, that was for wounds sustained on the ground. He was hurt during a mortar attack on Soc Trang last April 10. During the battle at Da Ngai on Dec. 27, a .50-caliber bullet smashed through his windshield between him and his co-pilot, WO Clarence Powell of Kansas City, Mo.

Hackett was graduated from West Point in 1960. He intends to make the Army his career. He's going home soon for eventual reassignment to the seat of Army Aviation at Fort Rucker, Ala. But first he intends to tackle what he calls a "priority mission."

That's his forthcoming marriage to a home-state girl, Miss Anne Byrnes. No date has been set, but if Hackett has his way, it will be quite soon after he gets home.

FEB. 8, SOC TRANG

The movie was "El Cid," a long one and a good one—so that most of the chopper pilots and their crews were still up when the first enemy mortar blasts came in.

It was 10:42 p.m., our time.

There was no doubt about what they were. The mortar fire hit in clusters of two to 15, all at the far end of the runway. They sprayed the parked Huey choppers with deadly shrapnel.

But it sounded as if they were landing just outside the movie theater. And "El Cid" acted out the last of his heroics before an empty house. No one stayed behind to turn off the movie.

By 10:44 p.m., the first of our choppers were airborne. In seven minutes all but one—which was laid up for repairs—were off the ground.

Even as the White House was announcing the retaliatory raids on the North Vietnamese training bases and staging areas, to avenge the bloody attack 24 hours earlier on Pleiku, the Viet Cong were taking this base under mortar attack.

Repeatedly in recent months incipient attacks here had been broken up. But now the Communists had slipped through and set up their mortars in the tree lines a half-mile away.

Men not attending the movie were sitting glued to their radios for word of the air raids on North Viet Nam, or were anxiously awaiting the release of the casualty lists at Pleiku, where many had friends.

The Armed Forces radio in Saigon had announced it would stay on the air all night to keep the troops informed.

Quickly the news of the attack on Soc Trang spread throughout the Mekong Delta.

In Can Tho, 50 miles distant, Lt. Col. Jack Mackmull of Dayton, O., in command of the 13th Army Aviation Battalion, hurriedly dressed and flew to Soc Trang.

Capt. Don Masters of Farwell, Tex., moved into the tactical operations center for the night.

Capt. Charles Teague of Oklahoma City and his armed Vikings were in the air over the besieged base—first circling, then firing rockets into the tree lines.

Angry Vietnamese artillery guns opened up.

Over Can Tho the skies were suddenly filled with churning, burping Hueys.

One by one the men settled down to wait out the night. Cots were set up in the terminal building for the crews. Some arrived in shorts, wearing shower shoes. Others had thrown flak vests over their pajamas. Bill Weeks of Fayetteville, N.C., threw down the book he was reading and was halfway to his Huey before it occurred to him he was stark naked

177

By 11:30 p.m. it was all over. The Viet Cong are deathly afraid of armed Hueys and had picked up their hot mortar tubes and moved away. Back in Can Tho, Col. George Bartin of Fairfax, Va., studied his reports.

"We weathered this one," he said.

Dawn came, and the Hueys which had moved out to safety during the night came home. Maj. Cecil Jist of Ellenwood, Ga., an infantry battalion adviser, squatted on the runway, digging for fuses and professionally estimating the enemy's capability.

"They had the azimuth," he said. "Another 200 meters and they would have been right on us."

With the dawn, Capt. Ken Griffith of Paducah, Ky., and a battalion of Vietnamese infantry moved out in pursuit of Soc Trang's attackers. Capt. Jim Bramlet of Harrisburg, Ill., and a second battalion stayed behind at the airfield in reserve.

In the mess hall, Col. Jim Keirsey of Durant, Okla., and Major Millard Whitten, Portland, Me., talked quietly over coffee.

"There's no doubt now what the target is," Keirsey said. "From this point on, it's 'get the American.'"

FEB. 15, HIEU DUC

It was the old man's birthday—his 75th—and his friends had gathered to honor him. They sat in a solemn, cross-legged circle, while the women, out back, prepared food and drink.

His name was Phan Van Hen, and he welcomed us solemnly. It was obvious Hen had not neglected the wine cup, but he was not drunk.

"I am," he said solemnly, with the air of one accepting homage, "an old man. I know nothing of politics. I have lived under many governments. More governments"—he fixed me with an owlish stare—"than you have years, young man. I have lived under the French, under the Emperor Bao Dai, under Ngo Dinh Diem and under Khanh."

He paused, took another drink, and his voice took on heavy volume.

"I know nothing of politics," he said, "but I have always deemed it my duty to obey and respect the government."

He looked about him, challenging denial. His cronies—men of his own age—nodded agreement.

Hen held the center of the stage—as befits a man on his 75th birthday—and had no intention of relinquishing it.

"Out here," he declared, "I sometimes think there is no government. Here, there is only war. War has been fought in these fields"—he paused to let this sink in—"young men have killed each other in front of these doors.

"I am an old man," he went on, obviously liking the sound of that. "And I have lived in this house for 60 years. No dog of a Viet Cong will make me leave it."

You wondered how much of this he really believed and what he told the Viet Cong, who control much of this area in the Mekong Delta, less than a mile from the Cambodian border, when they came to call. All this was said in Vietnamese and lost much in translation despite the bi-lingual ability of Le Van Van who sat beside me, whispering rapidly to keep up with the old man. We had wandered in on the party quite by accident. It was hot on the trail and we needed to rest. Phan Van Hen accepted us as his guests.

He took it for granted we had come to honor him on his 75th birthday.

"I am pleased," he said, acknowledging our presence, "that the Americans have sent you on this day. No foreigner—not even the French—have done this."

He paused, considered.

"Of course," he conceded judiciously, "I was much younger when they were here."

We sipped tea, and Le Van Van nudged me. I was expected to say something in return. Whatever I said, I was sure it would come out all right in translation, even if he had to improvise.

"My people have heard much about Phan Van Hen and have asked me to bring him their greetings and best wishes. His support of the government—which he knows we also support—means much to us. We know that we will have that support in

179

the years ahead, for we know that Phan Van Hen will live a long and illustrious life."

He nodded, and watched me closely.

Plainly, a gift was expected. But what would it be? All I had was a cheap cigaret lighter. But it bore the MACV (Military Assistance Command, Viet Nam) insignia.

"I commend to the venerable Phan Van Hen this insignia," I said. "I say to him that this is a token of our determination to remain at the side of his government until his people are free to live in peace. I commend it to him on this, his 75th birthday."

The old man's eyes seemed cloudy as he picked it up, examined it carefully and passed it around for his friends to admire. The old women had slipped quietly into the room, gazing at him with respect.

"Go in peace," he said. "This is the finest birthday I ever had."

FEB. 17, CAN THO

To many Vietnamese, the Americans are not advisers. They are providers.

They are loved for what they can acquire. They are the key to a rich storehouse of military and other supplies unavailable to the average Vietnamese commander. Said one recently quoted by Stars and Stripes:

"The Americans are very good. They can get us helicopters, air strikes and supplies very quickly. Their light reconnaissance plane is very good at spotting Viet Cong."

I have encountered this attitude frequently. I have queried Americans throughout the Delta about it. They say it is true more often than not. The American's advice seldom is sought. When it is volunteered, it is courteously received, and just as often ignored.

The American is important as a symbol, as a presence, and as a channel of supplies. As long as he is around, our helicopters and our planes will respond promptly to any call for help. His signature on a requisition automatically guarantees it will be filled. If it isn't, he'll find out why.

Otherwise, he is often a burden. At Cai Son, for instance, Capt. Nguyen Duy Hoe told me frankly he was glad to see weekends come. Then the three Americans assigned to him usually go to Vinh Long to relax.

"The Viet Cong attack only when the Americans are here," he explained. "When they are gone, the Viet Cong leave us alone."

Vietnamese commanders are acutely aware they are responsible for the safety of their Americans. If anything happens to them, they (the Vietnamese) will answer. They go to great lengths to protect their guests.

At Kien Binh, Capt. Nguyen Van Huynh will not let his five advisers to into town without an armed guard. Recently one slipped downtown for a haircut. Minutes later, guards appeared and took up positions at both ends of the street. They marched beside him when he returned to camp.

The Americans at Kien Binh sometimes feel they are prisoners.

The relationship between a Vietnamese and an American depends, in the final analysis, on their ability to get along together. Huynh's relations with Maj. Ralph Waara of East Lansing, Mich., are excellent. In other areas, however, relations are on a different basis.

I recently spent four days in a camp near the Cambodian border. During that time, the young American sent there to "advise" a Vietnamese of the same rank (captain) sent two ultimatums across the 100 yards separating their quarters. Each said in effect that unless the Vietnamese came across with certain information, "I shall be forced to advise my superiors that you have refused to cooperate." The Vietnamese will not even talk to his American adviser.

One reason the Vietnamese are disturbed by the setup is the frequency with which we change advisers. One Vietnamese captain pointed out that he had had eight different advisers in three years. None had stayed long enough to be of much use. Also, many of our advisers are young men with three or four years' military experience. Vietnamese with 15 or 20 years' service, much of it at war, do not feel they can be told how things ought to be done. A young officer unsure of himself insists on doing

181

things "by the book." Unfortunately it is our book, not theirs, he goes by.

FEB. 19, CAI SON

Capt. Nguyen Duy Hoe was playing his trump card.

He fired one of his mortar flares. It hung in the night air, brightly at first, fading and sputtering as it drifted down to earth. Hoe had only nine to begin with. Now he had eight. He had hoarded those flares. Only a dire emergency would account for his using one.

Firing broke out across a bridge spanning a canal 500 yards away. Automatic weapons chattered. A machine gun spewed tracers. Carbines and M-1's barked their angry challenges. Then there were sounds of guns being fired our way.

Back in an old French-built farmhouse protected by parapets of paddy mud, Maj. George Short of Columbus, O., checked hand grenades, stripping the adhesive off their containers. Dallas Hawkins of Clarksville, Tenn., checked out a machine gun. Sgt. Richard Quitman of Colorado Springs, Colo., picked up an automatic rifle and slammed a cartridge into the chamber. Capt. Richard Holbrook of Sauk Center, Minn., spoke quietly into the radio, advising Vinh Long, 14 miles away, that trouble could be brewing at Cai Son.

As suddenly as it had started, it stopped. An estimated 30 Viet Cong had slipped into Cai Son and almost reached us. They fell back under fire, taking three wounded men with them. It was obviously a probing attack. And, Dick Holbrook pointed out, they'd be back next time perhaps with enough force to stay.

Cai Son is a training camp for regional and popular forces, the backbone of Viet Nam's fight for survival. And nowhere else are the troubles which beset this nation's armed forces more poignantly illustrated.

One group of youngsters are in their second day of training. Only 48 hours earlier they arrived, city boys and farm boys. They spent the first day learning to march and salute. They spent their second day studying their weapons. Some don't even know yet which end of the rifle the bullet comes from.

Last Dec. 1, 14 recruits, in their first day of training, went out on patrol. A thousand yards outside camp they were ambushed. All 14 died. They didn't even have their rifles loaded.

Not a night goes by that the Cai Son is not attacked. The Viet Cong control the countryside. A few nights ago 200 of them came down the canal in sampans. Luckily a flight of armed Hueys—headed elsewhere, but the Viet Cong didn't know that—passed overhead. The Reds abandoned their boats and fled.

Day after day Captain Hoe begs higher headquarters for regular troops to defend Cai Son while he trains his recruits. His pleas go unheeded. All six outposts protecting Cai Son have been wiped out in the last two months. The Viet Cong kill everyone in an outpost, women and children included. Before they left us, last night's probers mined Hoe's rifle range.

Training recruits under such conditions is all but impossible.

The Americans and Vietnamese here do the best they can.

FEB. 20, CAN THO

The little plane swept low around the Cambodian border, from Mac Hoa to Don Phouc and back to Mac Hoa, looking for Viet Cong infiltrators.

Automatic weapons opened fire from both sides of the border. The plane's left front tank was hit, and it barely limped back to the nearest base.

Out here they call it "Guts Airline." The men who fly the little Otters refer to themselves as the Can Tho Ratfinks.

The Otter is a six-seater plane that can carry seven in an emergency. Guts Airlines flies passengers everywhere—everywhere no one else wants to go. The airline's exploits seldom make the headlines.

It drops supplies where outposts are under siege. It can land, and does, on uncharted and unapproved fields. It has pinpoint accuracy. It has dropped as much as 10,000 pounds in one day. Warrant Officer Paul Kelly, Koscuiusko, Miss., has made 65 drops in one week.

"It's a question of who has the guts," Kelly says with a grin. "Those who fly it or those who ride with us."

The Otter works primarily with the Special Forces, who swear by it. The bigger Army Caribous and the Air Force C-123's fly the main route. The Otter takes over from there to move men and supplies to the outposts. Frequently its crew chiefs—men like Specialists Bruce Yarian of Covington, O., Ramon C. Altamirano of Hatch, New Mexico, Jack Tressler of Steubenville, O., Pfc. James Grant of Murphys, Calif., Pfc. Daniel Pointer of Carnegie, Pa., Specialists Michael McNam of The Dalles, Ore., and Robin Smith, Neptune, N.J.—take off the doors and ride shotgun.

Because the Otter is relatively slow, it makes it a good reconnaissance plane. So, of course, is the helicopter. But choppers burn fuel so fast they can stay aloft little more than two hours. The Otter can stay up much longer.

A typical day for an Otter man begins at 5 a.m. It ends when he returns to his base after dark. Chow may or may not have been saved for him. A wise Otter pilot or crewman makes it a point to become friendly with the mess sergeant.

Otters, like the Caribous, are a Canadian-made plane. The contract has been cancelled to curb the drain on our gold reserves. We'll be sorry to see the last of them. The Otter has proved its worth in Viet Nam.

Pilots flying the Otter in the Mekong Delta include:

Warrant officers Kelly, Robert D. Orton, Holden, Mass., Allan Rebb of Fort Lauderdale, Fla., Donald Seymour of Sayville, N.Y., Donald Burrows of Palm Beach Gardens, Fla., David Kluborg of Milwaukee, Wis., and Capt. Wilfred Wittekind of Cincinnati and William O'Hara, Schenectady, N.Y.

FEB. 22, CAN THO

A U.S. Army colonel kept the lines open between Lt. Gen. Nguyen Khanh and Gen. William Westmoreland during the weekend's abortive coup. Westmoreland commands U.S. forces in South Viet Nam.

Col. George Barten, of Fairfax, Va., was playing volleyball just after noon Friday when he was notified that rebel forces had laid siege to Saigon's Tan Son Nhut airfield and other key points. Khanh had been taken, under escort, from his headquarters to that airfield.

At the same time Barten learned all Vietnamese communications had been cut. He went immediately to headquarters of Gen. Dang Van Quang, Fourth Corps Commander, and then to his own office. Our lines remained open.

Quang asked Barten to let him use our wires to contact his three division commanders in the Mekong Delta. It was a tough decision for a colonel to make. If the coup succeeded, Barten could be accused of siding with Quang. He undoubtedly would be relieved and sent home.

He decided affirmatively for two reasons. First, he was Quang's adviser and therefore under orders to help him whenever possible. A request to contact division commanders was a legitimate one for Quang. Secondly, by so doing, Barten would get to know what the Vietnamese were saying among themselves and be able to keep Westmoreland informed.

At 6 p.m., Khanh arrived at Can Tho by helicopter to sit out the coup. Air Force Chief Brig. Gen. Nguyen Cao Ky came soon afterward and both went to Quang's home.

Simultaneously Barten learned Khanh and Quang had ordered Brig. Gen. Nguyen Bao Tri, commander of the Seventh Division, to send a task force up Route Four to Saigon and halt at the outskirts for orders. Tri was trying to contact the Long An province chief to learn if the 25th Division—between his headquarters in My Tho and Saigon—would oppose his march.

Ky and Khanh then used our facilities to warn the rebels they would be bombed if they didn't stop the airfield siege. Only a few key persons in Saigon knew at this point where Khanh had gone. One report was that he had been taken prisoner; another that he had gone to Vung Tau.

Meanwhile, Quang deployed armored personnel carriers through Can Tho as "additional public security." Actually they were to protect Khanh. Several were posted outside the American compound and Americans were ordered to stay inside.

Only Barten was permitted to go outside the gates.

Soon after dark, machine-gun and mortar fire echoed throughout Can Tho. The Viet Cong were attacking Cai Rang, two miles outside the city. Three armored personnel carriers took off in that direction.

Westmoreland had been trying all this time to get in touch with Khanh. He asked Barten to relay his and Ambassador Maxwell Taylor's fervent hope that "bloodshed be avoided at all costs." Barten already had said this to Quang.

Khanh gave his personal assurances to this effect and Barten reported that to Westmoreland. Khanh left Can Tho at 9 p.m. for Vung Tau. He flew to Bien Hoa the next morning for political-military conferences.

By this time it was obvious the coup had failed.

Barten went to bed at 2 a.m. He was awakened at 4:30 a.m. Col. Jim Keirsey of Durant, Okla., adviser to the 21st Division in the southernmost part of the Delta, reported a battalion ambushed. He asked Barten to send armed helicopters at daybreak. Barten agreed and stayed up the rest of the night to follow developments.

Barten is a graduate of Gettysburg College. He has been a colonel since 1953, attaining that rank at age 38. He came here from the Pentagon.

FEB. 24, CAN THO

Coups d'etat certainly undermine an army.

After the last two here, one American colonel says: "It will be a couple of weeks before we get this war back on the tracks. If, of course, there isn't still another coup."

They throw everything out of kilter. Operations against the Viet Cong had to be canceled by the Vietnamese Seventh and Ninth Divisions, headquartered here.

The Seventh sent a task force, spearheaded by the 10th Regiment and Sixth Armored battalion, to the outskirts of Saigon. The Ninth division started to move when the first coup against

Lt. Gen. Nguyen Khanh fizzled. The 21st, deeper in the Delta, was assembling to move if needed.

If the Saigon crisis had lasted another 48 hours, the Mekong Delta virtually would have been without defending troops— against the crowding Viet Cong.

Then, two days later, General Khanh left Saigon. The Seventh Division had just got back here from Saigon. Each commander had to make a personal decision.

General Khanh called Gen. Dang Van Quang, Fourth Corps commander, and urged him to throw his corps behind him (Khanh) against the High Council. Quang was sweating blood over this. Khanh was his personal friend. He had upheld him 48 hours earlier against two other generals.

This time, he said, he would have to stick with the High Council.

Khanh flew to Vinh Long seeking a place to hold out until the crisis was over. A regimental commander there, under orders from the Ninth Division commander, Brig. Gen. Vinh Lac, took over the airfield. The Khanh plane buzzed the field, but didn't land.

One of the ablest province chiefs in the Delta, Lt. Col. Phan Thanh Thoi, stayed with Khanh. Vinh Lac put him under house arrest.

Thus, unavoidably, men who had been friends one day were enemies the next. It is hard to maintain morale when an officer realizes that the man sitting beside him at the mess table may throw him in jail the next day.

The coup disrupted American-Vietnamese relations as well.

Americans find themselves cut off from men they are supposed to advise on the conduct of the war. They are even barred sometimes from their own offices. And they aren't told what is happening.

Advisers to units actually involved in the coups must decide whether to accompany the units and become embroiled in the trouble, or remain behind—without any troops to advise. Nothing in their training touched on the tough question of coups and what to do about them.

187

Worse, Americans are often treated like enemies. A young U.S. soldier at Tan Son Nhut airport outside Saigon last weekend told about it:

"The military leaders who had deposed Khanh had gathered at the airport to prepare for any attempt by Khanh to shoot his way back to power. They declared a general alert at the field and geared their forces for a possible attack.

"Vietnamese fighter planes carrying bombs were overhead. Our helicopters would try to take off, but the fighters would buzz the choppers to try to keep them on the ground.

"An Australian Caribou (passenger plane) went to the end of the runway. They flew over it so low I was sure they would crash. The Caribou came back. Later one of our Navy planes tried to take off, and it got the same treatment.

"Those fighters had our markings on them and they were being used against us. It was sickening. All we were trying to do was to get in the air so we could get on with the war. What did they think we were up to?"

Later, he said, Vietnamese troops were posted around our aircraft and he was ordered away by gun-wielding sentries.

One saving factor is that the Viet Cong have been slow to act. Apparently they were unable to assemble quickly enough to take advantage of the turmoil. If the enemy had more mobility, we really would be in for it.

Also, says an American adviser, a great many of the Vietnamese army units do ignore the coups and keep on trying to flush out the Viet Cong and fight them.

FEB. 25, VI THANH

If all the units in the Vietnamese army were as good as the 33rd Battalion here, there would be no reason to have American advisers in South Viet Nam.

They come to grips with the Viet Cong wherever they find them. They have been bloodied, but never whipped. They spend much of their time on the march. Today they're moving along again, under a broiling sun, searching futilely for the enemy.

Their tempers have grown short. But they revive whenever we reach a canal and they plunge in for a refreshing dip.

Ground pounders of the Vietnamese Army, like ground pounders all over the world, consider themselves something special. They reserve their heartiest contempt for soldiers who have an easier life than theirs.

For the men of the 33rd any man farther back—in sector, division or corps—is a "lollipop," only slightly better than a "Saigon Commando."

It is important these men feel they are something special. It builds esprit de corps.

There are other such units, but not many.

Col. Jim Keirsey of Durant, Okla., senior U.S. adviser to the 21st Vietnamese Division, stood on the runway at Vi Thanh and watched members of the 42nd Ranger Battalion climb out of helicopters and form up. They had met with only moderate success on this particular Eagle flight, but they were not depressed at all.

"Those were the best soldiers in the Vietnamese army last year," he said proudly. "They collected almost a half-million piasters in bonuses for captured weapons.

"See that red baseball cap they wear under their helmets? They bought those with their loot. Let them catch some outsider wearing their cap! And they've used the rest of their prize money to build some pretty decent housing for their families. Their old man sees that any bonuses the battalion collects get right back to his men. That's why they're willing to die for him."

The 42nd has gone month after month without desertions or absences without leave.

Some day, perhaps, all units in the Vietnamese army will be like this. When that happens, we will have worked ourselves out of a job.

Meanwhile there is plenty of work to be done.

"The Vietnamese," says Col. Martin Sullivan of Falls Church, Va., "are compressing into one generation all we've done in four.

It is not surprising they have failures. What is important is that they're trying."

MARCH 10, BA TRI

The man broke from the brush like an actor who has muffed his cue.

Sgt. Raymond Bucks of Logansport, Ind., shot him. He tottered, then fell, clutching his side.

They carried him first to the village dispensary and when the wound proved superficial they locked him up in the police station.

Nguyen Van Thinh was the most important Communist in this, his own, district. He ranked as a deputy chief. But more important, he lived here. His home was 100 yards from the police station where he was now a prisoner.

Everyone in Ba Tri knew that he was a Viet Cong who had taken to the bush. His wife went to market with the other wives. His children attended school. But Nguyen Van Thinh stayed free, sometimes slipping into his own house after dark, slipping away again the next morning.

As long as Thinh remained free, he was a symbol of the government's inability to control Ba Tri.

It was only by chance that Bucks winged him. Nguyen Van Thinh was on the move, collecting taxes. His receipt book indicated he had had a good day, though the money apparently had been cached. Bucks had been on patrol, and their paths crossed.

Even in captivity, Thinh remained a hard-core, unrepentant Viet Cong. In his wallet he carried a picture of North Viet Nam's Ho Chi Minh. There were other pictures of Thinh in his black-pajama Viet Cong uniform with his weapons—a proud, angry man staring straight ahead.

Small matter, now. With Thinh's capture, the legend of his infallibility was shattered. That evening they even let his family bring him his meal.

The most dangerous Viet Cong, says Lt. Col. Tran Ngoc Chau, Kien Hoa Province Chief, is a fellow villager. Hard-core imports from the North are aliens speaking another dialect. Often they are resented, because they bring trouble. But local Viet Cong personify rebellion, somehow make it real.

To Colonel Chau, the villagers manning the mud forts which dot the countryside are "our real heroes." They know they can be overrun. Often they are. ("Two nights ago this bridge was hit; two of our men died.") If they have a mortar, it is home-made. Their pay is less than $10 a month, and slow in coming down the clogged pipelines of bureaucracy. If they die, their families wait six months or more for death benefits. Yet every day and every night they man their posts, defend their homes.

Such a man was Ngoc Dinh Gian, village chief of Tuong Da. When 200 Viet Cong attacked a few nights ago, Gian was one of seven government men to die. But so did 40 Viet Cong, and Tuong Da held out.

In many of his hamlets Chau has cleared out all resident Viet Cong and they are now considered secure. If strangers move in, block leaders report them. They are thoroughly checked out before they are permitted to remain.

MARCH 12, THANH PHU

The refugees came from the mangrove swamps which lie to the east of Thanh Phu. That is strong Viet Cong territory.

Stolidly they plodded down the dusty streets, ignoring and ignored by the village people, and made their way to the big shed which had been designated as their collection point.

Every line in their tired faces, the sag of their tired bodies, proclaimed they'd had it. They were sick and tired of the war, sick and tired of the Viet Cong, and of the artillery and bombs which have been their daily fare.

So they'd packed up what they could carry with them—a few chickens, a pig on leash, cooking utensils and a few clothes carried in a pack—and walked to Thanh Phu.

They were a varied and a frightened lot. The children among them were wide-eyed and staring, darting behind their mothers if noticed and peeking out again, unwilling to miss anything.

There were old men, village elders for whom the decision to leave their villages must have been hard. Old women, toothless, with gums stained by betel-nut juice. Younger women, plump and round of face; one had been terribly burned by napalm or white phosphorous and was in obvious pain.

They had one thing in common: They were afraid. For them, daily living had become a daily hell. The mangrove swamps along the coast are a free zone for bombing. We can practice there without worrying about what we hit, knowing it will be Viet Cong. Planes heading home with unexpended armament can drop it there. Even now, artillery is pounding the mangrove with a steady thump, thump.

Lt. Col. Tran Ngoc Chau, Kien Hoa Province Chief, is a compassionate man. Only Chau seems to be able to run Kien Hoa. He was here for three years, then they pulled him out for another job. His three successors made such a mess they brought Chau back. He has a way with the people. They stop him on the street and talk with him. He never fails to listen—then act.

Chau spoke briefly, assuring the refugees of their welcome; and then listened. His face brightened. Their leader, a wizened old man, was asking about the air strikes in North Viet Nam. They had heard about them, the old man said, but the Viet Cong was putting out denials on their radios.

Graphically, in Vietnamese, Chau described the retribution against the North. As he spoke, his excitement mounted and his voice became shrill. The refugees clustered about him, openmouthed, nodding occasional approval. It was good, their spokesman said. It was right and just that the Viet Cong suffer.

It has been this way since the first strike, Chau said later. People have come from Viet Cong areas asking about the bombings. They have gone home to spread the word.

Chau controls 50 per cent of his province. He estimates he has the loyalty of 80 per cent of his people. Kien Hoa and An Xuyen are the two provinces with the heaviest concentration of Viet Cong. Yet Chau says firmly:

"We are winning the war here. This war has gone on for years. There have been too many unfilled Viet Cong promises, too many threats not made good. The people of Kien Hoa are disillusioned with the Viet Cong. Here, they have lost credibility.

"I do not mean the Viet Cong will go away or we can get rid of them without bloodshed. I do not mean the people will actively help us until we are strong enough to guarantee they will not be revenged. But the people no longer believe, or believe in, the Viet Cong. They want them out as much as we, the government, want to be rid of them. Time is on our side."

MARCH 17, PHUNG HIEP

Three miles down the Xeo Vong Canal out of Phung Hiep, five men waited patiently to die.

They were Viet Cong. They had slipped across the Bassac River from Vinh Binh, where their unit had taken a beating, and had been spotted. A thousand of them, the first reports had said. Three hundred, they amended when—at dawn—we moved into Phung Hiep from Can Tho with the big 155 mm. howitzers.

And now there were five. And they were trapped. The others, if they were ever there, had moved on during the night or found places to hide. Armed Huey choppers had rocketed the trees along the canals, hoping to smoke them out.

At first, the five men had tried to save themselves. They ran in one direction and stopped short when they saw regular army troops ahead of them. They cut back and ran the other way. Regional forces were there. It was the same on the other two sides. So they sat down in an open field and waited to die.

Methodically, our men in Phung Hiep went about the business of killing them. They were pros—experts in their business—and this was a mathematical equation, a problem in co-ordinates and range, altitude and wind.

A spotter plane swooped low over the five and called back a tentative fix. They did not look up. In Phung Hiep, Lt. Col. Douglas Harper of Palo Alto, Calif., relayed the message.

"Down 500, right 500," he said

The guns roared moments after the recess bell clanged in a

schoolhouse 75 yards away. The children crowded around, as close as the school guards would let them, the bigger boys up front, the younger ones holding back timidly.

The spotter called again, and the Colonel frowned.

"I said right, not left," he said. "Make it right 800. An easy target, Captain, is no excuse for a sloppy performance."

The 155's fired again. All the older schoolboys chattered learnedly, pretending to understand and discuss what was happening. The younger ones gazed at them with open-mouthed respect.

A native ice-cream cart was pushed into the schoolyard, and Jim Mead of Big Stone Gap, Va., edged through the chattering boys and girls to buy a home-made popsicle.

The Colonel made another correction, and the guns fired again.

The smaller boys had lost interest and started a game roughly resembling tag and football. The little girls clustered in groups, gossiping. A few put their fingers daintily to their ears.

Finally: "Fire for effect."

That meant we had found the range. The big guns opened up for the kill. Then they fell silent. The smoke lifted, and the spotter plane made his last sweep.

"The target has disappeared," he called.

The waiting is over. Now the five could only be dead.

The school bell rings and the kids line up. A teacher slaps one of the boys and a little girl giggles.

APRIL 3, WASHINGTON

It comes as no great surprise to those who know him that Brig. Gen. Joe Stilwell, who is 53, has seriously injured himself jumping out of a helicopter.

General Stilwell, son of the late Gen. Joseph (Vinegar Joe) Stilwell, is commander of the Special Forces Training Center at Fort Bragg, N.C. He suffered fractures of the lower back, pelvis and both heels when his main parachute failed to open fully and his reserve 'chute failed to deploy.

Stilwell went to Fort Bragg from Viet Nam where he headed the Support Command. This gave him control of all of the U.S. Army's helicopters in that war theater.

The General is a person no one can be neutral about, if he knows him. The men who served under him either hated or loved him. There were many occasions on which the whole group would swear Stilwell hated everybody, including himself.

Whether he was as tough as he made out was one of those topics men discussed endlessly in their bull sessions in Viet Nam. The concensus was that he wasn't; no man could be. General Stilwell did his best to convince people he was a hard one. Greeting an incoming company commander who was noted for his cockiness, he said:

"Think you're good, don't you? Let me tell you something. You've never been harassed before in your life. I'll have you on the carpet every day, many times a day. After you've served under me, you'll be a wreck. You'll be begging for mercy."

Some believed Stilwell felt he had to live up to Vinegar Joe's reputation for toughness.

Helicopters and Joe Stilwell went together. He was no desk man. He spent most of his time in the field. Invariably, he manned one of the machine guns and did his share of firing. His superiors in Saigon frowned on this, and any reporters about were asked please to forget they'd heard the General's rasping voice over the radio shouting:

"That ought to teach the b———!"

On one occasion, the 121st Aviation Company in the Mekong Delta decided to experiment with .50-caliber machine guns mounted on its Flying Bananas. The experiment was less than a success. Stilwell heard about it, flew down to Soc Trang to see what was going on. He insisted on firing the first test.

The gun jumped off its mount and smote the General in his face. His finger froze on the trigger and it continued to pound him in the teeth while his subordinates almost went out of their minds. Stilwell wound up with a split lip and minus several molars. He thought it was hilarious.

Among other things, however, he fought for the enlisted men

in his command. When one of his commanders invited several Embassy girls, including the Ambassador's secretary, down to the Delta for an anniversary party, General Stilwell was on the phone.

"Did you invite anyone for the enlisted men?" he asked.

"No, sir."

"The party's canceled."

And it was.

APRIL 6, WASHINGTON

Thousands of Americans in Viet Nam are daily involved in a dirty, grueling, bloody war against the Communist Viet Cong.

Their living conditions range from primitive to merely adequate.

They subsist for weeks on native food—including a vile-smelling sauce called Nukman which should be included in disarmament talks—and canal water laced with iodine.

The strain is constant, frustrations incessant.

Trouble is everywhere, and usually comes when it is least expected.

Most of these Americans are family men and they miss their families.

Yet in 13 months with our troops in the field, most of that time in the Mekong Delta, I do not recall one who broke under the strain.

Today we have 27,000 men in South Viet Nam. This figure will grow.

Until recently we have stubbornly insisted they were there strictly as advisers. This has never been quite true. At one time Americans were directly responsible for better than half the Viet Cong killed in the Delta.

Our armed helicopters and fighter planes, which support every major operation, still account for large numbers. It is not difficult, surveying the field after a battle, to spot the fatalities our side has caused. They have head and upper-body wounds.

Our rockets and machine guns quite literally decapitate them.

We send only our best men to South Viet Nam—the First Team, the Cream of the Crop. This has been said so often, it has almost become a cliche. But it is still true.

No one who has been passed over for promotion need apply.

Anyone else interested in future advancement had better pull strings to be sure his records reflect a Viet Nam tour.

Selection of our four senior Corps advisers is as painstaking and thorough as the selection of a new U.S. Chief of Staff. The process takes months. These four colonels do four generals' work, and sometimes have even greater responsibilities.

In a very real sense, these advisers live on beleaguered little islands in a sea of Viet Cong. Our side controls only six per cent of the ground south of the Bassac River. A mile or less outside the bigger towns the Viet Cong are often supreme. Only in an extreme emergency will roads be used without an armed escort.

At night the Americans retire to their little compounds and await the dawn. Even there they are not always safe; Pleiku and Qui Nhon showed that. If they go out at all, it is on patrol, seeking the enemy and often finding him in greater numbers than they had expected. Helicopters and small planes are their principal means of transport.

They are apt to feel, at times, that they are forgotten. What are they saying about us, what are they doing back home, they invariably ask the visitor from the outside world. The news they get is days old.

Our men are professionals doing a professional's job. They do a year in Viet Nam—six months in the field and six in a higher headquarters—and when it is over inevitably they say it has been the most rewarding tour they've ever had. They go home seasoned and matured.

There is a reason for this. The reservoir of experience we built up during World War II has, for all practical purposes, been exhausted. After 15 years, the Korean reservoir is fast being dried up. Men who fought there as second lieutenants are in South Viet Nam as majors and colonels. Few of our junior officers have had combat experience, and combat is the best teacher. So they are learning more in a year there than they could learn in their classrooms in a decade.

There is another side to this coin, however.

Every man we lose in Viet Nam is a severe drain on our investment capital. Many are potential generals. For example, it was widely agreed that Capt. James Spruill of Suffern, N.Y., couldn't miss. But Spruill died when his jeep hit a mine near Binh Minh.

Gen. William C. Westmoreland is their boss. A former West Point Superintendent, he knows many of the younger officers as a father knows his son. Lt. Ron Hines of Abilene, Tex., was the first of Westmoreland's boys to die. Ron was killed last spring when he leaped from the security of his armored personnel carrier to run to the assistance of a wounded Vietnamese officer, who was also his friend.

Since then, General Westmoreland has averaged at least one funeral a week.

Lt. Thurston A. (Turk) Griffith, 25, of Alamos, N.M., was to have been Westmoreland's guest on Christmas Eve. They never got to the dinner table. A terrorist bomb blasted a U.S. billet in downtown Saigon and Griffith rushed off to help dig out the survivors. Less than a month later, Westmoreland saw Griffith's body put aboard a plane for the flight home. He had been killed in an ambush.

The equipment of our men gets better every day. They don't have the push-button stuff, but Viet Nam is not a push-button war. I have seen a dramatic improvement in the quality of equipment in the last several months. The old T-28 plane, held together by chewing gum and bailing wire, is gone and the Skyraider, replacing it, fills the bill.

The Army has washed out the old Flying Banana helicopter—and has gone exclusively to Hueys. Some communications equipment is of World War II vintage and hard to maintain, but newer materiel is coming in.

The Marines near Da Nang are experimenting with classified weapons and detection systems. A few new jeeps have shown up. Ammunition supplies are adequate to abundant, though we occasionally get a load of duds. This is particularly true of flash bombs. Some time back, I flew on a night mission and we kicked out 10 flares. All were duds. But instances like this, and the unfortunate issue of World War II medical kits, are increasingly rare.

Logistical problems are staggering, as in all wars. A limited amount comes by air; the bulk by sea. Pirate attacks on the Saigon River are the rule. Once in Saigon, the stuff must be distributed either by air or—in case of the Delta—by canal. Barge traffic is risky.

Assignments of personnel are frequently wrong. Far too many artillery officers are serving as infantry advisers and vice versa. There could be a good reason for this, but the men involved fail to see it. They are interested primarily in their career fields. Among enlisted men there seem to be even more square pegs in round holes. I know of one radar repairman assigned as a supply clerk, handing out paper clips and carbon paper.

They work and fight, day after day, under rules of engagement that tie their hands. They can't approach the Cambodian border, though the Viet Cong and the Cambodians are free to strike them at will. They can't shoot until they've been shot at.

Requests for air strikes, even in dire emergencies, have to be approved by both the Americans and the Vietnamese. Such rules, one officer told me, are not only stupid, they're damned near criminal. Our men resent them but—with exceptions—abide by them. Some of these rules now are being eased.

But, as for our man in Viet Nam—he may ply the rivers and canals for days at a time, he may guard the Cambodian border, or he may live and fight with a Ranger battalion. He may fly an armed helicopter at tree-top level, daring the Viet Cong to shoot at him so he can shoot back. He may pilot an unarmed spotter plane or an Otter, he may be a sub-sector adviser living in a small district town surrounded on all sides by Viet Cong, or he may bounce across the paddies in an armored personnel carrier.

Whatever his role, we can be proud of him.

* * *

Essentially the war in Viet Nam will be won, or lost, by the Vietnamese themselves.

We can only help.

Just how good are the South Viet Nam armed forces?

After 13 months in Viet Nam—in the Mekong Delta and along the 16th Parallel around Da Nang—I can report that the South Vietnamese soldier is far better than when I first met him in January, 1964.

There are more good Vietnamese army units today than there were a year ago, and even more are due next year.

They cannot be created overnight. There is no substitute for training and experience. Patience and time are required.

Whether the American people have that patience, or history will give us that time, are the unanswered questions.

I remember an operation in which I took part shortly before I came home. We had been chopper-lifted into a Communist controlled area near Vi Thanh. Resistance had been fierce, but brief. There had been casualties, but the Viet Cong fell back, then disappeared. We spent a hot, fruitless day hunting for them.

"The troops hate it when it's like this," a young American captain told me as we plodded through the paddies. "They hate it worse than we do, looking for the enemy and not finding him."

The men of the 33rd Regiment's 33rd Battalion, under Maj. Le Ngoc Dai, are good troops. They spend much time on the march. They lock horns with the enemy where they find him.

The Viet Cong tries to avoid these contacts. The 33rd whips him more often than not.

For these tough little troops—midgets by our standards—any man farther back, in sector, division or corps headquarters, is a "lollipop." A lollipop soldier is only slightly better than a Saigon Commando.

The 33rd Battalion is what we are aiming for; why we are in Viet Nam. If every battalion were as good, we wouldn't need to be there. We have a long way to go.

There are still some incredibly bad units in the Vietnamese army.

Last December an operation off the Gulf of Siam was meticulously planned. From the start, however, nothing went right. There was no reason for anything to go wrong. All that was lacking was direction; someone to insist that schedules be met, plans be executed, things be done right. Because no one did, the Vietnamese went ashore hours late. While they were stalling, the Viet Cong wiped out a command post ashore. Fourteen men, including three Americans, died needlessly.

I reached the point I would not go on an operation if I knew in advance the 15th Regiment, commanded by a Lieutenant Colonel Bich, would be involved. If this officer ever actually tangles with the Viet Cong—and so far he hasn't—it will be strictly an accident. When he locates them, he manages to stall until they get away. Then suddenly he becomes a real Tiger. Even his lukewarm defenders concede this officer is "overly cautious." Yet Bich stays on. He is a political officer who knows someone in Saigon.

There are far too many political officers in the Vietnamese army. Too often, command depends on whom the officer knows and to whom he gives political support.

A unit's performance depends on its commander. Thus the 21st Division, under Gen. Dan Van Quang and later under Col. Tran Van Phuoc, always managed to catch and maul the Viet Cong in its area.

Across the Bassac River, the Ninth Division never seemed to get going. The Ninth is commanded by Gen. Vinh Loc, a cousin of ex-Emperor Bao Dai. Staunchly loyal to Free Viet Nam, he seems to have such royal bearing he cannot accept counsel gracefully. His American advisers invariably have a hard time.

Since 1961 the Vietnamese have had 62,700 casualties. That should be answer enough to the blanket charge they will not fight. Unfortunately, the burden of war falls on too few Vietnamese. For a variety of reasons.

Saigon's trouble-making students are draft-exempt. These urban commandos look down on soldiers. Because our side controls only six per cent of the ground in the Mekong Delta, recruiting there is strictly pro forma. This means the bulk of the Vietnamese GI's come from villages under our control or from the working slums of Saigon.

In the Delta last spring, authorities undertook a drive to round

201

up 16,000 draft dodgers living in our areas. It netted 3051. Whole communities turned against the army. Old men and women lay down in front of trucks taking the draft dodgers away. At Vinh Long, they started a riot and 600 or 800 detainees got away again.

The Vietnamese Air Force, which supports the army after a fashion in the Delta, is still testing its wings. It leaves a lot to be desired. Presumably it does better elsewhere. Their helicopter and fighter pilots are reluctant to go where there is trouble. Time after time we have implored them to fly out their own wounded. When all else fails, they develop "engine trouble." In recent months, however, they have begun night flying, and there is some hope they will come around.

Many educated young men prefer to become interpreters for the Americans. The risks are no less, but the pay and living conditions are better. Some do turn up in the ranks, however. I recently sat beside one flying out of Cha La, deep in Viet Cong country, who told me he had been a high-school teacher in Saigon.

The Vietnamese GI is pleasant and friendly as an individual. He invariably owns a wrist watch and a transistor radio, his status symbols. He prepares his own meals, usually rice balls, and carries them with him. It is not unusual to find him going into battle with a live duck or chicken tied to his knapsack. He endures hardship without complaint. He can carry incredible loads through difficult country. Wounded, he seldom cries out, even when dying. His best buddy, however, often will weep like a baby.

On the books, desertion is a capital offense. In practice, it is something else. Americans are amazed to see deserters welcomed back and even given their back pay. The Vietnamese apparently rationalize that if a man's reasons are good—if, for instance, there was sickness at home—his offense is to be condoned.

On the other hand, I have seen men confined to barbed-wire coops in a broiling sun merely for going AWOL for a few hours or getting drunk.

In many units junior officers are free to refuse orders with which they disagree. Yet I have seen a general slap a major and relieve him from his command for responding too slowly to an order to advance.

Relations with the Americans are spotty. In such Vietnamese Divisions as the 21st, they are good. In others they are strained. And then there are units in which our advisers are tolerated—but ignored. One Vietnamese battalion commander told me he had worked with eight Americans in less than two years. Small wonder he didn't bother to listen to any of them.

In such units Americans are regarded as providers, rather than advisers. They are viewed as the key to a rich storehouse of military and other supplies not ordinarily obtainable.

But whether Vietnamese or Americans, the men in the field are convinced that national mobilization of South Viet Nam is necessary. Too few Vietnamese are personally involved in the war against the Viet Cong.

* * *

In South Viet Nam, the enemy is always masked.

He can be a houseboy. He is sometimes a soldier on our side. He may be a taxi-driver, or the cute chick who asks you to buy her a drink in a Saigon bar.

Behind that facade he is tough, dedicated, fanatic. He is capable of unspeakable brutalities—and unexpected kindnesses when it serves his purposes. In most cases he believes in his cause with an awesome single-mindedness.

Recently the bag of prisoners in a battle near My Tho turned up a young lady obviously out of place. She proudly identified herself as a Saigon high-school teacher who voluntarily spent her weekends with the Viet Cong. Undoubtedly there are more like her.

Militarily it is not difficult to identify—or at least sort out—the Viet Cong.

Starting at the top, there is the hard core.

Hard-core Viet Cong are professional soldiers. They are commanded in the Mekong Delta by two North Vietnamese major generals. Early in December we were convinced we had killed

203

one of them, Luu Thanh Duc. Agents reported in detail on his death and burial.

Just before I left, Col. George Barten, senior American adviser, told me Duc was still alive.

Hard-core Viet Cong have either infiltrated down from the North through Laos and Cambodia (some come by sea) or have remained in the Delta after the 1953 Geneva Armistice ending the Viet Minh war with the French. The majority fall in the latter category. Instead of submitting to repatriation north of the 17th Parallel as the Armistice permitted, they took off their uniforms and became farmers. Actually they never ceased to be soldiers.

Those who have come down from the North arrive emaciated. The journey takes months, through jungles and along terrible trails. Once in the Delta, they need more time to regain and rebuild their strength.

Then there are the regional forces. Such a unit is the Soc Trang Dynamic Battalion. Commanded by hard-core officers, the battalion is made up of men from the area around Soc Trang where we have a major helicopter base. Their threat against it is unceasing. Fighting is their full-time occupation. Knowing the region as they do, they are hard to find. In fact, if they don't want to fight they're never located.

There are others—the two U-Minh battalions operating out of a mangrove forest which our Special Forces have been unable to penetrate, and several bearing numerical designations.

The hard-core and regional battalions are tough. They can march without rest. They can hide in canals and breathe through reeds. They dig caves which we find only by accident.

Not all regional force men serve voluntarily. Many are impressed into service. Others are kidnapped. A few escape and return to their villages or report to our units. But the majority are indoctrinated and eventually become loyal Communists.

Finally there are the hamlet guerrillas. These are the local boys, the recruits working their way up. They operate in small groups, often in pairs. They snipe at us, mine our roads, toss bombs into our compounds.

But there is still more to the answer of what makes a Viet Cong.

The captured diary of a hard-core man killed near Long Xuyen provides further light.

He quietly entered a hamlet and started work as a tinsmith.

Eventually the village elders went to him and asked his identity. "I am a Viet Cong," he said candidly. "I have to live among you."

As time went on, he was careful to avoid creating antagonisms. He became popular, particularly with the young people.

One day word came of the approach of a Vietnamese army company with a tax-collecting mission. The army's methods of tax collection are not always gentle or fair.

The hamlet's Viet Cong resident quietly suggested that the village organize and fight back. He offered to show how. The elders were shocked at the idea.

Very well, he said (according to his own diary), I'll do it myself.

So he planted spiked booby traps in the road and—unaccountably—the army stopped and withdrew. Apparently it suspected a trap.

The villagers were impressed. The young men volunteered to help the newcomer next time; they were ashamed. Eventually this one man enlisted 70 per cent of the hamlet's males into a guerilla unit. He became the leader. Once in authority—again by his own account—he acted ruthlessly to wipe out all opposition.

Still he was not satisfied. When he died, his diary was found to complain that too many of his followers were motivated by self-interest, that they failed to understand "the true meaning of the people's struggle."

Instinctively you know it when you move into Viet Cong country. The trees look the same. The paddies are no different. The people wear the same kind of clothes. There are water buffalo, pigs and chickens on both sides of the line. But the line is there. And you know when you've crossed it.

Offer a child a piece of chewing gum and she runs. A lieutenant hands a small boy a five-piastre note, worth a few cents. His mother yanks it from his tiny fist and throws it back. She spits and turns her back.

These are the Viet Cong's assets. He indoctrinates the people. If that fails, he intimidates them. He is capable of prodigious feats of courage and endurance.

But he is not seven feet tall.

As the war has expanded, he has lost much of his mobility. Heavy equipment—mounted .50-caliber machine guns, for one—makes it hard for him to get away and take his weapons with him. He is increasingly tied down. He has found it impossible to ignore creature comforts completely, so he has rest and recreation areas. These are our favorite targets.

As a result, the enemy has been clobbered in a number of Delta operations beginning last November. His losses have been heavy. Many of those killed have been hard-core men. They are not easily replaced.

Again, as a result, 15- and 16-year old boys who normally would have become hamlet guerrillas have been pressed into service in hard-core units. The 21st Division recently captured one who had come directly from his father's barbershop in Bac Lieu. This lad hardly knew which end of the rifle to point.

When I first went to Viet Nam, prisoners were the exception to the rule.

When I left, they outnumbered the dead 10 and 20 to one.

Green troops break or do foolish things under fire. These boys obviously had little stomach for combat. They surrendered with their weapons—unheard of earlier—and seemed relieved to do so.

Time may be running short for the Viet Cong.

In Hanoi, Ho Chi Minh talks of a 10- or 20-year war. The Delta people, sick of it, are less interested, and without the people, the guerillas are in trouble.

Lt. Col. Tran Ngoc Chau, Kien Hoa Province Chief (governor) says there have been too many unkept promises, too many threats not made good. He believes that, in his Viet Cong-infested province, the enemy has lost credibility.

When we first bombed North Viet Nam, people streamed out

of Viet Cong country to get the news. They seemed pleased. I saw this happen.

This does not mean, of course, that the Viet Cong will go away or the war will end without more bloodshed. But Chau believes this is a significant—and generally overlooked—development in the Delta War.

As this has happened, the Viet Cong have turned more and more from the carrot to the stick. Whole villages have been massacred. Women and children are not spared.

This is our enemy.

We would do well to get to know him better.

Part Three

APRIL-DECEMBER, 1965

Bill Barschow of Cleveland, Lieutenant USN, is dead. And suddenly the war, 10,000 miles away, becomes very personal again.

It seems ironic now, but we used to call him "No VC Barschow."

"Send Barschow along," we would say, "and nothing will happen. No Viet Cong will show up."

Bill was always sorry about that.

"I want to apologize for that last one, sir," he said when he invited me on the last river assault we made together. "I thought for sure we'd find something. I'm pretty sure we'll hit something this time, if you'd care to take the chance."

Bill "sirred" everybody older than he was.

We were to take off at 4 a.m. and when I went to get Bill he had overslept. I stood there in the morning dark, pounding on his door and shouting:

"Damn it, Bill, get up. It's time to go."

Two or three other Bills were in that row of huts, and they all came tumbling out of their bunks, too.

We did hit some Viet Cong that day, and Bill Barschow was pleased. But someone had made off with his jeep when we got back to the Vietnamese naval yard, and we were 15 minutes too late for chow. I was sore.

"I think, sir," he said with a big grin, looking me up and down, "you can afford to miss a meal or two."

Living in a compound no bigger than half a city block for months at a time, we would all get to know each other. Bill was one of those everybody liked. He'd walk past, full of good cheer and good health, and invariably some senior officer would remark:

"That's a fine young man."

If Bill went to the club, it was to read. He spent most of his time in his room, writing letters or listening to his hi-fi. He wanted good music. When I was in Saigon processing out to come home, I heard him interviewed on a radio program called "Pacific Report." He gave a succinct, well-thought-out account of his work. He also gave most of the credit to the Vietnamese navy, which he admired. That was like Barschow.

I intended to write him and tell him I liked it. But I never did.

It seems to me that death is a much more personal matter in a little war like Viet Nam. In bigger wars, such as World War II and Korea, it was a constant thing. Men died in bunches, and the shock was somehow muted. In Viet Nam, it happens often, but it usually involves one or two men, and it always is unexpected. It's a lot like losing a member of the family.

Bill Barschow will be missed. He was decent, honorable, intelligent. More important to me: He was my friend.

"If it's any satisfaction to you," said my Pentagon source, "they killed 309 Viet Cong."

It isn't much satisfaction.

Bill Barschow was worth every one of them.

APRIL 20, WASHINGTON

Defense Secretary Robert S. McNamara is in Hawaii today to begin implementing plans to step up the war against the Communists in Viet Nam.

The decisions were taken "in principle" when Ambassador Maxwell D. Taylor was in Washington recently. McNamara left for Honolulu last night with instructions from President Johnson that the decisions be put into effect immediately. Meeting with him are Gen. Earle Wheeler, Chairman of the Joint Chiefs of Staff, Adm. U. S. Grant Sharp, U. S. Commander, Pacific, and Gen. William Westmoreland, head of the U.S. Assistance Command, Viet Nam.

Among policy decisions ready for implementation are those which would:

1. Add 160,000 men to the Vietnamese armed forces, which

obviously calls for heavier support, in U.S. advisers, training facilities, money and logistics. This would give the Vietnamese about 600,000 men.

2. Eventually boost our military strength in Viet Nam to 50,-000 men, or more. We now have an announced 32,000 there. The bulk of the additional buildup would be in combat-ready units, like the U.S. Marines now based near Dan Nang, but also would include more advisers for the Vietnamese armed forces.

Decision to increase the Vietnamese armed forces is more easily taken than carried out. Since the Communists control much of the countryside the draft often exists in name only. Experts from our own Selective Service System have been sent to Saigon, but there is a limit to what they can do.

Among other things, they have recommended a sharp curtailment in deferments and exemptions, particularly the blanket exemption extended to Saigon's troublesome university students. Obviously, the bulk of draftees must come from the cities. In the past, the people in some fringe areas have physically resisted the drafting of their young men.

No announcement of an additional buildup in our military strength will be made in advance. But the authoritative Journal of the Armed Forces said over the weekend that plans have been developed "to boost U.S. military strength in Viet Nam to 50,000 men." A Defense spokesman would neither confirm nor deny the report today. But it was pointed out that when McNamara was asked about reports that an additional 2000 men would be sent to Viet Nam, he replied he would not limit himself to that or any other figure.

The spokesman said McNamara was not worried about aircraft losses in the Vietnamese war so far. We have lost 34 tactical planes to date, but this year we will buy another 865. So far, no additional aircraft orders have been placed, though major aircraft companies reportedly have been asked how rapidly they could expand production if Red China entered the war. All eventualities must be taken into consideration.

As a direct result of the air war in North Viet Nam, the U.S. Army apparently is bestirring itself to rebuild decimated anti-aircraft strength, and the Air Force may be forced to take a second look at its decision to equip its wings only with fast jets.

With the advent of jets and missiles several years ago, the Army all but abandoned conventional anti-aircraft defense on the theory it was useless. Now, the spokesman said, the two services have found that jets can be knocked down with bullets and shells. Once hit, the more sophisticated electronics marvels virtually disintegrate, while the older propeller-driven planes usually manage to limp home.

JULY 22, OVER THE MEKONG DELTA

For one awful moment on the fifth strafing pass we both figured we'd had it.

The ground—a whirling montage of trees and canals and burning thatch-roofed huts—had come up to meet us, as it always does. The acrid smell of burning wood and cordite had filtered into the cockpit, and that we had come to expect, too.

Our big Skyraider—a Navy job with fold-back wings gone Air Force—strained and yawed as her wing guns cut loose, as she'd done a few minutes earlier when her napalm cans slipped their pinions and tumbled into the pineapple groves below us.

We level off, just over the tops of the shattered tree stumps, and suddenly there's something headed toward us and we're plunged into darkness.

I glanced at Capt. John Larrison of Terre Haute, Ind., and he was sweating, too. But he grinned.

"M-U-D," he spelled out. Our heavy machine-gun slugs had hit the wet rice paddies and thrown mud 75 feet into the air.

The altimeter needle is inching upward now. One thousand feet. Eleven hundred. Twelve hundred.

This is Mission 96639, out of Bien Hoa. During the morning, while we were being briefed, the Viet Cong had launched a short mortar attack as a welcome to American troops arriving from the States. Our target—a pre-planned strike—was to have been the hamlet Ap Phuoc Lo. There was one reported company of Viet Cong in the area.

214

Once airborne, however, our target was changed. Either Ap Phuoc Lo's Viet Cong had been tipped off, or our intelligence was faulty, or they'd moved out, or a better target had turned up elsewhere.

Five Skyraiders are on Mission 96639. Capt. Duane Rice of Roswell, N.M., is in 548. Capt. Van Brown of Shreveport, La., is in 876. Capt. Tom Dwelle of Visalia, Calif., is in 885. We are in 987 and Capt. Lee Greer of Voldosta, Ga., and Sgt. Jack McRoy of Sunnymead, Calif., in 938. McRoy is a photographer.

"You'll discover, before too long, it's a brand-new war," Lt. Gen. Joseph Moore, Commander of the Second Air Division, had said back in Tan San Nhut, outside Saigon. "When you left in March we were frustrated. Now, the wraps are off."

Moore's third star, pinned on him a few weeks ago, is evidence of that.

"584 to Paddy Control," Duane Rice's voice cut through your reverie. "This weather is closing in. We'd like to expend while we can still find the target."

Paddy Control is Capt. Marshall Hill of Winfield, Ill., in a small spotter plane. His job is to lead us in. He's local; he knows his country.

Duane Rice and Van Brown carry 500-pound bombs, armed to explode before they bury themselves in the Delta mud.

They go in first. We circle. Their bombs burst among the huts in the trees. Hill had warned we'd find 40-knot winds on the ground. Under those conditions, this is very accurate bombing. We find ourselves cheering.

"Do you have napalm?" Hill asks.

Tom Dwelle in 885 and Larrison in 987 are loaded with napalm. Two large cans on their wing tips weigh 750 pounds each. Six smaller ones carry 500 pounds each of liquid death.

So, now it's our turn. Tom Dwelle has preceded us by 15 seconds and already the hamlet is in flames. Smoke pours skyward in mushroom clouds. We tear through them. John Larrison presses a lever and old 987 lurches skyward. He banks. A second wall of fire has erupted behind us. Four passes we make, and then come in with machine guns blazing. The ground erupts ahead of each Skyraider as it makes its deadly pass.

It's our eighth pass now, and again John presses his trigger. He swears quietly.

"We're out of bullets," he says sadly.

"Good show," Marshall Hill calls. "I'm awarding you 75 per cent target destruction. It could turn out to be more."

Other flights are reporting as we head back to Bien Hoa, to park alongside the shattered wreckages of American planes destroyed by the Viet Cong and their mortars.

"Three sampans definitely destroyed, four sampans damaged, 20 per cent target destruction," one calls.

It's a brand new war, General Moore had said. And for every ton of bombs we drop on North Viet Nam, we drop two in the South.

It's about time.

AUG. 7, LON DINH

Most of all, he remembered the faces, Lt. Billy Tabb of Paducah, Ky., said afterward.

First the faces of the Viet Cong—the enemy. There had been at least 20 of them, out in the open near a small grove across the highway that leads from Saigon to My Tho.

Those faces swam before his eyes when he brought his small spotter plane down on top of them. The VC hate and detest anything that flies, most of all the small L-19's that sneak up on them when they least expect it and call in the artillery. Death usually follows an L-19.

The Reds ran—firing back—when they realized he'd seen them, of course, and Billy Tabb followed across the paddies in his L-19. Theirs were the faces of fear, anger and hate. Billy got that close.

Then there'd been the face of his Vietnamese spotter, Lt. Hy Ahn Quang. Quang had always impressed Billy as a mild-mannered kid who spoke halting English in a high treble, capable enough in his profession, which was identifying Viet Cong and terrain, but invariably polite and never angry.

216

Now Quang's face was alive and flushed with something Billy Tabb hadn't seen in his three months over the Delta. His Colt .45, almost half as heavy as Quang himself, was out and Quang was firing over the side at the VC below.

His voice took on timber and crackled with authority as he called in co-ordinants and affirmed—it takes a Vietnamese to do that, no American has such authority—that these were Viet Cong beneath their wing tip. Tabb saw two of them fall, heard Quang's full-throated yelp of triumph and realized he hadn't, until now, really known his man.

Finally, there was the face of the paddy as it came up to meet him. Tabb had seen it before, but theirs was but a passing acquaintance. Now they were about to meet, and the paddy was at once lonely and savage.

Back in My Tho, the call had come during lunch—"May Day, May Day"—and the voice had been that of Lt. Billy Tabb.

May Day means a plane is going down. Tabb had swarmed over the VC at 100 feet and then tried to take his ship back up again. But the controls were suddenly lifeless. He tried again and again. The L-19 quivered and nosed down. Desperately, Tabb worked it into a glide.

In My Tho and Lon Dinh men came alive.

"Try to get as near to us as you can," Maj. Norbert Gannon of Washington, senior adviser to the 11th Vietnamese Regiment, called over his radio from Lon Dinh. "We'll head out to meet you."

I headed out with the rest.

By now the Viet Cong knew Billy Tabb, their tormentor, had troubles of his own and no longer was a threat to them. They'd stopped to watch from Lon Dinh. Vietnamese regulars were already moving out. Tabb saw all this, too.

At the last minute he braced himself and his little ship crumpled in. Its landing gear struck a dike and was sheared off. The craft veered crazily as it struck. The wings folded back and Tabb was thrown forward violently, but his locked shoulder harness kept his face from the windshield. There was a blinding, grinding smash. Then silence for both men.

217

How long he was out, Billy doesn't remember precisely. It couldn't have been long. Billy first remembers seeing Quang's face, flaked with blood and paddy mud.

Seconds later they were out and moving away from their dead aircraft in the direction of friendly troops. Norbert Gannon—less than a mile away—was in the lead.

Overhead there was a shout: "There he is!"

Lt. Pat Deck of Chevy Chase, Md., and Warrant Officer Bob Kinlaw of Columbus, Ga., put their graceful Huey into a slow, looping dive—across the highway and back again—while their gunners, Paul Martin of West Milford, N.J., and Louie Seagers of Auburndale, Fla., tore into the VC below.

Along the highway, buses, trucks and bicycles moved in a steady stream, unmindful of the drama above and around them.

We're on the ground now, and Billy Tabb is flushed, excited and shouting to be heard above the rotors. There's firing on both sides, but there's too much to be done to worry about that. We strip Tabb's wrecked craft of everything which might be of use to the enemy. His radio must be left behind, but the earphones come out. I took off for the chopper with an armload of maps.

"What's to be done with that?" Gannon yells, gesturing toward the wrecked plane.

"Burn it!"

A thousand feet. Two thousand. Three. Billy Tabb and Hy Ahn Quang relax. Slowly, their faces crack in smiles.

"Good boy," Tabb says. "You shoot VC. I see."

"You get airplane down good," Quang responds.

Artillery opens up in a sullen, angry roar.

Tabb puffs gratefully on a cigaret.

"That," he says, "is the longest 10 minutes I ever spent."

Ten minutes in which another American saw the ugly face of war.

AUG. 11, PHOUC TO

I landed flat on my back in the rice paddy, and prayed that the M-113 wouldn't run over me.

218

That is how I busted my coccyx—which I know now is the end of one's vertebral column, or spine.

Things were pretty vague for a while.

"Don't move," someone said. Small worry about that.

Pretty soon I got up, only to pass out again, on my back. I don't know how long I lay there this time, but finally a medical chopper showed up.

The young pilot hadn't wanted to land so near a tree line, but he did.

Everybody seemed to be hurrying—everybody but me.

They handed me aboard the chopper and I lay on a stretcher, flat on my belly this time. My eyes refused to focus.

The little Vietnamese attendant was solicitous.

"How you?" he asked, using all the English he knew.

"How me?" I answered. "Oh, I'm fine."

I never told a bigger one.

But all that was a couple of weeks ago, and now I can write about it.

First, let me explain what an M-113 is. More correctly, it's called an M-113 (APC). The APC means "armored personnel carrier." One carries about a dozen soldiers.

I was riding atop the M-113 with the rest of the troops. The personnel are supposed to ride inside the carrier for their protection behind the armor. But they don't and won't, for two reasons: because it would be certain death if the carrier hits a mine, and secondly, the fumes make people sick.

So there we were on the way to Hau My, a village menaced by the Viet Cong. Altogether there were 29 carriers in the troop (or company) I was with.

Our objective was the evacuation of Hau My, which once had a population of 3100, civilians and militia. Most of the civilians already had come out by sampan. The troops, with their livestock and in some cases families, were to come out with us. After that we would blow up the place.

In the final briefing before we set out, Col. Robert Guenthner of Carlisle, Pa., had indicated a half-dozen spots on the map the enemy was holding with a total strength of 1200.

For his mission, Colonel Guenthner had been given everything but choppers. He had Navy and Air Force planes to bomb and strafe any targets he could spot.

The planes had been at it since dawn that day. At the village of Ap Tan An, the red-and-blue Viet Cong flag was still flying brazenly from a big tree, less than 100 yards from our column of personnel carriers as we passed.

We didn't even bother to shoot it down.

Atop our ugly mechanical beast, things were crowded.

A few miles back Capt. Wilber McPherson of Albuquerque, N.M., and his sergeant, Roy Manows of Corpus Christi, Tex., came aboard our vehicles with a company of Vietnamese troops. There was hardly breathing room. And no handholds.

The little Vietnamese soldiers—who do this every day—were vastly amused at my efforts to keep my balance. They insisted on sharing their rations—they could skip that—and their warm soda pop.

A half-mile to the right, Air Force Skyraiders and jets were pounding a tree line. A half mile to the left, Navy planes were strafing.

We stopped in our tracks and put out yellow identification panels. They're not apt to mistake us, says Capt. Jim Boehme of Tulsa, Okla.—and we hoped he was right.

We watched the bombs drop, saw the explosion, and then waited for the blasts to shake us up on the carrier.

But now we were going into the woods to see what was there. We headed toward a small canal. We had crossed several canals before on this trip, and always our M-113 would span them with its caterpillar tracks.

But this time the carrier's nose went down—straight down—and suddenly I was fighting desperately for my balance.

Slowly, ever so slowly, it seems, I went over the side. Jim Boehme grabbed me, but couldn't hold on.

I turned a double flip and landed on the base of my spine—and that was it.

The chopper flew me to My Tho where a medic injected something which made me sleep 24 hours. Then I was told I was only bruised. But later I flew on to Can Tho where an X-ray confirmed the breakage of my coccyx.

I've had to take it easy since then—but I now can write the story.

P.S. Without me, the mission was accomplished: We got them out of Hau My.

AUG. 13, VI THANH

It was the night the skies rained death on Chuong Thien Province.

That wasn't the way they phrased it in Saigon, of course. But they weren't in Vi Thanh and Chuong Thien that night. The communique mentioned it on page five:

"Six mortarings and two attacks were reported in Chuong Thien Province early this morning, in an area about 100 to 125 miles southwest of Saigon . . . Friendly casualties were light."

Lt. Ron Clarke of Plainsfield, Ill., remembers it differently.

"It was the kids I remember most," he said angrily in the cold light of dawn. "Even they didn't cry. I carried a little girl—I guess she was about eight—to the chopper. She died in my arms. But she never cried. She even smiled at me. She knew she was through, but she never cried."

The Lieutenant shook his head, as if to clear something away. Ron Clarke has been here for eight months now.

I had seen them flown into Can Tho, to the nearest big civilian hospital. The wounded had come out first; the dead could afford to wait. They'd been horribly burned, tragically mangled. A mortar is a deadly thing. They had been asleep, most of them, when the first shells hit. They weren't prepared. They should have been ready. And they weren't.

It was a well-planned attack. The Viet Cong had mortared eight outposts between midnight and dawn.

From Soc Trang, medical evacuation helicopters had come in while it was still dark. Lt. Ron Carlson of Bismarck, N.D., and WO Don Cook of Savannah, Ga., landed their ship at Vi Thanh at 4 a.m.

They took off again five minutes later with 13 badly wounded Vietnamese. Most of them were women and children. The little girl Clark tried to put aboard was left behind.

I flew into Vi Thanh with Col. Martin Sullivan of Falls Church, Va., acting senior American adviser in the Delta. Dick Scheiderer of Columbus and Joe McCoy of Washington manned the guns on Sullivan's command chopper as it swung low over the Snake River and put down outside Vi Thanh.

Vi Thanh, one of the smallest of the Delta's provincial capitals, went quietly about its business, despite the beating it had taken from mortars the night before.

Colonel Sullivan was upset.

"How could it have happened? Had you no warning?" he asked.

"Yes, sir, I suppose we did," Maj. Thomas LeVasseur of Minneapolis admitted miserably. "We heard, around 4 o'clock, we might be mortared. But we'd had those reports before. And these were vague. Nothing we could really credit. Every day we hear that sort of thing."

Colonel Sullivan nodded grimly.

LeVasseur motioned across the big, muddy canal.

"Over there," he said, "that's all Viet Cong country. We run patrols out there at least once a week to show the flag and keep it from being more hostile than it is. We hope, some day, to reach out and take it into our pacification program. Right now, we've got all we can do to hold what we have. So they have free run out there, four kilometers away. We can't count on anyone telling us when they show up. They can set up their mortars and fire away."

"How soon did your artillery fire back?" asked Sullivan.

"Not soon enough. It was at least 15 minutes. We were disorganized."

The Viet Cong have taken some of their worst lickings recently here in Chuong Thien. This is their way of striking back, killing women and children.

A young captain takes over at an impromptu briefing.

"The Viet Cong's tactics from now on seem to be to discredit us, to convince the people that we cannot protect them," he said. "We've got to be honest. So far, they've done very well. They've terrorized our three northernmost district towns"—he indicates them on the map—"they've cut our roads. And now they've hit Vi Thanh. They could easily have got us Americans in our compound. They weren't after Americans. We don't frighten. They were after their own people."

This got two lines in a Saigon communique. I wonder if it made the papers at all back home.

Ron Clarke shakes his head sadly.

"It was the kids," he said. "Even the babies didn't cry."

AUG. 16, GIAO HOA

I was less than 24 hours out of the hospital when the call came for a medical evacuation helicopter.

I chose to go along because the boys had laid out a stretcher in the craft and I could lie on my stomach—rather than sit on my still-sore spine end—and watch or listen to the battle below.

Lt. Ron Carlson of Bismarck, N.D., and Warrant Officer Tom Cook of Savannah, Ga., were at the controls.

We were going out after the call had come from Capt. Robin Miller's armed Huey chopper saying they were down. Pass after pass, the big Army captain from North Manchester, Ind., had taken his ship over the target—a Viet Cong-occupied hamlet on a winding canal a few miles out of Bac Lieu.

Their guns had spoken with authority. Their rockets had plowed into the muddy paddies and smoking tree lines.

And now . . . we were going in to save them.

Bullmoose—Col. Bob Spilman of Fort Worth, Tex.—is aloft in a command chopper nearby, busily searching out the two enemy companies he knows are down there, moving his troops about like chessmen. The enemy are the remnants of the Viet Cong's Soc Trang Dynamic Battalion, already badly whipped but the nucleus around which they seek to regroup and reorganize. It's important they be destroyed.

If Bullmoose doesn't find them here, he'll move his force.

Moments before, too, Howard Crotty had been hit on a low pass over Giao Hoa. Enemy fire had shattered his windshield; one round had passed within an inch of his head, filling the cockpit with glass slivers. Crotty, from Spout Spring Park, N.C., had been cut about the face. Another round had come up through the floor as he leveled off.

For a time, Howard's anguished, startled cries blotted out everything else on the air.

Carlson dives steeply, so steeply my ears plug up.

I see them now, in the paddies below. Rather, it's a small lake. The wounded chopper is down; it looks like a big water bug. The men are out of it, waist deep in mud and water. They look like ants.

The ground comes up to meet us, and with it the war. Giao Hoa, a half mile away, is an inferno. The smoke creeps into the cockpit. I see men—armed men—scurrying along the dikes; some are in the water, too. I hope they're ours, that they're friendly.

Jack Blundell of Madill, Okla., and J. T. Spruill of Rocky Mount, N.C., in our craft man their guns, but they will hold their fire until fired on.

We're down now. Miller's chopper is smoking, but its engines still turn, its rotors strain angrily at the brakes which hold them immobile. Miller and his co-pilot, Warrant Officer Charles Poulton, Okmulgee, Okla., are back in the cockpit. Their crew chief, A. L. Smith of Miami, Fla., and Gunner Cpt. Keith Griffin of Hutchinson, Kan., struggle desperately to dislodge a smoking rocket pod.

It's a race against time. Enemy gunfire had set the pod on fire. Once the flames reach those rockets . . .

There's gunfire in the distance, and more F-100's come in, pounding the enemy to keep him down.

Minutes pass, and they seem like hours. Smith and Griffin work slowly, their hands bleeding.

Dear God, I pray, let them succeed!

There's a cheer as the smoking pod comes loose. It tumbles into the water below the ship.

Poulton's thumb goes up in a gesture of triumph—of victory—

and the two paddy-soaked crewmen tumble back into their ship. It rises slowly, arches gracefully and is airborne.

Ron Carlson and Tom Cook release their controls and we follow. For a couple of miles we fly low over the battlefield. Then we seek the safety of altitude. One thousand feet. Two thousand. Three thousand.

We've made it.

Spruill, the medic, and Blundell, the crew chief, fix my stretcher and I climb onto it again, the better to protect my aching tailbone.

Thirty minutes later at Bac Lieu, Carlson and Cook bring their chopper in for a new load of fuel. There's time now to stretch our legs, eat a tin of C-rations and relax.

Charlie Poulton strolls over.

"Thanks for coming in after us," he says casually. Too casually, I suspect. "It's a mighty comforting feeling."

Ron Carlson grins.

"Any time," he says. "Hell. That's what we're here for."

AUG. 17, ABOARD CARRIER *MIDWAY* OFF NORTH VIET NAM

Those of his shipmates who could be spared from the war quietly assembled on the hangar deck, dressed in their cleanest whites.

For Lt. Cmdr. Harold E. Gray, a memorial service is to be held.

The South China Sea is calm. The sky overhead is blue and cloudless. The guided missile frigate *Reeves* trails in the Midway's wake.

A makeshift ship's band concludes the stately, poignant strains of "Eternal Father, Strong to Save" as R. Adm. M. W. White and his Chief of Staff, Capt. B. N. Charbonnet, take their places.

And, overhead, the war in which Commander Gray died goes on.

"The Navy today announced the loss of a single Skyraider in an attack on Communist installations at Dong Hoi, North Viet

Nam," a communique had said. "The pilot is presumed to have been lost. Secondary explosions were observed on impact."

That was four days ago, on a bright afternoon like today. Less than an hour after he had downed a final cup of coffee, strapped on his harness and catapulted from the flight deck above, Harold Gray—35 years old, father of Harold, III, and Tracy—had taken his attack-bomber over the target and hadn't pulled out. His bombs exploded when he hit the ground.

This is his shipmates' farewell.

"Harold Edwin Gray, Jr.," Chaplain M. A. Lawson of Springdale, Ark., intones, "was born in Brownsville, Texas, on Oct. 6, 1930. He was graduated from St. George's School, Middletown, R.I., and attended Yale University before he entered the U S. Naval Reserve on active duty in June, 1953."

Harold Gray is the first from the Midway to die in this war.

He was the son of the president of Pan American World Airways—and Operations Officer for Attack Squadron 25. He chose the Navy because he loved it. He lived, worked and played in this tight-knit community of 3700 men.

His shipmates stare straight ahead.

"We sat stunned beside our radios, in our ready rooms and about ship when the word came in," painfully the Chaplain recalls the memory of it. "We were not ready for death to take so young a life with so much potential unrealized, so many years unfulfilled, small children to be raised without a father. Why did it happen to him, our friend, our shipmate, son, father and husband?"

One of the planes which Gray flew from the Midway has been lowered on an elevator from the flight deck overhead to a spot behind the Chaplain. His men have cleaned and furbished it, but the signs of war are not easily removed. This is their memorial to him. "We must remain steady in an hour like this," the Chaplain says. "We can and will.

"When a man believes in a great cause, and believes in it so fully he is prepared to defend it with his life, he has achieved nobility not limited by the barriers of time."

Suddenly the first of the planes on today's strike hits the flight deck overhead with a muffled thump. Its tail hook snags the arresting cable and its roar is like that of an angry, trapped animal.

"Lt. Cdr. Harold Edwin Gray, Jr.," the Navy has announced, "was killed in action during a combat strike against insurgent Communist guerrilla forces in Southeast Asia on 7 August 1965. He has been awarded the Air Medal and recommended for three Gold Stars, the Purple Heart and Distinguished Flying Cross."

The Midway is turning into the wind now, and the services are drawing to a close.

"We have lost a shipmate," Chaplain Lawson says. "Attack Squadron 25 has lost a pilot and a friend, the Navy one of its finest officers, the nation a dedicated citizen, a wife and two children one they cannot replace, his parents a son. We pray he did not give his life in vain."

The sad, aching strains of taps float over the South China Sea and a Marine honor guard fires a final salute.

On the flight deck above, Attack Squadron 25 is launching its planes.

Its target for today is Dong Hoi.

AUG. 24, ABOARD DESTROYER *HENRY B. WILSON*
IN GULF OF TONKIN

The Russian merchant ship increased her speed to 15 knots.
We went to 20.

So, a few minutes later, did the Russian—and we went to 25, then 27.

Lt. Lance Swenson of Potomac, Md., grunts in the darkness.

"He knows he can't outrun us," he says.

It's unusual for a merchantman to attempt these speeds. This lad must have a good reason for wanting to get away.

The chase started shortly after 3 a.m. The Wilson—a guided missile destroyer—had slipped out of the Gulf of Tonkin to refuel alongside the Cimarron, an oiler, in the South China Sea. I had come over to the Wilson on a high line; two downed aviators, plucked out of the Gulf during the day, had gone over to the Cimarron en route back to their carriers. As we pulled away, lights had appeared off the Wilson's port, seven miles away.

"Find out who he is," ordered Cmdr. Earle West of Comstock, Neb.

Signal lights flashed on both ships. Then:

"It's garbled, sir. All I can make out is 'Singapore.'"

The other ship swings around, opens his throttle and skitters away. The Wilson goes after him. The chase is on.

A new voice comes out of the darkness.

"I want to close with that guy, near enough for a positive identification," it says. "But don't bear directly down on him. Some of our 'friends' have complained recently."

Navy Capt. Arthur Fischer, Jr., of San Diego, Commodore of Destroyer Squadron 21, has come up the ladder to the darkened bridge.

"We know what they're taking in there—SAM's among other things—but we can't stop them," he says.

By now the gap has closed to four miles. The other skipper decides to change tactics. He's ready, apparently, to talk, in the language of the sea. His signal lights blink steadily. A signalman on the bridge overhead calls out the letters but they make no sense.

We've closed to less than three miles. A radio whistles and, minutes later, a signalman calls down from the bridge:

"He says he's Russian, he's headed for Singapore out of Haiphong, and he's either from—or he's named—Minsk," the boy shouts.

(Minsk is an inland Russian city and Jane's ship registry lists no vessel of that name.)

Iron Curtain-country ships, in and out of Haiphong—North Viet Nam's chief port—often alter or remove their nameplates. The Minsk—if that is her name—is clearly visible now, plowing desperately ahead, riding high out of the water in ballast. Obviously she had discharged her cargo and is on the way out.

"She's turning away from us!" someone shouts.

The Russian has turned, in a final, desperate lunge to avoid identification, toward the only rain squall on the horizon. A dark thunderhead looms and soon the rains are coming down hard. Men line the decks. No one is asleep on the Wilson. The Minsk is a scant 200 yards off our starboard.

We pull alongside. The other ship's lights go out and she plunges ahead. Five minutes, then ten and we hold our position off her port. Neither ship gives any sign of recognition.

But that's the end of it. Slowly the Wilson turns away because we are due back on station, a few miles off the coast of North Viet Nam at dawn. Our ship's job is to pick up downed fliers.

The Minsk holds a steady course. A mile away, her lights come back on. Luck was with her. She got away.

AUG. 31, ABOARD DESTROYER *WILSON* IN GULF OF TONKIN

The voice of the female commentator on Radio Peking is shrill.

"The Gulf of Tonkin is *not* an American lake," she storms. "The sooner the imperialist aggressors realize this fact, the easier it will be for them to face their inevitable, shameful defeat."

The 400 "imperialist aggressors" aboard this guided-missile destroyer finish their evening meal. They still have 45 minutes before time to darken ship. A few linger over coffee. Still others are on watch.

Few bother to listen to the gal from Peking. A switch of the dial and another channel brings in a rebroadcast of the Dodger-Pirate baseball game. Baseball takes priority. That's how it is with imperialists.

The young lady in Peking favors us with a blow-by-blow account of the doings of the peace-strikers, the draft-card burners and the troop-train blockaders back home.

"The American people," she says, "have risen in full-scale revolt against the aggressive war policies of the Johnson regime. Lyndon Johnson's crimes are thus not only against the people of Viet Nam and the democratic republics, but against the American people as well."

A bell clangs and the imperialists charge to battle stations.

MIG's are in the air over Hanoi, 70 miles away.

They've never bothered us out here in the Gulf. But we take no chances. We go to Condition Red.

But soon the MIG's are gone and we "stand easy."

Thunderheads have gathered over the mainland directly ahead. But the Gulf is smooth and peaceful.

The gal from Peking is back on the air. Now it's India getting blasted. Indian troops, we're told, have "cracked down on the people of Kashmir." The Kashmiris, however, can be counted on to "shake off the yoke of the Indian Army."

Now it's South Korea's turn. Seoul's "puppet assembly" has voted to send a full division to Viet Nam as "cannon fodder for the U.S. aggressors."

It's 7:15 p.m., and we darken ship.

"The United States," Radio Peking drones on, "is bound to go bankrupt. In order to save itself from defeat in Viet Nam, it has resorted to sabotage, violence, murder and blackmail."

It's been a long day and a hard one. On deck it's 100 degrees hot. In the engine compartments, it's near 140.

"Attacked at home and abroad," Radio Peking assures us, "the Johnson Administration is in a difficult position. Braving bloodshed and prison, thousands of American Negroes have revolted against its oppressive policies in Los Angeles, Chicago and Springfield, Mass."

On the beach, around Hon Me and Nui Cao, our Air Force planes begin dropping flares. They're 50 to 60 miles away, but they seem to be just off our side. Distances are deceptive at sea. In the war room, we listen to the chatter of our pilots. They've apparently spotted a big truck convoy. Ack-ack is moderate to heavy.

The Wilson stands ready. If a pilot is hit and heads out to sea, it's our job to pick him up.

The last flare flickers and the attack ends.

The men drift back to the mess deck for a final cup of coffee. Radio Peking is still belaboring the Los Angeles riots.

In the Wilson's war room, radar is tracking a bogie—any un-

230

identified aircraft. This one is moving out from the mainland toward us. We go to a condition of "modified gray" alert.

At 30 miles, the plane identifies itself. It's one of ours. The pilot had forgotten to turn on his squawk box.

Taps sound at 10. All but a handful of the Wilson's crew turn in.

The Gulf of Tonkin is peaceful beneath a full moon.

But, like the gal said, it isn't an American lake.

Or is it?

SEPT. 3, ABOARD CARRIER *CORAL SEA*

Cmdr. David Leue of Buffalo, N.Y., studied the aerial photos, dripping fresh out of the lab, with grim satisfaction.

They were good. They showed clearly the smashed trucks on the North Vietnamese highway.

"The Old Man taught us that," he said.

It's hard for Leue to realize that he's the "Old Man" now. His squadron hasn't had time to get used to the idea that Cmdr. Harry Eugene Thomas of Taft, Calif., won't be back.

"In North Viet Nam, day and night, through a hundred barrages, he taught us and led the way. His leadership and experience were our shield. To him we owe our lives," said Commander Leue. "May God help his family understand."

Navy people are a clannish lot. They have two homes: one where they were born, grew up and went to school; the other where they leave their families when they are away at war. These men live in rented houses and trailer camps clustered around the big, new, naval air complex in a rich farming region near Lemoore, Calif. Their kids go to the same schools. Their wives share their letters home. When death strikes, they close ranks instinctively.

They held a memorial service on the hangar deck for Commander Thomas. It was Navy all the way: a brief lesson from the Scripture, the Navy hymn he loved, a final volley from the shipboard Marines, then taps.

It's not easy to watch men grieve.

"This one hit me hardest," said Rear Adm. Ralph Cousins of Eldorado, Okla. "You don't replace a man like this."

The "Old Man" was an independent who liked to fight his own style.

He moved; he didn't talk about it. At 38 there was much maturity in him.

"We found some barges—a lot of them—around Vinh last night," the Admiral said. For two years, until May, Admiral Cousins was Military Assistant in the Pentagon to Deputy Defense Secretary Cyrus Vance.

"There's a lot of anti-aircraft in there, so we tried something new. We sent Crusaders in at 24,000 feet. Their anti-aircraft somehow isn't very good at that altitude. Then, as we were turning away and their guns were trailing us, we sent Skyhawks in on a low-level run. They never got their guns turned around."

The "Old Man" taught them that, too.

Dave Leue had been on that run. So had Lt. Cmdr. Bill Majors of Henryetta, Okla. The weather had been too much to see what they'd done. The Coral Sea is working the night shift this week. At dawn she turned the job over to a sister carrier.

Leue was with the "Old Man" on another low-level run a week earlier when it happened. Squadron commanders are a strange, a vanishing, breed. In an age of specialization in which most troop commanders, of necessity, stay behind and follow the battle on a TV screen, they still say, "Follow me." The "Old Man" flies the lead plane. He asks nothing of his men he hasn't already done himself. If he's good, he's greatly respected. If he's not, he's soon found out.

Harry Thomas was good.

Leue came back from that raid with a big hole in his left wing. But he made it back. The "Old Man" didn't. It has been a week now, and this is the first raid of another day.

Dave Leue is the "Old Man" now.

Three of his men—Bill Majors, Lt. Howie Alexander, also of Taft, and O. J. Greene, Jr., of Charleston, S.C.—are suiting up. Leue will fly the lead plane, of course.

It's time to go. They walk onto the flight deck, proudly, a little cockily.

The "Old Man" taught them that, too.

SEPT. 8, SAIGON

The fast buildup of American forces has greatly depleted U.S. food supplies in South Viet Nam, and "the next two weeks are going to be touch-and-go."

That outlook was pictured today by a high-ranking American supply officer in an exclusive interview. But he said $30,000,000 worth of food was on the high seas en route here and in time should restore military pantries to normal levels.

"The critical period is right now," said Navy Capt. Archie Kuntze, 45, of Sheboygan, Wis., commander of support activities in Saigon.

The Navy feeds, clothes and houses all American military personnel in South Viet Nam. This responsibility is scheduled to go to the Army's logistics command but no date has yet been set for the transfer.

The Navy's Saigon agency is the largest single shore command overseas.

Kuntze said the food shortages were the direct result of the tremendous increase in the U.S. military population here, and not of poor planning.

"We looked ahead," he said. "We foresaw what would be needed. But we ran into a snag on shipping. The bottoms weren't available."

There will be meatless days in the next two weeks but no American "will actually go hungry," he added. "We have plenty of canned stuff."

Another problem is that "we have run out of refrigeration space and have no place to put additional fresh and frozen foods arriving daily."

The Navy has leased all available cold storage in Saigon and now is planting "reefer farms" all over the landscape, some perilously close to Communist Viet Cong country.

Kuntze said he was trying to "spread the shortages evenly," and most units would take 10 to 15 per cent cuts in rations.

Americans here now consume $5,000,000 worth of fresh foods every nine days, the Captain said.

"Saigon is the bottleneck," he emphasized.

In the future, direct shipments will be made to the big American complex around Da Nang instead of routing supplies through Saigon. This should take off some of the pressure.

Kuntze said the troops require 400,000 pounds of potatoes a week and 25 per cent of those spoil.

"We have tried to get our people to eat rice instead of potatoes, but they just won't," he added. "Americans are stubborn in their eating habits."

Kuntze said that Saigon, where he now operates 42 hotels exclusively for troops, has reached the saturation point—"in fact, we've gone a little beyond it."

It is impossible to rent a hotel room at any price, he said.

"I am boarding 900 (civilian) transients tonight," he said. "If I could get rid of them it would go a long way toward solving my problem."

Many of these transients, he added, were official visitors with impressive credentials.

Adm. U.S. Grant Sharp at Pearl Harbor last week issued orders "establishing new criteria for visiting Saigon," Kuntze pointed out. "People can't come here simply because they want to, or to get 'oriented.' They have got to contribute something."

Kuntze now pays $6,000,000 a year for hotel space and is "eyeing anything down to small apartments."

By next February he will have 5500 rooms under lease in 60 hotels. They cost an average of $11 a day.

SEPT. 10, ABOARD CARRIER *CORAL SEA*

From dawn to dusk, nothing moves in the area south of Hanoi to the 17th Parallel, which divides North Viet Nam from the South.

Below the line, South Viet Nam is a beehive of activity.

Navy pilots who are over North Viet Nam every day, several times a day, report the situation this way:

Once the sun comes up, North Viet Nam's highways are deserted. Most bridges are out. It has been weeks since they've spotted any daytime traffic.

North Viet Nam's railroads can't operate. All rail bridges are out; much of the rolling stock has been destroyed. There still is some movement by rail between bombed-out bridges; cargoes are off-loaded onto barges or trucks. But North Viet Nam doesn't have the tunnels in which the North Koreans hid their locomotives. One by one the locomotives are being knocked off.

By night, whenever possible, truck convoys stick to side roads. But the number available is limited, and in some areas they must risk the highways. Besides, our pilots are now familiar with most of the access roads and patrol them, too.

Trucks travel in groups of four to ten. They move with lights on until they hear our planes. Then they switch off their lights and race to the nearest village, where they'll be safe because we avoid civilian targets.

For river crossings, the North Vietnamese resort to ferries. Often these are simply sampans lashed together. They can carry only one truck at a time.

Trucks are heavily, and often skillfully, camouflaged. Waiting for the ferries, they are driven off the roads and into the brush. By day, ferries are moved several miles up or down stream and camouflaged. We knock out two or three a night.

"Ferry crossings are easily spotted," said Cmdr. David Leue of Buffalo, N.Y. "A road goes down to the river on one side and comes out on the other. We know if we hang around long enough we'll get one."

The North Vietnamese have turned more and more to barges. Red China apparently has given them such craft. Barges now have top target priority.

Navy and Air Force planes reconnoiter all North Vietnamese highways around the clock.

"If we quit patrolling them during the daytime they'd start

using them again," one pilot pointed out. "We're keeping the pressure on."

No figures are available here as to how seriously this has hampered the movement of men and supplies to the South. Navy pilots are convinced, however, that such traffic has been much curtailed.

"After all," said one pilot, "daylight is half the day. The better half at that."

Air strikes against the North are rigidly controlled, presumably from Washington. I was aboard the Midway recently when a SAM (surface-to-air missile) demolished one Skyhawk and badly damaged another. I asked permission to talk to the surviving pilot and to cable a story from the ship. Within six hours, the Midway had its reply from Washington: There would be no interviews. The story was released in the Pentagon.

Some officers aboard ship wish we were permitted to hit the Hanoi-Haiphong complex. From the air, day and night, our men see trucks moving between Hanoi and the port of Haiphong and along the streets of both cities.

"As long as they have that sanctuary," one pilot said, "we're not hurting them as much as I think we should."

All this has not been accomplished without heavy cost. A marked step-up has been noted in the quantity and quality of North Viet Nam anti-aircraft. Nam Dinh, Dong Hoi, Vinh and Thanh Hoi bristle with it. We try not to fly over these areas unless we have to. It is not our policy to tell our enemies when—or how much—they have hurt us. But it's true they have been hitting our planes.

SEPT. 11, WITH A RIVER ASSAULT GROUP

Operation Flying Dragon 928 was conceived a few days ago when a defecting Communist Viet Cong district chief told us about a big arms cache.

He said he would lead us to it, in a mangrove swamp near the mouth of the Bassac River in South Viet Nam's Mekong Delta area.

We set out at midnight aboard a fleet of river craft. We picked up our troops along the way. We were using six battalions from the 13th Vietnamese Regiment.

Two battalions would land with us. At dawn two more would land by helicopter back of the mangrove. Two would be held in reserve. We had no idea what we'd encounter.

It turned out to be a mess. The proposed landing zone was completely under water. No one could land there. So we steamed down Cai Co Creek firing blindly as we went.

Where we put the troops ashore wasn't much better. The minute a man stepped off a barge he was out of sight. It took a little urging. These are city and Delta boys.

The renegade district chief never did lead us to the arms cache. At 10:30 a.m., however, we killed two Viet Cong—they had rifles—and picked up another.

He was talkative. He promised to lead us to 30 pro-government Vietnamese prisoners of war.

At noon one of our boys picked up a "dud" rocket. That was the last of him. They wrapped what was left in a poncho and put the body aboard one of the boats. By mid-afternoon the stench was awful. The skipper put the body in a small boat and rowed around trying to get one of the others to take the dead man off his hands. No one would.

Still later, we picked up a couple of peasant women toting carbines. We tied them up and brought them back with us.

By 4 p.m. we had all we wanted of the mangroves. As we were pulling out, we heard a couple of shots.

Lt. Col. Tran Binh Qui, the regimental commander, put on his most innocent face and swore it was a signal of some sort. Maj. O. M. Padgett of Madisonville, Tex., Qui's friend and adviser, was skeptical. He was aware that the captured Viet Cong who said he could lead us to the prisoners hadn't come through.

"Qui will never tell me," the Major said. "Last time he shot a prisoner, I gave him hell."

Minutes later, we were in more trouble. It's surprising, sometimes, how little these people know about their own country—they had picked a landing zone where they couldn't land and now the tide had gone out. We couldn't get back to the Bassac River. We were stranded up Cai Co Creek.

"If the VC have any sense," someone said, "they'll mortar us."

All we could do was wait. Four sailors waded ashore and shot a water buffalo. They cut big, bloody chunks from his haunches and left the carcass to rot.

Our fighter planes and helicopters came back at dusk with bombs and napalm. Five miles back, artillery opened up. We hoped that would keep the Viet Cong off balance. Mushrooming clouds blotted out the setting sun.

All night long we listened for the sound of enemy mortars. We were lucky. They never came.

At 2 a.m. the tide came back and we floated free. Operation Flying Dragon 928 was over.

SEPT. 13, ON THE BASSAC RIVER

The ship is quiet. All eyes are on Lieutenant Phong.

As the skipper, he must decide.

A searchlight catches him briefly as it wheels past, and his face mirrors his anguish.

Phong's shoulders sag, and he turns back to his bridge.

"Don't fire," he says.

His men turn away from their guns.

U.S. Navy Lt. Larry Hope of Vallejo, Calif., lays a friendly hand on the young Vietnamese officer.

"I concur," he says softly.

Phong drops his head into his hands.

"Did I do right?" he asks.

"You did right."

A few minutes ago, alarms sounded aboard our infantry landing ship, the LSIL-158, as it steamed down the Bassac. Its crew rushed to general quarters. LSIL-158 is the biggest warship in the South Vietnamese River Navy. Lieutenant Phong is its skipper.

Straight ahead, a big sampan loomed in the water. Under the

curfew, no river traffic is allowed after dark. It was 8:10 p.m. by the ship's clock.

Our guns fired three warning shots between the sampan and the river bank. Our searchlights came alive and focused on it.

The little boat wheeled and headed toward us. Had it continued on course, Phong would have sunk it without a second thought. Now he intended merely to search it.

Larry Hope undoubtedly would argue it ought to be seized and its passengers arrested. Phong would just as predictably let them off with a tongue lashing.

Our searchlights follow it as it draws closer. We can see two men rowing, one at each end. Eight women seem to be huddled between them. But this doesn't mean much. The Communist Viet Cong often disguise themselves.

The boat comes abreast, a hundred yards off starboard. For perhaps 10 minutes, the two men fight against the current. Suddenly, they turn and head for the shore.

A sailor on our ship shouts through a bullhorn. The boatsmen only row harder. Phong reaches for a rifle and fires into the air. Still they move away.

They reach shore, pinned in the glare of our searchlights. Phong watches them through binoculars. He fires another warning volley.

Slowly, they drag their boat out of the water. If they're Viet Cong, someone says, they have nerves of steel. Now they're walking, not running, toward a line of trees. Once there, they'll be safe.

Finally, Phong speaks: "Don't fire."

The ordeal of Lieutenant Phong on the muddy Bassac tells a great deal about the kind of war this is. Phong is a North Vietnamese. Those in the sampan were natives of the Southern Delta. They speak different dialects. But they, too, are Vietnamese.

Phong faces the same hard choice almost every night.

Earlier, he had not hesitated. Five men in a sampan darted for shore as soon as our ship came into sight. They beached in a small creek and disappeared into the brush. Thirty seconds

239

behind them, Phong's guns roared. They were right on target.

Some of Phong's officers would not have hesitated in the second case, either. Take, for instance, Ensign Van Truug Quan. His family once owned much of the rich paddy land around Bac Lieu. Now the Viet Cong have it. An uncle was kidnapped by the Viet Cong and held for ransom. The Quans paid, but the Communists killed him anyhow.

Ensign Quan would have fired.

"There was one chance in three those people in that boat were Viet Cong," Larry Hope said. "But when it reaches this point, there's nothing I can say, no advice I can give. It's Phong's decision. Because it's his country."

Larry Hope lit a cigaret and stared into the night.

"After all," he said quietly, "suppose this were the Mississippi and those had been Americans?"

SEPT. 15, CA MAU

Napalm cut huge red gashes in the Mekong Delta night.

"That's good," said Air Force Capt. Skip Robinson of Seattle, Wash. "Now move a bit to the right."

This was one of the first night-bombings in the Delta. Living and fighting with the Communist Viet Cong at close quarters, each side learns the other's habits.

The Viet Cong take it for granted we'll knock off bombing promptly at 6 p.m. We always have. But now it was 8:27 p.m. And we were after them. They must be puzzled.

Just before dark, Robinson had spotted a couple of camouflaged sampans.

This is Viet Cong country, and the canal is their supply route. For two nights a lone, friendly outpost at Cai Tai had come under attack. Robinson figured the two sampans might be loaded with ammunition for another attack. I was flying with him.

Those who say we bomb indiscriminately out here don't know Skip Robinson. Skip is a FAC—a Forward Air Controller. He flies a small spotter plane. He selects targets and leads bigger planes to them. Skip has the eyes of a hawk, the instincts of an eagle and the selectivity of a deb at her first prom.

"See that sampan covered with foliage below?" he said just before dusk. "A new man would say that was a camouflage job. It isn't. It's carrying rice seedlings. It makes no attempt to blend with the scenery. It's next to an open field. People are working there.

"That's why we use local people for FAC's"—Skip now considers himself local to the Ca Mau Peninsula. "We try to be selective."

Skip proved that. He had come across a half-dozen potential targets in the last two hours. He held off from all of them.

First, we spotted a big, heavily loaded sampan in a small canal. Skip buzzed it—"the safest altitude here is above 500 feet or below 50"—and drew no fire. Instead, it turned around and headed back.

We left it alone.

There'd been several sampans around a Viet Cong burial ground.

"They could be civilians caught by the curfew," Skip said. We left them alone, too.

Skip knows the Ca Mau Peninsula like the palm of his hand. No foxhole is too small or too well camouflaged.

He has learned the work habits of the people below. He knows how many sampans should be docked at Nam Can. If there are too many, or too few, he becomes suspicious.

He talked about enemy tactics:

"For a while they fired at all planes. Then they wouldn't fire at any. After that, they'd fire at Army spotters but not at the Air Force. Don't ask me why. Now they'll fire if you give them a target.

"And they camouflage. They're good, but from their point of view it's a mistake. Anything that's expertly camouflaged gets hit. Sooner or later they'll come up with another tactic, and we'll have to adjust to that."

Now we were over a free-bomb zone. Theoretically, we can bomb here at will.

"But we don't," Skip said. "Take that house down there; I've no reason to hit it. Sure, those people live in VC country and pay VC taxes. But they're simply trying to make a living.

"Now take that bombed-out hamlet to the left. It stood for months after I got here. Then one day we got a lot of ground fire from it. So we knocked it out."

The two camouflaged sampans on the canal are something else. We intend to get them.

It had been a game of hide-and-seek. The Skyraider planes were late. Their pilots were strangers to the Delta. So Skip went in first.

His rockets whooshed, then thudded into the Delta below.

Now our Skyraiders were overhead. Skillfully Skip guided them in. Their bombs and rockets tore into the night. Fires were set on both banks.

"I thank you," Skip Robinson said as they headed back to Bien Hoa. "You did a real fine job."

SEPT. 20, VINH LONG

"The legs [ground troops] have run into Viet Cong out there," said Capt. Bob Molinelli of Pocatello, Ida. "That's what's holding us up."

It couldn't be much. Molinelli had asked if they needed help from his armed choppers. Capt. George Griffin of Fayetteville, N.C., had said no, thanks, they'd handle it. Just give his men another 30 minutes, he said. He'd let us know when they got moving again.

I suppose you'd call this a mercy mission. That's an overworked term, but I know of none better.

There are 38 men, 36 women and 43 children in An Phu Thuan on the Rach Xa Tau Canal five miles out of Vinh Long. For the past week, they've lived off rats and rainwater. In Viet Nam right now we have plenty of both.

"We found out last night they haven't been resupplied in more than a month," Molinelli said. "We decided to do something about it."

Vinh Long is one of our biggest Delta helicopter bases. But the Viet Cong are just off its runways. Landing and taking off, we sometimes draw hostile fire. An Phu Thuan is one of a dozen or so little outposts around it. Actually they're decoys. They draw some of the fire we'd otherwise get.

Several times a week An Phu Thuan comes under attack. The Viet Cong have fixed gun positions and foxholes directly across the canal. When they open up, Molinelli's Cobra Platoon of armed Hueys takes to the air. By now, they know where to deliver; they've spotted those foxholes.

"People who say the Vietnamese have no will to fight," said Lt. Col. Bill Maddox of Washington, D.C., Molinelli's boss, "ought to come to An Phu Thuan."

Two companies of regional troops kicked off from Duc Tan at 8 a.m. George Griffin and his medic, Sgt. Billy Cook of Atoka, Okla., went along. They were due in An Phu Thuan at 9:30. But this is the rainy season, and they often were in water up to their armpits. On top of that, they'd run into Viet Cong. It was now 10:30 a.m.

One Vietnamese had stepped on a poisoned stick. It'd gone through his rubber sneakers and his foot. In falling, he'd driven another through his hand.

Lt. Phil Brunstuder of Abilene, Kan., and Capt. Fred Terry of Worcester, Mass., had flown out to pick him up. Col. Maddox and Lt. Frank Mayer of Medford, Ore., flew cover.

Soon we landed at desolate An Phu Thuan.

The regular supplies came off first: 200 pounds of flour, 400 pounds of rice, 266 pounds of cooking oil, 360 pounds of powdered milk, 100 pounds of cloth, 60 spools of thread, 20 pounds of soap. They needed it badly. But it was the extras that meant the most. That's human nature.

Molinelli's Cobras had chipped in to buy 60 bottles of beer, 40 cartons of cigarets, 50 cigars, 40 packages of chewing gum for the kids, a transistor radio and—unbelievably—200 pounds of ice. The ice got them. They hadn't seen ice at An Phu Thuan for two years. They held it aloft for all to see. They licked it. The radio was almost as big an attraction. They'd never had a radio.

Naturally this called for a ceremony. Major Hoa, the deputy province chief, made a long speech. Then Molinelli spoke.

"We feel mighty close to you people because we're out here so often," he said. "We just want you to know how much we appreciate what you're doing for us. There is no call we'd rather answer."

The Vietnamese platoon leader at the outpost showed us a couple of bamboo cages, each containing a big rat. "We'll still keep these to fall back on," he said, laughing.

We started back to Vinh Long. Maj. George Derrick of Austin, Tex., fell off the monkey bridge across the canal and got soaked. I did, too.

SEPT. 21, DON CHAU

This could be what hell looks like.

Minutes ago—before 8 a.m.—these were mangrove swamps.

Thick, impenetrable, the lair of snakes and Communist Viet Cong.

Then the B-52's came 3000 miles from Guam.

Came with their 1000-pound and 750-pound bombs.

Flew over the mangroves, at the mouth of the Bassac River, at 22,000 feet altitude. Turned on their radar. Released their deadly loads.

We never saw them. But we saw their bombs hit. Hit with the deadliest accuracy.

Fifteen minutes later they were on their way home.

Back to Guam, another six hours away.

Then came the smaller planes—the F-100's, and AIE's and the armed helicopters—with their napalm and white phosphorous. With their machine guns and rockets. Swooping out of the sky in graceful patterns, sweeping back up again.

They took 30 minutes.

Now, at 9 a.m., in an unarmed helicopter, we are over the target.

Flying through the smoke.

Choking on the fumes.

Others have watched B-52 raids from the air. I did, earlier this month. Others have walked through the bombed areas later. But we are the first to fly through the carnage minutes after the big bombers struck. It is an awesome sight.

Fires are everywhere. Seven huge swaths, each three-quarters of a mile long, have been cut through the swamps.

The bombs fell in strings.

Where each hit, there is now a circular clearing, roughly the size of two football fields.

The trees, the brush, the mangroves, all are gone. We call that "blow down." In each cleared circle there is a neat, round hole. Already these holes have filled with water.

The target was 1.2 square miles of jungle.

In 15 minutes, 20 per cent of it was cleared.

While the planes were over target, a Vietnamese Navy River Assault Group lay off shore. One string of bombs thudded through the mangroves and out into the Bassac River. The Navy, and the ground troops with them, had a moment of panic. But the last bomb hit some distance away.

Now they are going ashore. Walking through the clearings. Staring in awe.

Trees weren't just knocked down. They disappeared. Disintegrated.

We don't find the Viet Cong. We didn't really expect to. Our Intelligence reports weren't that good.

But this has always been one of the Viet Cong sanctuaries. Here they could relax, retrain, regroup. And now it has been taken away from them. In 15 minutes, they lost it.

They'd been here. Our troops found 400 tons of rice.

They burned it.

Cruel?

Certainly. War is a cruel business. And food is a weapon of war.

Long before the first of the big B-52's returns to Guam, we've finished walking through the mangroves. No man ever did that before. No one on our side, anyhow. And it wasn't too hard. Our men aren't even winded. River boats are waiting on the other side to pick them up.

The Viet Cong?

They're still somewhere around. Looking, undoubtedly, for a place to spend the night. Trying to convince the peasants, who want no part of them now, to let them stay. Looking for another sanctuary.

SEPT. 30, CAI CAI

This is the newest U.S. Special Forces camp, next to the border of Cambodia in western Viet Nam.

Authorities in Saigon were hesitant about building it. We had never tried putting one down in the middle of strong Communist Viet Cong country. But Cai Cai is still here, after six months, and gradually extending its influence.

"The people hated us when we arrived," said Lt. Pete Crummey of Cincinnati. "They still may not love us, but they are no longer living under the Viet Cong."

We've taken 30,000 people and 50 million piastres in taxes away from the Viet Cong just by coming to Cai Cai, Saigon estimates. The men here believe that might be overstating it. But they have made friends and they have plans for building a new village, if the waters ever go down.

And they've made it tougher on the Viet Cong. Once the Reds could use the river as their infiltration highway. Now they must use the smaller canals.

"This is where we'll prove or disprove our tactics," said Crummey. "Here everything is just like the textbooks say. It couldn't be more ideal, or any tougher."

Cai Cai gets its supplies by airdrop or by helicopter. Last week a chopper didn't make it out. It's still in the river. A part of its motor crashed into a hut and tore a man's arm off.

Two days ago an Air Force plane overshot and dropped a cargo of what Crummey thought was gasoline in Cambodia. That happens every now and then.

Crummey called the Air Force HQ and told them, matter of factly, they had just made the Cambodians and the Viet Cong a nice present. "Hell," the Air people said, "those things were mortars."

That wouldn't do. So Crummey, John Learson of New Orleans and Sgt. Rafael Lopez of Cleveland set out to recover the cargo even if it had landed across the border.

They found it—not in Cambodia but 100 yards inside our lines. And it turned out to be gasoline after all. They promptly machine-gunned it and set it afire.

"After all that time," Crummey explained, "we knew it was booby-trapped."

Life is never dull here. There are Vietnamese Airborne Rangers and Vietnamese Special Forces in camp, and no love is lost between them.

It makes trouble.

There have been three incipient riots in 11 days. Crummey quelled one by standing on a small bridge between their encampments and daring either side to try to get past him. Just like Crummy!

The Viet Cong are everywhere. Pointing to a map, the Lieutenant said:

"You can get a fight here . . . and here . . . any time you want it."

But the Reds aren't too hot as soldiers, he added. He explained:

"They're downright stupid. They fire at our planes always from the same spot. And so the planes turn around and drop everything they've got on them.

"Recently we hurried out and policed up the area. We found a couple of dead still there—both teen-agers, thin and full of sores. Really pitiful specimens.

"They've mortared us 13 times. But until last night, we hadn't been mortared in 50 or more days.

"We figure that when they mortar us, their Chinese or Cambodian advisers have turned up. Maybe they bring in the mortars.

247

"The locals themselves aren't much to worry about as individuals. It's just that there are so damned many of them."

OCT. 4, CAI CAI

The United States and South Viet Nam are trying to seal the Cambodian border—a major Red-infiltration route—with money provided by the U.S.

The effort has failed completely.

In the Fourth Corps area, there are 18 Special Forces posts along the border with her pro-Communist neighbor. The posts have a border surveillance mission to spot and halt the clandestine movement of men and arms into the Mekong Delta. Each has a section of border to patrol. On a map it looks impressive. Surveillance sectors are interlocking.

Theoretically, the border has been closed, but only theoretically.

These 18 posts are manned by members of the Vietnamese Civilian Irregular Defense Group (CIDG). These are civilians, hired at better than prevailing local wages and higher than those paid regular soldiers.

In addition, each outpost has a team of nine to 12 American Special Forces men. It has a smaller team of Vietnamese called the LLDB (Luc Long Dai Bach).

This setup is absurd. The CIDG obviously has no intention of patrolling the border. It has no intention of moving outside its defense perimeter. It has no intention of clashing with the Viet Cong. Casualties invariably are the result of Communist initiative; such as ambushes and mines. These men are free to refuse any order they choose. They frequently do.

I spent five days at Cai Cai this week. On two successive days patrols were canceled because the CIDG preferred not to go. The third day they went; but in the opposite direction, away from the border. This was listed, belatedly, as "training."

Cai Cai is a mile and half from the border. It has the job of patrolling a 25-mile stretch. To seal it would be a real contribution to the war effort. Cai Cai was set up six months ago. I asked each American here how far, in those six months, he had been out of camp. None had gone farther than three miles. The rest of that 25-mile border is wide open.

The Americans are embarrassed. They want to go. But they lack authority to take their troops with them.

When Cai Cai was built in April we brought in 438 CIDG. Two weeks later, 87 were still in camp. The rest deserted. Those 87 were officers and non-coms who brought their families with them and couldn't easily take off. Cai Cai is the dirtiest, remotest, ugliest, most dangerous outpost along the border. It has been mortared 13 times. The CIDG want no part of it.

Another 507 were brought in recently, but they are now in the process of deserting.

The CIDG is recruited locally. Province chiefs are interested primarily in looking good in Saigon. Given a quota, they fill it. But they are not too careful whom they hire. Infiltration is a constant danger.

There are four CIDG companies here. This month, their commander asked for wages for six company commanders. When we refused, he said our attitude would result in "bad feeling."

Americans say the LLDB commander here stays in his sack 18 hours a day and plays cards the other six.

CIDG men make a practice of touring the border, enlisting, drawing wages until they are tired or bored, and then moving on to another. There is nothing we can do about this.

No one I've talked with defends this setup. They all concede it's quite useless. The only thing said in its favor is that it is speedy. Our Special Forces, like other hush-hush outfits, apparently have unlimited funds and little red tape. Ordered to recruit 500 men, Special Forces can do it in two days. Otherwise, it would take months. But the men we recruit are something else.

Meanwhile the border is still wide open.

OCT. 12, DA NANG

The young Marine had been shot in the face.

"It's a jaw wound," said Comdr. Almon Wilson of Hudson

Falls, N.Y., "and this is the period of maximum swelling. For the moment, we have him under sedation. In another 48 hours he'll be out of the woods."

Commander Wilson is with "Charley Med"—or Medical Company C. The company is stationed at the foot of a big hill near the sprawling Marine base here. Of the base's 24 Navy doctors, eight are with Charley Med.

In the two months since it was established, Charley Med has been busy. Operation Starlite strained it to capacity. But every day, several times a day, wounded Marines are brought here. Most survive.

The story of Navy medicine in Viet Nam is one of the more heartening in this war.

"If they are alive when we get them, we have a good chance of saving them," said Wilson. "I'd say we've lost no more than two men, where we had a chance to pull them through, since we've been here."

Until July, Commander Wilson was based at the Naval Hospital in Chelsea, Mass.

"We're Marines," he says of his staff. "Our job is to save lives and get men back to duty as quickly as we can. If they can be returned within 120 days, we evacuate them to hospitals in the area, to Japan, Okinawa or the Philippines. If they're more seriously wounded, we send them home."

By any standards, Charley Med is still a primitive tent-hospital complex. Two of its pre-fabricated operating rooms are air-conditioned. But its doctors sometimes have to perform surgery elsewhere on the grounds. Commander Wilson hopes soon to have four more air-conditioned operating rooms.

"We've finally got the equipment we need," he said. "We're more sophisticated every day. From now on, we'll concentrate on expanding our facilities."

Most wounded men are brought here by air. A huge helicopter landing pad takes up what would be the parade ground. Medical evacuation choppers come and go. At the moment, dust is a problem, though oiling has kept it down.

"This is war," Wilson says, "and these boys are green. They

sometimes take too many chances. But they're learning. And they have courage and stamina. After all, we are dealing with healthy young bodies, not with people with heart conditions and the like. These lads are likely to pull through if anyone can."

He paused and smiled.

"We're learning, too," he said. "This is our first war. But we handle each bunch of wounded men a bit more professionally. It's heartening to me to see them brought off the choppers with a minimum of fuss and dispatched where they should go, where we can do the most for them. An outsider, I suspect, would be struck by our matter-of-fact attitude. But an excited doctor is no doctor at all."

The doctor says there is a high incidence of belly wounds. And the Viet Cong inflict considerable tissue damage with high-velocity shells.

"We get whole blood from Americans in Japan," he said. "We know it's good blood, from healthy people. It's helped save many lives."

Next January the hospital ship *Repose* will be anchored off Da Nang. And a 400-bed Naval hospital is under construction nearby. All this means additional life-saving equipment, more doctors and nurses.

But it's at dusty, sprawling tent-city Charley Med, at the foot of a hill near Da Nang, that wounded Marines go first.

Many of them will survive because it's here.

OCT. 15, DA NANG

The Marine lieutenant sat by the field telephone in the darkened tent. He seemed a bit lost.

"I often suspect," his colonel said, "that this young man doesn't know what fear is."

Lt. George Connell, Cheverly, Md., overheard. He broke into a grin.

"Sir," he said, "that might have been true once. Before this morning."

This is the command post of the Fisrt Battalion, Ninth Marines, a few miles from the new Da Nang air base along the South China Sea. Nearby there is an old French fort. A few miles back, there's a big Seabee camp. Closer at hand, a 400-bed Navy hospital is nearing completion.

And Viet Cong are everywhere.

George Connell had taken a small patrol out at dawn. His mission was to listen and observe. He had four men with him. They'd taken up a position in a rice paddy near a small hamlet known to be Viet Cong.

"Tell him about it," Lt. Col. Verle Ludwig of Kokomo, Ind., suggests.

"Well, sir," George Connell recalls. "We lay there watching. A bunch of kids herded some water buffalo through. What we didn't know then was the Viet Cong were right behind them. First thing we knew they opened fire. Two of my men were wounded."

He stopped, remembering it all.

"I looked up and saw two grenades floating down on me. That's the only way I can describe it. I tried to shout a warning, but I couldn't think of the word 'grenade.' All I could say was 'Oh, hell!' I buried my face in the ground.

"The grenades detonated, wounding the two men who'd already been hurt. I came up firing. And, believe it or not, my carbine rammed into the cheek of a Viet Cong just as I pulled the trigger. He was that close. It blew his face apart."

George Connell seemed almost to shudder.

"I had to change when I got back," he said. "I had Viet Cong all over me. And that, sir, is why I am perfectly happy to be where I am tonight.

"I think, now, I do know what fear is."

OCT. 22, CAI SON

Why, dear God, do they have to kill kids?

What could the planned murder of an eight-year-old boy conceivably prove?

That one political system is stronger and better than another?

That it cares more for the people? That it will win this awful war?

That one bunch of angry adults is stronger and braver than its foes?

If it does, then there was a reason for Le Van Binh to die.

If it doesn't . . .

Little Le Van Binh's only crime—as the Viet Cong reckon such things—was that his dad was a schoolteacher.

It takes guts to teach school in a place like Cai Son. I wouldn't have the job; I don't own that sort of courage.

A Vietnamese schoolteacher is a marked man. The Viet Cong go hunting for him. And, more often than not, they get him eventually. He's lucky if he's the only one they get. They go for his family, too, with the heartless, methodical planning that marks everything the Viet Cong do.

So little Binh died at two o'clock one recent morning. His dad, Le Van Hai, died, too. The same grenade got them both.

Little Binh's mother was luckier, though she wouldn't call it that. She happens to be the village midwife, and a neighbor woman was in labor.

Le Van Binh wasn't one of those caught up in this war, mowed down in its deadly crossfire, as so many have been. His was a political assassination, as diabolical as it was impersonal.

Somewhere out in the brush which has grown up around this once prosperous farming village, a group of adult men had met and condemned him to death.

The assassination squad crept up to the hut where Hai and little Binh slept. They seldom slept twice in the same place. This morning, the Viet Cong knew precisely where they'd be. Somewhere in Cai Son today, there's a traitor who told them.

Ten yards away they loosed a grenade. Hai's thatched roof was no protection against it. Little Binh always slept next to his dad. He died immediately. Le Van Hai, the village teacher, lived until they got him to the landing pad where an American helicopter waited. There he died, too.

I didn't know little Binh. But I've known thousands like him.

Dateline: Viet Nam

Mischievous little imps with dirty faces and sparkling eyes and grimy hands reaching out for "chew gum" and candy. "Bad" little boys, invariably, who play hooky to sail their home-made boats on the canals, kids utterly without guile, so anxious for your affection they'll cling to your legs like leeches if you notice them at all. Which, of course, you do.

Little Binh's mother reaches out to touch his mangled little face and the tears come. Brokenly, she says something in her own tongue. But the language of a mother's grief is universal and you understand her.

After they killed Binh and his dad, the Viet Cong moved down four huts, across another canal, and killed Nguyen Van Cua, 68, and his wife, Chung Thi Tan, who was 64. Here, too, their planning was admirable. They knew precisely where the old couple would place their sleeping mats. One grenade was enough.

The Cuas were much respected in Cai Son. But they, too, had sinned, and for their sins they were condemned. A son, Nguyen Van Bay, 33, is a sergeant in the Vietnamese army, stationed in Saigon.

Captain Nghia, Cai Son's Regional Force commander, sent his troops after the assassins. They killed at least one. His body lies where he fell outside the old couple's hut, where their neighbors have gathered to pay their last respects.

Lt. Col. John Swango, Quincy, Ill., hopes this was the one who tossed the grenade. You hope against hope that John is right.

At mid-morning, Air Force jets, guided by a Vietnamese spotter plane, swarm in and all but obliterate a grove of trees where Nghia's patrols say they'd chased the killers. The blasts shake the huts where the four bodies are laid out.

A sampan brings in four ornate coffins.

Helicopters drop down to carry out eight soldiers wounded in the chase.

Little Binh's dirty-faced classmates, urchins with sparkling eyes, are hopping with excitement. Their elders cuff them into unchildlike silence.

They are saying goodby to little Binh, who had to die because his dad was a schoolteacher.

OCT. 26, CAN THO

Not the least of the qualities of good fighting men is their ability to endure. Bravery, military knowledge, marksmanship—these things have their place in the making of a soldier. But they are as nothing if a man cannot endure the unendurable.

— Farley Mowat, Canadian military historian

This is the story of two young Americans who have endured the unendurable.

Capt. Jerry Devlin of Waltham, Mass., and Lt. Bob Walsh of Red Bank, N.J., are two of the bravest soldiers and finest men I have ever known.

The quotation above was taken from the framed motto on the wall of the hut here in Can Tho where Bob Walsh occasionally sleeps. More often, however, he sleeps in the field. He has always tried to live by the words that hang on his wall.

Jerry Devlin is one of those rare young men who seems to embody all of the fine qualities one hopes to find in a professional officer. It is rare to find them all in one package.

For the past 10 months, Jerry Devlin has served as the principal U.S. adviser to the 44th Vietnamese Ranger Battalion in the Mekong Delta. The 44th Rangers are South Viet Nam's best fighting outfit. Ask President Johnson. He recently awarded the 44th his personal unit citation. He has never done that for any other Vietnamese unit.

In those 10 months Devlin lost, by death, two young lieutenants. This hurt him deeply. He brooded about it.

Bob Walsh came to the 44th Rangers in August after the death of Lt. Bob Fuellhart, a former West Point football star.

Devlin and Walsh, in the three operations they ran together, worked well in harness. There was a bond between them. For one thing, both are devout Catholics and, whenever possible, attended Mass together. Father (Capt.) Thomas J. Endel of

Chicago says of the two: "They are men in the best sense of the word, each with a strength and dedication."

Walsh greatly respected Devlin. But he was not afraid to disagree with him nor to tell him he was wrong. Walsh sensed Devlin's fear of losing another officer, and fought against any attempt to protect or withhold him from his share of the danger.

Walsh is an intense, soft-spoken young man. He is deeply devoted to his wife, who is expecting a child and to the Army. He has an intense pride in himself as a man and a soldier.

Two other things about Bob Walsh are worth mentioning. He has a deep respect for the Vietnamese Rangers. And he is a lover of William Shakespeare—if not a Shakespearean scholar.

I have had to wait a week to write this story. I was not there —for which I am thankful—and there were too many conflicting accounts from others who were not there to sort fact from fiction. I flew to Saigon to see Devlin, but he had undergone five hours of surgery and could not speak. Walsh was under sedation, but I was able to talk to him later.

I feel this story was worth waiting for. The story of young Americans who endured the unendurable.

It all really began, Bob Walsh recalls now, around 1 p.m. on the afternoon of Oct. 13.

"We were just getting ready to eat," he said, "and I was starving. I'd had only two eggs for breakfast."

That morning, Lieut. Walsh and his sergeant, Ben Barnes of Pensacola, Fla., had worked with two companies of Vietnamese Rangers searching for Viet Cong along a line of trees on the banks of a canal in Phong Dinh Province.

They had taken three prisoners and flown them out by helicopter. More importantly, however, they had liberated 28 Vietnamese prisoners.

"Some of them were Rangers," Walsh recalled. That seemed important to him, for Rangers are a special breed in his book.

At 1 p.m., from his command post, Capt. Jerry Devlin had called over his radio for Walsh to get ready to move to another location where the hunting looked more favorable. Helicopters arrived minutes later and they piled aboard, skipping their meal.

"I was weak with hunger," Bob recalled.

It was 5 p.m. when they flushed their first Viet Cong. "For a half hour," said Walsh, "we assaulted. Then we consolidated our position. I remember there were many enemy dead around. I didn't count them—I was too busy."

At 7 p.m., Devlin again called over his radio and said he was sending a man to bring Walsh and Barnes to his post a scant 300 yards away. So, as darkness fell, four Americans were gathered, including Devlin and Sgt. David Halbauer of St. Paul, Minn.

"We sat down and had a cigaret and opened a can of C-rations," said Walsh. "Mine was ham and eggs. It tasted like caviar."

The Viet Cong struck about 8:30 p.m.

First there were mortars. They came from the front and from the flanks. Suddenly came mortars and automatic-weapons fire from the rear.

"I'm intuitive about these things," Walsh said. "I've been in the Army only five years, and this was my third combat operation, so I'm a neophyte. But I knew, instinctively, and Jerry did, too, that this was the pay-off. Sometimes a man will come at you and you know he intends merely to frighten you. Other times, you know he intends to hurt you. But then there are times you know he intends to kill you.

"I knew, and Jerry knew, they intended to wipe the Rangers out. If they could do that, they could regain the initiative they lost in December. And they came prepared to do it."

It is impossible, Walsh said, to describe what followed. Rangers were dying all around them. Eventually the four Americans found themselves wading deep in the water of a small canal. As a matter of fact, Walsh said, this being the wet season, the entire battle was fought in water "only some was deep and some not so deep."

A mortar dropped among the four Americans. They were just a few feet apart, but it hit closest to Captain Devlin.

"It blew me out of the canal and up against a small tree," said Walsh. "I felt something very hot and very hard in the small of my back. I can best describe it as the way I felt when I was tackled on the blind side playing football."

Walsh saw Barnes against the opposite bank and called to him. Barnes said his hip was shattered. He asked about Devlin.

"The Captain is dead," Barnes replied.

Walsh called to Halbauer.

"Take Barnes, however you can, and get out of here," he said.

Devlin was not dead. But the concussion, in water up to his armpits, had shattered his innards. Practically all of his organs, in one way or another, were badly damaged, the doctors were to find later.

In pain, fading fast, almost incoherent, Devlin struggled to the bank and found Walsh. A few yards farther they saw Captain Dai, the Ranger commanding officer, struggling to reorganize his forces. Then a mortar obliterated Captain Dai.

The Rangers lost their leadership and they were in danger of becoming disorganized.

Fast losing consciousness, Devlin cornered a young second lieutenant, calmed his fears, and helped pull the battalion together. How a half-conscious, almost fatally injured man could do this, no one—certainly not Bob Walsh—can explain. But Devlin did.

Devlin decided to hold. The 42nd Rangers, the 44th's friendly rivals, were in the area and were "tying in." If the 44th broke that contact, he shouted in Vietnamese, "they'll destroy us, every man of us."

"The Rangers were magnificent," Walsh said. "I saw one boy stand up, firing his weapon until they got him between the eyes."

Devlin told Halbauer to collect as many wounded as he could, at one point so the helicopters could get them out. Halbauer walked a few feet toward the paddy dike—which was the only high ground—and died. He was shot through the mouth.

Walsh said it was then midnight.

"Jerry was coherent but starting to go," he said. "I had never been so tired in my life."

In that condition, Walsh rolled back into the canal. He had a heavy radio strapped to his back, a helmet on his head and his weapon in his hand. He went to the bottom. He shed his radio, took off his helmet and—this he can never forgive himself —discarded his weapon. He attributes this to his utter exhaustion.

"I knew I was drowning," he said. "As a kid of seven I was almost drowned and was revived. I felt the same way this time.

"Then Jerry came after me. Wounded as he was, out of his head, he came down into the water and got me. He brought me back onto the bank. We lay there face to face for I don't know how long."

The mortars still came and Walsh's radio was gone. He could reach no one. He knew the 42nd and his friend, Capt. Max Powers of Fayetteville, Ark., were nearby. He stood up, intending to go look for them.

"Someone started shooting at me so I got down," he said. "It may have been Viet Cong or Rangers, I don't know. Anything that moved got shot at. That's how it had to be."

Walsh was afraid Devlin was dying. To bolster the Captain's morale, he began talking about a medical helicopter, urging him to hold on. Actually, he had no means of summoning one.

But the Viet Cong, frustrated, broke off around 3 a.m.

"One last mortar round and they withdrew," Walsh said.

Devlin asked for morphine. Walsh had one vial. He urged Devlin, if he could, to wait until nearer dawn. He feared they might still "have to walk out and I knew the later he took it, the better he'd be in condition to walk if he had to."

But Devlin could not wait. The pain was too severe. Walsh recalled it took him 30 minutes, lying there in the darkness, to administer the shot.

"He went to sleep and was peaceful until the choppers came after us at 8 a.m.," he said. "They flew us to Saigon."

Bob Walsh is back on duty. Jerry Devlin—protesting he must not desert his Rangers—has been flown home. He faces a long pull before he is whole again. There will be long periods of surgery. One Army doctor says "whole pieces of vital organs are floating around inside him still."

Devlin's ambition is to become a regular Army officer. A former enlisted man, he had completed two years of college and hoped, when he went back home, to be stationed at a post where he could obtain his degree. His superiors are urging that the college requirement in his case now be waived.

Ben Barnes' leg was shattered. He, too, has been sent away. Meanwhile Bob Walsh is alone with his Rangers. One by one they come by to thank him, to kiss him on both cheeks, to shake his hand, to weep a little.

Bob Walsh is thankful.

"The Chaplain asked me, there in the hospital, why I thought I was still alive," he said. "I don't honestly know. But I know there must be a reason. God always has one."

OCT. 28, CHU LAI

The Marines here, hard-pressed on supplies, have begun to cannibalize crippled planes and helicopters in order to keep better craft flying.

This is part of their report to representatives of the Senate Armed Services Investigating Subcommittee. The group, headed by Chief Counsel James T. Kendall, has been in Viet Nam interviewing senior officers in connection with Washington hearings. Accompanying Kendall were Marine Brig. Gen. S. R. Shaw (Ret.) and Ben J. Gilleas, a subcommittee staff member.

It boils down to this:

Marine aviation units left their bases in the United States with a 90-day package of supplies and spare parts.

This is standard procedure in priority and alert units. At all times, and in all circumstances, they must be prepared to subsist on their own resources for three months if they have to.

But this is the extreme.

Most of the helicopter and fighter teams here and in Da Nang now have gone 45 days or more without material resupply. And "significant shortages" have begun to develop.

The situation is not yet critical enough to interfere with military operations. One fighter squadron at Chu Lai boasts of an 89 per cent aircraft availability rate. This is considerably above average even for stateside operations. But it is straining its resources, and it is doubtful how long it can keep this up. And once an aircraft is down it is stripped of needed parts.

Resupply may very well be on the way.

"We have no way of knowing," one unit commander told the investigators. "All we can do is file requisitions. We have done so every day. They simply disappear into channels. The stuff may show up soon. On the other hand, it may not come for several weeks. They've got problems at the other end, too. We know that. But in that case we'll be in some difficulty. We're getting nervous."

Resupply, in the early stages of troop movements as large-scale as ours have been, always presents problems. It is inevitable, perhaps that shortages develop. Commanders expect them and are ingenious enough to cope with them. On the whole, Marines feel they have done well.

There certainly are no shortages of medical and surgical supplies. Navy doctors serving with the Marines have been able to get the latest and most sophisticated tools of their trade. A 400-bed Navy hospital is being built near Da Nang. The fatality rate among wounded Marines is low.

After a month and a half, some ground units still are eating C-rations. Down to the regimental level, fresh meats and vegetables usually are available. Battalions get meat maybe once or twice a week; most of the time their chow consists of bulkier B-rations. Below battalion, at the company and platoon level, C-rations are the rule. The men do not seem to mind. Each man prepares his own. Usually they pool their rations and have come up with some unusual concoctions.

As in all wars, there are problems peculiar to the locale.

The airfield here, for instance, was built on a sandy beach. This had never been done before. It involves initially laying down aluminum planking. The planks consist of two sheets of aluminum joined by a network of strong cross-bars.

Maj. Gen. Lewis Walt, the Marines' top commander here,

helped develop this when he was in research and development before his assignment to Viet Nam.

To provide a solid base, they laid down a coating of asphalt and oil. This has proved almost totally unsatisfactory. Whole sections of the field at Chu Lai are now inoperative. The base was capable of taking small fighters, which weigh 20 tons. Larger transport planes, which must also land here, put it out of commission. Even a jeep driven over it causes the planks to tilt and wave.

So now the field is being rebuilt. The planks are being taken up and another base of concrete, mixed with beach sand, is being laid to a depth of several feet. While this is being done, however, air operations continue. The Marines use carrier tactics. Arresting cables enable their fighters to land on that part of the field which is still usable.

NOV. 1, PLEI ME

Dick Sundt brought the word to our jungle command post about 10 o'clock on a dark night.

There are, he said, major elements of two Viet Cong and North Vietnamese regiments between us and Plei Me, five miles away. Despite constant bombing and strafing attacks, their morale is high, he added.

"They're waiting there to kill more Americans," said Sundt.

Lt. Col. John Stockton said: "They may just get that chance. And we're waiting to kill Viet Cong."

Captain Sundt is an Army 'brat,' who calls New Mexico his home. On this night Dick was our liaison with the generals in Pleiku. He had come by chopper to give us the latest battle plan.

Plei Me has been under fire most of the day. I've been in and out of the post. Now I am with Stockton's air cavalry squadron—the eyes and ears of our First Cavalry Division—ready to move in against the Viet Cong. At the moment Plei Me is quiet.

Captain Sundt outlines the plan he has been given. Stockton doesn't like it; his tactical area is smaller than he wants. The bulk of the attack mission falls to the First Armored Brigade.

The Colonel is inclined to blame the Captain—why didn't he speak up? But Sundt is apparently used to these squalls. He points out the area is still big enough to carry out a plan nearest the Colonel's heart: a surprise mortar attack at dawn on Chu Ho Hill.

All night long Stockton's jungle lair buzzes with activity. Capt. Gene Fox of Washington, D.C., commanding Alpha Company, and his executive officer, Lt. Paul Mobley of Rockville, Md., push through the tall elephant grass for last-minute instructions.

Air Force Capt. Les Holland of El Reno, Okla., hovers over his radio, tying in with fighter planes which already have flown 600 or more sorties against the Viet Cong around Plei Me.

Sgt. Maj. Lawrence Kennedy of Tupelo, Miss., is everywhere at once. Capt. Jack Williams of Wilmington, Ohio, the battalion surgeon, prepares his hospital tent. Chaplain Maj. Harry Treude of Philadelphia works with him.

We sleep fitfully and before the first light of day we are heliborne, ready to spot for the mortars which have been helilifted to the sites. Warrant Officer Charlie Greene of Wellsville, N.Y., is at the controls of the Colonel's chopper. Sgt. Bob Worrell of LaGrange, Ga., sits in the co-pilot's seat beside him. Sgt. Lowell Pirkle of Albuquerque, N.M., is riding shotgun, along with Marion Dittmer of Green, Kan., and Paul Eddy of Orlando, Fla.

Pirkle is more out of the plane than in. The chopper has no doors and he wears harness. But he's actually standing at times on the landing floats and leaning out.

The chopper makes a steep turn and I close my eyes. When I open them I note that Pirkle, miraculously, is still there.

"I haven't shot any Viet Cong all week" he says, "and I am embarrassed."

Suddenly we are being fired on. The jungle below is slowly turning from black to dark green as the sun comes up.

Pirkle, Dittmer and Eddy fire back. Charlie Greene holds a steady course and we move out of range. Slowly Bob Worrell adjusts the range for the mortars below us. Right there, in the trees under our whirling rotors, we are told, was the Viet Cong

101st Regiment. The 102nd Regiment was on Chu Ho Hill.

Maj. Rob Zion of Helena, Mont., commanding C Troop, and Maj. Billie Williams of Linden, Tex., commanding B Troop, are within 4000 yards of the enemy's rear line atop that hill.

This is John Stockton's surprise party. Now his mortars speak. The first few rounds fall short. The next few are too long. Bob Worrell, in his heliborne outpost, makes adjustments.

Now he's right on target.

Chu Ho is being plastered. Mortar after mortar drops in on the Viet Cong soundlessly. White smoke rises in mushroom clouds until Chu Ho Hill is lost from sight.

As planned, both our A Troop and B Troop fire 50 times each. Then the men climb back aboard their choppers and are gone.

Plei Me is quiet. The Viet Cong have their heads down. This is one morning they won't forget. As we move out, the Air Force fighters swarm back in with their napalm.

NOV. 2, PLEI ME

The kid stood stock still, his face frozen in a foolish grin.

The thing had come at him out of the elephant grass, nicking his side and burying itself in the earth.

It was a primitive spear, five feet long, its bamboo point needle sharp and hard as steel. The Viet Cong had planted them all about, lashed to bent saplings like bows and arrows and triggered when a man trips over a vine or a root.

They are fired silently and fly with a barely perceptible whoosh. They can go right through a man.

But so far we have been lucky.

Pfc. Jose Sanches, 19, of Puerto Rico, held his side and the blood oozed through his fingers. But fortunately Jose had approached the booby trap obliquely and he wasn't badly hurt— just frightened.

We were all frightened. This is something you can't fight.

The Colonel patted him on the back and ordered him to the rear.

Since early afternoon we'd been camped here in the jungle,

waiting orders to go in against the Viet Cong attacking Plei Me. Artillery nearby roared without letup.

But this is their jungle—not ours. They were born here. They know it like the palms of their hands. They were here ahead of us. When they left they planted their spears and their punji sticks in the elephant grass around us.

Two months ago our kids were back in Fort Benning, Ga. They're here for the first time.

Soon after dusk Mike Peltransky of Riverside, Calif., a tall crew-cut lad of 20, was brought in from patrol. He had been the lead man of his unit. He was carefully pushing through the elephant grass when a punji stick jabbed him in the right leg.

A punji stick is the Devil's own contrivance. They're needle sharp and coated with manure by the Viet Cong so they will produce infection. Mike's wound was ugly and painful.

Capt. Russell Prince of Spartanburg, S.C., battalion surgeon, swabbed the bleeding sore.

"I'll have to send him out," he said. "He'll need five days of penicillin and antibiotics."

Father Joe Rogers of Ottumwa, Ia., the Chaplain, brought Mike a canteen cup of water.

"You'll be all right," the Chaplain said.

"Sure I will, Father," said Mike.

A few hours before, I'd flown with Lt. Col. Jack Cranford of Roanoke, Va., and Maj. Dave Johnson of Lima, Ohio, over jungles around Plei Me. A long column of Vietnamese Rangers was making slow progress down a province road leading to the besieged outpost. They had been ambushed earlier. Smoking trucks were still along the road.

Suddenly Pfc. Jim Bailey of Cleveland opened fire. In the jungle below, Bailey's sharp eyes had picked up gun flashes. The Viet Cong were after us.

Cranford poured on the gas and we zoomed out of range.

Our radio crackled. A helicopter was down between Plei Me and Pleiku—and this was Viet Cong country.

We spotted it along Highway 14 and Major Johnson eased our chopper down beside it.

The downed pilots, Capt. Evart Robeson of Rapid City, S.D., and Warrant Officer John Dill of West Point, Va., were inspecting the damage.

Then another craft came in with Maj. John Persch of Sharon, Pa., battalion maintenance officer, who checked the crippled chopper and said it would have to be airlifted out.

A bigger ship, a Chinook, was summoned from Pleiku.

A half-hour after the tiny Huey had gone down it was moved out, slung beneath the belly of the giant Chinook headed for Pleiku.

So we took off, too, continuing our aerial spying over the Viet Cong lines.

NOV. 3, DA NANG

"Young man," the four-star General said, "I think I'd like to fly her for a while. I've had 200 hours in these birds, but I haven't handled one recently."

Gen. William C. Westmoreland was speaking, and we were in a helicopter on the way here.

Marine Capt. Tim Common of Wilkes-Barre, Pa., the pilot, raised both hands to show he was no longer at the controls and Westmoreland took over.

"I hope," he added, smiling, "I'm not giving anyone heart failure."

For two days recently, I traveled with Westmoreland, the top U.S. commander in Viet Nam, throughout the Central Highlands and along the parallel where the Viet Cong are strongest.

Out itinerary included An Khe, where the First Cavalry Division has its command post. We spent the night here. Our schedule was subject to frequent change, for Westmoreland is nothing if not flexible.

At 51, he sets a fast pace. It doesn't bother him, the General says, if he gets enough exercise. This includes 25 push-ups each morning and tennis. He tries to get seven or eight hours sleep a night. But he can do with less if he gets the exercise.

An inordinate amount of his time is taken up by important

visitors—more than 500 last month. There will be as many this month. General Westmoreland gives them as much time as he can. But they cut deeply into an already overcrowded schedule.

He does not spare his subordinates. He expects them to keep up with him. If they can't, they're replaced. Excuses aren't enough. This is war, and General Westmoreland expects results.

He is, however, capable of unexpected kindnesses.

At Da Nang, he decorated a number of officers and men waiting at the airfield. He had learned that Marine Col. Bob Conley, the Marine Air Group Commander, and I were old friends from Korea. He halted the ceremony and called me forward to shake Bob's hand.

At An Khe, he was told that an old friend had been injured aboard ship and was in the hospital in Hawaii. "Is Priscilla with him?" he asked. "I'll have Mrs. W. drop by and see him."

But his principal concern is his job.

"No man enjoys being away from home and his loved ones," he tells his troops.

"But we have a job to do. And we're professionals."

He talks a soldier's language. He has two themes:

—We are here to help the Vietnamese win *their* war.

—And we are here to make friends.

The Vietnamese, he reminds his men, have known other foreign troops in times past. Those memories still rankle. But Americans came to fight for an ideal—the ideal of freedom. Our conduct must be such that we will win the people's confidence, their friendship and, most important, their respect.

To senior officers in the briefing tents, he says: "We can beat this Viet Cong, but we must never underestimate him. He's tough and he's resourceful. He'll adapt his tactics to ours. We are one jump ahead of him. Let's stay ahead."

To all, he pounds home this message:

"You're professionals. No bunch of professionals has ever been so fortunate, has ever had this God-given opportunity to test his doctrine and tactics against a live enemy. Stay flexible. Stay loose. Learn as you go."

To the paratroopers, he says simply:

"I sent for you men because I needed you."

His concern for the Vietnamese is real. He inspects their messes as thoroughly as our own. At a training camp outside Da Nang, he stopped several recruits, fresh out of their native hamlets, and questioned them through his interpreter. Are they getting enough to eat? Did they enlist or were they drafted? Why had they joined up? One question he asked every man: Why are the Americans here? The answer, from each man, never varied. To help Viet Nam.

"That's right," he said. "To help you."

At Hoa Vinh, a hamlet recently liberated from the Viet Cong, he listened patiently while a team of young Marines told of their plans for the people, including rebuilding a school burned by the Communists. Then he spoke briefly.

"We know what you have been through," he said. "You have our respect. We hope the worst is past."

Westmoreland is convinced the tide of war has turned. But he does not delude himself that the road ahead will be smooth. We are no longer losing, yet it will be some time before we win.

And winning is Westmoreland's job.

NOV. 15, BAC LIEU

The sign on the command bunker reads "Fort Martha Raye."

Martha Raye, 52, of Butte, Mont., and Hollywood, Calif., is, in the language of the younger GI, "something else." And she is on her way to becoming the sweetheart of this war, as Mary Pickford did in World War I and Marlene Dietrich did in Europe in the last big one.

Bigger names, perhaps, than Martha's have come to Viet Nam. But those have been one-night stands. Martha has been in this country five weeks on this, her second trip.

"I've just got my extension," I heard her stage-whisper to Col. Bob Spilman of Fort Worth, senior adviser to the 21st Division. "They're going to let me stay until Dec. 28."

Martha, like most everyone in Viet Nam, has been under fire. The last time she was in Bac Lieu, around 4 o'clock in the morning the Viet Cong attacked an outpost 900 yards away, killing four Vietnamese sentries.

Bullets were whipping through the compound. Practically every man here had but one thought: Get Martha into the bunker. She was literally dragged there by dozens of anxious, but not always gentle, hands. Once inside, she gave them an impromptu performance. Later they named the bunker after her.

Martha Raye's name means little to the younger generation. She's had to sell them from scratch. And she has. She needs only to say "good evening" in that familiar, big-mouthed pout of hers to convulse them. And Martha has been around long enough so that the other two members of her troupe—Ollie Harris of Chicago and Earl Colbert of Collinsville, Okla.—have their own following, too. This pleases her immensely.

"They don't just crowd around to see the big movie star," she said last night. "They come up to talk to Ollie and Earl. Big movie star. Ugh! Who am I kiddin'? Last time I did a picture, you were in diapers."

Martha has gained her place in South Viet Nam with a minimum of publicity. The cast of "Hello, Dolly!" was here and put on shows in Saigon, Bien Hoa and Nha Trang. U.S. Ambassador Henry Cabot Lodge threw a party. It is doubtful Lodge knows Martha is in the country. Not that she minds.

The other day, for instance, was to have been her day off. But she put on eight shows, the last in the little outpost of Cha La, so deep in Viet Cong country in the Ca Mau Peninsula they won't send a single chopper in there alone.

Give her as many as three lonely GI's and she puts on a show that Las Vegas and Lake Tahoe would pay big money to see. She doesn't spare herself or her companions.

The Vietnamese love her, too. At one of her shows here, the Vietnamese 21st Division commander showed up with most of his staff. Martha talked with him in excellent French. In no time she had the Vietnamese rolling in the aisles. She has done a lot to cement the relations of our two countries.

Recently she said she'd like to visit some remote outposts along the Cambodian border. Col. William Desobry of Washington, D.C., arranged to fly her to the places, including Cai Cai, the remotest of them all.

At Cai Cai she put on a 90-minute show, then sat around drinking beer with the boys for another hour. It's that way wherever she goes.

Occasionally she rates a line or two in *Stars and Stripes*, but the press at home seems to have ignored her.

"I'd like to think," says Ollie Harris, "that we are shaming the rest of Hollywood into doing something for the GI's out here, too."

NOV. 20, TAN HIEP

The wounded lay in rows along the highway near here, 25 miles south of Saigon. A Viet Cong suicide squad was still holding the south end of the airfield.

"Let's move out these casualties and then get on with our main business," said Maj. Sam Vincent of Indianola, Miss.

That "main business" for the next several hours would be to find and destroy two Viet Cong battalions which hit and over-ran Tan Hiep, the flying field for My Tho, the provincial capital.

The Vietnamese Seventh Division is headquartered at My Tho and lately it has been mauling the Viet Cong in the area. In sweep after sweep, the Division seized eight tons of enemy arms and destroyed three camouflaged arms factories.

The Viet Cong evidently decided to hit back hard. The attack began at 2 a.m., and Col. Sid Berry of Washington, D.C., Seventh Division adviser, said the two enemy battalions had been strengthened for the fight.

First they blew up all 14 trucks belonging to the 32nd Rangers and destroyed four of the five U.S. Air Force observation planes parked behind the sandbag revetments.

Every building on the field was destroyed or damaged. Then long before daylight the Viet Cong's battle with the Seventh became vicious hand-to-hand fighting.

At daylight I flew in with Lt. Col. Bill Maddox of Washington, D.C., and Maj. Wayne Dutton of Tomah, Wis., at the controls of our command chopper. We tried to land, but were waved off because the field still wasn't secure. Not until 9:30 a.m. did we come down.

It was a bloody sight. Lt. Don Crysler of Albany, N.Y., the Ranger adviser, said one mortar shot killed 12 of his men.

Our chase of the retreating Viet Cong began as soon as the wounded were moved out. But the enemy had several hours' start. I went along as the Maddox chopper took to the air again.

Capt. Bert Rice of Glendive, Mont., leader of an armed-chopper platoon, spotted a camouflaged sampan. His native observer identified it as Viet Cong. It was a good clue.

Soon our Air Force planes joined in and there were dozens of strikes. Napalm exploded with bright red flashes along the canal. Bombs came down with muffled roars. Artillery shells thumped in.

The Viet Cong broke into small groups to get away. But still they fought.

A chopper flown by Lt. Allan Pritchard of Brownwood, Tex., and WO Gordon Hall of Portsmouth, N.H., was hit. It wobbled wildly, but Pritchard managed to right his craft and come down into a paddy.

Maddox sat down beside the crippled plane and two of our crewmen leaped into the waist-deep water to help strip Pritchard's chopper of its guns, ammo and radios. Then came a medical chopper to pick up the crew, which included Pfc. Marvin Phillips of Gruetli, Tenn.

Later Captain Rice spotted a convoy of camouflaged sampans along another canal. The tide was low and two men on each side of the eight sampans were in the water, pushing the craft.

Rice's choppers swarmed in for the kill—and drew heavy fire from foxholes along the levees.

But our helicopters proved superior, and in time all eight sampans caught fire, one by one. Then they would settle in the shallow water to burn.

Apparently they were carrying dead and wounded from the night's battle.

We saw the bodies floating away from the burning boats. Some gunners along the dikes panicked and tried to run.

Maddox put his chopper into a dive and our machine-gunner, Pfc. James Shatz of Lancaster, Pa., poured it into them.

By noon all was quiet. Tan Hiep had been avenged.

NOV. 24, SOC TRANG

The first mortars crashed into this crowded helicopter base at 1:45 a.m.

Ten minutes and 25 mortar rounds later, it was over. But it was a hellish ten minutes, in which men lived a lifetime. Ten minutes that meant life would never be the same again for some who were there.

Soc Trang was asleep when the Viet Cong hit—except for those men detailed to be on watch. Always before they've hit Soc Trang prior to midnight.

Capt. Robin K. Miller of East Manchester, Ind., chief of the Thunderbird armed helicopter platoon, was in his bunk when the first mortar round crunched home.

Hurriedly Miller pulled on his trousers and, in slippers, sprinted across the runway.

As he ran, mortar fragments caught him in his side.

Bleeding, hurt, Miller managed to climb into the pilot's seat of his chopper. WO Robert Johnston of Gordonsville, Va., got in beside him. Johnston, incidently, had two helicopters shot out from under him in one day last week. He was not hurt. But some guys are just luckier than others.

As their propellers began slowly turning, shrapnel tore through the windshield. A piece of the glass caught Miller in the forehead, stunning him. This—on top of taking mortar fragments on his way across the field.

The Viet Cong continued their heavy fire. They struck hard in an area occupied by an aviation company under command of Maj. Don Elmore of Effingham, Ill.

One shell hit a latrine. Another hit a barracks. A crew chief named Cook sprinted for the door. He had celebrated his 23rd birthday earlier in the evening. Now he was hit badly in the knees.

Cook was carried to the infirmary where doctors tried to stanch the flow of blood. One medic used a pair of scissors to snip away what remained of the youth's left leg.

And Cook's blood was a rare type, not available here.

A sergeant named Clevis was hit in the head and brought into the hospital unconscious.

Miller and Johnston took their helicopter aloft. Other ships went up.

Despite his injuries, Miller began directing his helicopters, leading them to areas where the enemy was firing from. Then they would saturate the Viet Cong with rockets and tracers.

Twice Miller passed out and slumped against the shattered windshield. Then he would regain consciousness—and resume command of his platoon.

Medical choppers were brought out to fly the wounded men to Saigon. Cook, weak from loss of blood, was carried aboard one chopper, screaming: "Please, please—get me out of here."

It was the fifth time Soc Trang had been mortared. And no two attacks were alike.

NOV. 29, HOA THANH

With darkness coming on fast, Capt. Paul Yurchak of Pittston, Pa., and his battalion were pinned down.

Machine guns on both flanks poured deadly, grazing fire over their heads.

Yurchak's Vietnamese counterpart, Major Phung, had been wounded. So had his radio operator, Clifton Howard of Shreveport, La. Phung's radioman was dead.

Yurchak's voice, over the radio, was surprisingly calm.

"We cannot move," he said. "Charger will have to go without us."

Charger is the American adviser to the 42nd Rangers, Capt. Max Powers of Fayetteville, Ark. Yurchak is Stormy Two, call sign for the Second Battalion, 33rd Regiment.

This was Operation Dan Chi 182. It will be recorded, as it should be, as a victory over the Viet Cong. For two weeks we've

273

sought out the enemy's crack Ta Do battalion, knowing it was here.

This time we dropped down on top of them.

Our losses were light; eight dead and 33 wounded. As dusk closed in, counted 47 dead Viet Cong. Undoubtedly there were more. We took prisoners and picked up heavy weapons. Generals and colonels in Bac Lieu, Can Tho and Saigon were greatly heartened.

But this is the story of a story behind a victory; of the agony and suffering in the price we pay, and of the men on the ground who pay that price.

As dusk closed in, Col. Robert Spilman of Fort Worth decided on one more air strike.

"Put out your panels," he called. "We're going to let the armed ships soften them up a bit."

Captain Yurchak acknowledged.

"Remember," he cautioned, "those guns are on the dikes, in some trees and bushes. They're not on the canal."

The armed choppers, led by Capt. Robin Miller of East Manchester, Ind., swarm in, rockets blazing, machine guns spewing red tracers.

This time Yurchak's voice edges on panic.

"I said fire to the south, not to the west!" he shouted. "He's firing to the west! He's firing right into us!"

"He's not firing at you," said Spilman. "Those are shell casings."

"The hell he's not . . . Sir."

The Colonel called off the armed ships.

All day Yurchak's men fought over miles of wet paddies and muddy dikes. They were desperately low on ammunition. Two flights of helicopters were circling overhead, one prepared to fly out the wounded, the other with ammunition.

With ten minutes of daylight remaining, Col. Spilman faced an agonizing choice. Without hesitating, he made it.

"There will be no evacuation until we have resupplied," he ordered.

That meant no evacuation until morning. The wounded, including Maj. Phung and young Howard, had to lie in the wet paddies under the muzzle of enemy guns until daylight. Some might not live through the night. But other lives were involved. Without ammunition, everybody could die.

Five supply helicopters dropped their loads behind a troop of M-113 personnel carriers on the far side of the canal. It was comparatively quiet there. During the night it would be ferried across to Yurchak in sampans.

Capt. Art Littlewood of Wayne, Pa., hovered overhead in a small observation plane, relaying messages, watching for enemy movements. Flare ships kept the skies lit as night came. Badly hurt, the Viet Cong battalion was on the move, trying to slip away as it always does under the cover of darkness. Armed choppers exacted a heavy toll for the enemy's escape. We found more bodies at dawn along his escape route.

At dawn Yurchak sent his men forward, but the Viet Cong had gone. There were blood stains and pieces of men everywhere, but the enemy had vanished.

Then the choppers came down to pick up the wounded.

NOV. 30, PHUNG HIEP

The young Vietnamese soldier had been shot through the back of the head and through the face. It seemed a miracle that he was still alive aboard our medical evacuation chopper.

Jim Wright of St. Louis, a medic, asked me politely if I would hold the boy's head down "sideways." Otherwise, he explained, the soldier would choke to death. When they're shot in the head, they vomit a lot.

This youth had been conscious when he was brought aboard. He had chewed his fingers until they bled, to keep from screaming. But now he was fading, and he simply groaned and fought.

Wright and Mills Boyette of Richmond, Va., the crew chief, had strapped him down as best they could in a rolling helicopter. But he somehow managed to struggle free and try to sit up. Or he tried to turn his head, or thrashed back and forth.

For us—3000 feet above it at times—the war in Viet Nam had

resolved itself into the job of keeping this nameless youngster alive. There had been wounded men down there since just after dawn.

And we had tried several times to get in and bring them out. Maj. Arlie Price of East Lynn, W. Va., and Capt. Bob Cloke of Chicago tried the last time at 2 p.m. But a fire-fight always broke out just below us and we were driven off.

We picked this one up at 3 p.m.

"Unit having med evac (medical evacuation), throw smoke," Capt. Bob Weatherbie of Alexandria, Va., had called, but no one immediately answered.

After 10 minutes we spotted smoke and dropped down. Major Price flew an erratic pattern to avoid hostile fire.

It was touch and go whether we'd get the Vietnamese to surgery in time. We were perilously low on fuel, and wasted precious time flying to Vi Thanh for more. We'd refueled in a driving rain. Wright was busy giving the boy an injection and I fought to keep his head down. The struggle made him bleed all the more, so that when—30 minutes later—we finally got him into an ambulance at Can Tho, I walked away and was quietly, but desperately, sick myself.

This battle, just off a heavily traveled highway, had been a strange one indeed. It took a couple of hours to figure it out. First one battalion adviser and then another would accuse still-another "friendly" battalion of shooting into it. And often the other guy would plead guilty. Friendly fire is as deadly as hostile fire.

The Viet Cong obviously hadn't planned it, but it turned out they were right in the middle of us. They'd fire at one of our outfits, and our men would shoot back. A friendly outfit on the other side would receive that fire and return it with interest.

The enemy was busy shooting in all directions, and our men were bitterly denouncing each other. The air was charged with acrimony.

It stopped suddenly when someone said via the radio:

"Damn it, I'm not shooting. If you're getting fire, you're getting it from Charley." (Charley is what we usually call the Viet Cong.)

After that we knew what to do and we did it. We damn near wiped him out, one whole battalion of the enemy.

Two Virginians, Bob Johnston of Gordonsville and Howard Crotty of Princeton, had a couple of helicopters shot out from under them.

Arthur Britt of Marianna, Ark., a helicopter crew chief, was shot in the foot. The bullet lodged in the bone and he'll be sent home.

It ended well. We won. They took far more casualties than we did.

I wish I could say the kid we fought so hard to save—the boy with the head wound who bit his fingers to the bone to keep from screaming—came through, too. He didn't. He died during the night.

DEC. 3, CAN THO

The little Vietnamese fort of Cai Tau had been under attack for three days. Enemy mortars on all sides were still firing into the post.

Our medical evacuation chopper answered their call. Though we were on a mercy flight we had drawn heavy and deadly fire from automatic weapons when we came within range.

Capt. Murray Pittman of Beaufort, S.C., and Lt. Bob Cottman of Baltimore were our pilots. As soon as we landed, Medic Jim Wright of St. Louis and Crew Chief Mills Boyette of Richmond, Va., leaped out to bring the wounded aboard.

Boyette still held his machine gun ready, but what could he do against mortars?

First a dead Vietnamese soldier on a stretcher was shoved aboard. The candles at each end of his stretcher showed that he already had had the Buddhist last rites.

Another bundle, wrapped in a straw mat, was tossed on top of him. It was a nine-year-old boy. His tiny feet stuck out. The top of his head was gone. A woman and another small boy followed.

All this had taken less than a minute. It seemed like hours. We climbed back into the heavy storm clouds, glad to get away. Anything was better than Cai Tau. The town the fort once defended was gone.

The call to take out the wounded first had come to the Vietnamese Air Force (VNAF) in Can Tho. It never responded.

After two years it's a sad fact that the VNAF still won't rescue its wounded countrymen if there is the remotest possibility its planes or personnel will be shot at.

I reported this sad truth early in 1964. The Pentagon said I had insulted a gallant ally, a group of earnest beginners who were getting better every day and soon could shoulder their responsibilities. Gen. Nguyen Cao Ky, now Premier, called a press conference to denounce me.

I wrote it again early this year. The Pentagon's anticipated improvement in VNAF performance had not then materialized.

I write it again today. Not with any sense of satisfaction—I have great respect for Vietnamese fighting men—but because it should be written. There may have been an excuse for it 18 months ago. There is none in late 1965.

I do not say this is true of all VNAF pilots. Many have distinguished themselves. I know it is true of VNAF helicopter pilots in this area, however.

At 2 p.m., the VNAF rejected the mission because Cai Tau was not on their list of secure areas. Men seldom get wounded in secure areas.

At 3:30 p.m., it said it could not fly the mission because it had no fighter escort. We offered it a convoy of American armed helicopters.

After 4 p.m., it said it had engine trouble. All its helicopters were down.

This invariably happens. When all else fails, so do VNAF engines.

We left the bodies at Ca Mau. The old woman held the little boy by the hand and stood in a pouring rain. She was a pathetic sight. Her man was dead.

At 11 p.m., back in Soc Trang, another call came. A Vietnamese soldier at Binh Chau had been shot in the head by a sniper. His life hung in delicate balance. He was waiting at the airfield in Bac Lieu.

Bac Lieu is a secure field. But VNAF does not fly after dark.

Smudge pots lined the strip as Pittman and Cottman nosed down. Wright helped the stretcher aboard. En route to Can Tho, he administered blood. The man was alive when we arrived. Wright and Boyette helped put him aboard a waiting ambulance.

Parked along the runway were four VNAF helicopters.

We never saw their crews.

DEC. 6, CAN THO

The daily poop sheet out of Saigon listed Capt. Larry A. Thorne as "missing."

That was all. No other clue.

I called a friend in Saigon and he said it was true, but that he couldn't discuss it over the telephone. That made it all the more strange—and I still haven't found out what happened to Larry Thorne. (He pronounced it Torny.)

Everything about Thorne has been mysterious. That, in a way, was his appeal.

Some who knew him said Larry was a Finn.

I remember the first time we met early in 1964, at an outpost along the Cambodian border. Larry's accent was incredible. But his men loved him. They would do anything he asked. He was a leader.

Larry had fought for Finland against the Russians. When Finland lost, he fought against the Russians for the Germans. He hated Russians. He never confirmed it—Larry Thorne never confirmed the time of day—but it was rumored that he was under death sentence in his homeland; that the Finns condemned him under pressure from the Russians.

But they also said, and it wasn't hard to believe, that he went home regularly to visit his old mother. True or not, it contributed to the legend about the man.

279

Larry got out of Europe and into Argentina. Next he showed up in Mexico. Finally he appeared on the pay roster of our Army as an enlisted man. One who has known him some time recalls Larry's cleaning out a German beerhall when some drunken GI's took exception to his accent. I could believe that, too.

When the U.S. organized our Special Forces, Larry went with them. It was the natural thing for him to do and, in time, South Viet Nam was the natural place for him to be.

I've been running across Larry Thorne off and on for the past two years. He's been back to the States a couple of times, but somehow this war drew him like a magnet. He's always been glad to see me, anxious to buy us both a drink, but as close-mouthed as ever. I never tried to pump him. Maybe I remembered the story of that German beerhall.

Now the poop sheet says he's missing. I don't believe that.

Sooner or later, he'll come strolling in.

Nobody will be surprised.

And nobody will learn where he's been.

Part Four

FEBRUARY, 1966 -

Inland, back of Dong Hoi, only hours ago a Navy A-4 jet fighter from the carrier Ticonderoga was hit by two Russian SAM's (surface-to-air missiles).

Miraculously, it seemed to us listening aboard the *Ranger*, the pilot made it out into the Gulf of Tonkin and parachuted into the water just before his plane disintegrated.

He was picked up by one of our destroyers patrolling the Gulf. It was the first time the North Vietnamese used their telephone-pole missiles since we ended our 37-day bombing lull.

Also, it was the first time any of our men survived a hit by a SAM.

This was important to us in a converted prop-driven Skyraider because our job was to spy out electronic emissions along the North Vietnamese coast. We were particularly interested in SAM sites.

Now tiny puffs of white smoke appeared off the starboard from Tiger Island. But we were still 10 miles away at 10,000 feet. It was a safe bet that they were not shooting at us. Besides, this was conventional stuff.

"That bit of real estate—Tiger Island—belongs to the enemy," said Lt. Cmdr. Devon Hurd of Grover, Wyo. "We are not going any closer. That is, not unless we have to."

Tiger Island takes lots of punishment. Its defenders are jittery. It's a dot of land in the South China Sea off Cap Thuy Can, and has become a dumping ground. Planes returning with unexpended bombs and rockets have permission to dump them on Tiger Island. It would not be safe to try to land with such weapons slung beneath the plane wings.

The island's garrison by now is well dug in. But it can't be a very happy life for them.

Three days back, not expecting anything to come of it, I had asked to fly with a combat mission—any combat mission off the

Ranger. Other correspondents have made the same request of the Navy and Air Force in the past and nothing happened.

This time, unexpectedly, permission was granted to me. Rear Adm. Maurice Weisner of Knoxville, Tenn., commander of Carrier Division One, told me about it at dinner.

My jet qualification card is seven years old, so I was put aboard this electronic scouting plane.

"We fly across the Parallel to Tiger Island, then up the coast to Dong Hoi," said Hurd. "That's where any action will be. We will patrol the coast until we run so low on fuel, we will have to turn back."

I rode in front with Hurd. Lt. Freeman Ford of Pasadena, Calif., and AT3 Gary Beck of Lawrence, Kan., would ride in the rear, manning the complicated spy-detecting gear.

Beck couldn't have cared less about SAM's at the moment.

"I got another letter from a girl I don't even know," he said, waving it aloft. "I bet my mother hands out my address with change at her store."

His grin faded. "Two of them got married after they started writing me," he added soberly.

Jets went off the carrier first. One developed a rough engine and had to dump its fuel and return. Tension eased after he made a successful landing. Then it was our turn. Hurd wheeled his Skyraider onto the catapult, gunned the engine and waited for the deck officer's signal.

The big ship surged forward, anxious to reach the skies. It tucked itself together, drawing in its landing gear.

After Tiger Island, Dong Hoi appeared off portside. The city, principal marshaling point for supplies headed south, was clearly visible.

Lt. Dave Maples of Nashville, Tenn., was riding shotgun in a single-seat prop fighter. Dave had four machine guns and six rockets. We had two machine guns; everything else is thrown out to make room for radar.

Maples swooped low, looking for enemy shipping in Dong Hoi's harbor. But we were disappointed. The harbor was empty.

One by one the jets peeled off, dropping payloads on the

highway, going after bridges around the port city. Most of these are makeshift affairs by now. All the major bridges long since have been destroyed.

There's something eerie about it all. The paddies around Dong Hoi seemed peaceful. Our jets appeared out of nowhere, swooped low over the target like angry insects, then disappeared back into the clouds. But we've lost lots of men in this area in the past year. For some reason the defenders are not shooting back today.

Slowly, methodically, Hurd traced the coastline from the Parallel to Dong Hoi and back. I watched the fuel gauge, wondering when we'd head back.

Suddenly the Ranger was beneath our wing tips, plowing the South China Sea, waiting to recover her birds. One by one the jets went in, their 1100-pound grappling hooks grabbing the arresting cables.

Finally it was our turn. Hurd put the Skyraider expertly onto the deck. The canopy rolled back and blessed sea air flowed in. Minutes later other planes were taking off for another strike against North Viet Nam. That's the way it is out here.

FEB. 14, ABOARD *RANGER* IN SOUTH CHINA SEA

It is 4 a.m. The weather is marginal.

But a patrol plane has flown over North Viet Nam to check it out. The pilot reports our planes can get through. Just barely.

It has been like this for days. It'll be like this for more days.

A sleeping ship is a lot like a sleeping city. And the Ranger is a town of 4600 men. ("The biggest monastery in the world," its skipper calls it.)

A single mess hall and one of the carrier's four wardrooms—all-night eateries—are open for breakfast. A handful of flight-suited jet jockeys, scheduled for the first mission of the day, wander in.

Sometimes the men start flying at 2 a.m. Other days at 3 a.m. Today we begin at 5:30. Tomorrow we'll start at 4:15.

"We don't want them (the North Vietnamese) to start setting

their watches by us," said the Ranger's skipper, Capt Lee McCuddin of Sioux City, Ia. "They're smart.

"They build signal fires, hoping we'll go after these instead of the trucks on the highways or the bridges or the freight yards. Sometimes they fire; other times they don't. They wait for us to get careless."

In a dozen war rooms and ready rooms throughout the ship, the briefings are under way. I wait for them to finish the classified (secret) part. Then they open the door and let me in.

In one, Lt. Cmdr. John Stovall of Kermit, Tex., briefs the crews of his Skyraiders. They'll be flying Rescap (Rescue Patrols). They'll stay out over the Gulf of Tonkin, go in if there's trouble.

There'll be 14 jets and four propeller-driven planes on his mission. Stovall and his wingman, Lt. David Franz, of Castro Valley, Calif., will be up for eight hours, through five missions.

Unless they get some business up there, it'll be a long, do-nothing day. They hope they get no business.

"Use as steep a dive angle as possible," Stovall says. "We may have to go right in on the deck."

At another briefing, Lt. Cmdr. Jerry Dougherty of San Diego holds forth. His men fly Phantoms, the fastest fighters in the air. They'll be looking for traffic along the coastal highway out of Dong Hoi.

"I'll be the flight leader," he says. "Mike, you'll be the alternate."

Lt. Mike McCarthy of Oakland, Calif., nods over a cup of coffee.

Dougherty is talking about ditching procedures.

"The Phantom doesn't ditch well," he says. "Eject if you can. If you can't, hit the water with your landing gear down. That'll break some of the impact. It's the only way you'll come out with only a broken back and not a broken neck."

No one says much.

They're on their way now. From the bridge I watch them on the flight deck below. It's slippery, and only a washdown in port can clear the deck of its coating of oil.

286

All signals are by lights—red ones, green ones, purple ones, yellow ones. The catapults belch steam. Captain McCuddin speaks from the darkness, his eyes glued to the scene below.

"You couldn't photograph this," he says. "No one would believe it."

One by one his birds fly off into the morning dark. The weather is still marginal. But North Viet Nam is just over the horizon. Waiting with its signal fires, its ack-ack, its SAM's.

There's nothing to do now but wait. Slowly the big ship, the sleeping ship, stirs to life.

The air war against North Viet Nam knows no letup now.

FEB. 15, OFF NORTH VIET NAM

The waves were still cresting 12 feet high as Lt. Joe Heye's helicopter hovered above the damaged destroyer in the Gulf of Tonkin.

The night before, the Destroyer *Bass* had collided with another ship during a sea-air rescue patrol. A work crew from an accompanying oiler had been transferred to the Bass to help keep it afloat.

Now it was dawn, and Heye—who studied eight years for the priesthood before winding up as a helicopter pilot—was ready to take the work crew back to its own ship.

"It was a rougher sea than I've ever seen in my life," recalls Heye, whose home is in Olympia, Wash. "The rear deck of the Bass was pitching so much that the doctor decided not to risk transferring two stretcher cases. I'm thankful for that."

One by one, however, 11 other crewmen from the Oiler *Navasota* were hoisted aboard the chopper in a helicopter sling. And Heye set off to complete his mercy mission.

But 40 feet up and 40 feet from the Bass, his helicopter went out of control.

"In two seconds we made two complete turns," he said. "I hit the water in as level a position as possible. I shut off my motor immediately. Otherwise, we'd have gone down. The chopper turned over and I went out the window."

His co-pilot, Lt. Dan Bathold of Seattle, Wash., went out the other window.

"The waves were so high, we couldn't keep everyone in sight," Heye said. "You'd see a man on top of a wave and then he'd disappear into a trough.

"Three men were lost, and I don't know what happened to them. But without Kelly, we'd have lost more."

First Crewman J. E. Kelley of Kennewick, Wash., gathered the eight survivors around the still floating helicopter and made them "hang on to the tail wheel" until they were plucked out of the sea 25 minutes later.

One man lost his life vest, Heye said. But Kelley took care of that. He simply held the man's head above water until help came.

"That boy deserves a medal," said Heye.

The two fliers and the 11 seamen were picked up by another helicopter from the nearby Destroyer *England*.

Meanwhile, 60 miles away aboard the Carrier Ranger, Lt. Cmdr. Richard MacDonald of Lexington Park, Md., had heard of the accident. He set out in another helicopter for the scene. By the time he got there, he found nothing.

MacDonald then decided to complete the transfer of the seamen to their oiler. He took five of the men off the England and started for the Navasota.

"I was beginning my approach when, with no warning, we got a loud bang in the tail assembly and the whole aircraft began to shake," said MacDonald.

"At this point I still had full control. But rivets were popping, and I had to put down in the water. I kept my rotors turning for stability, so we didn't turn over."

Quite understandably, the five survivors of the previous accident panicked. They threatened to leap from the stricken helicopter as it shuddered 30 feet above the waves.

But, MacDonald said, they were prevented from jumping by Crew Leader John T. Baker of Kershaw, S.C., and Petty Officer J. R. DeJong of Academy, S.D.

Baker and DeJong held the terror-stricken sailors back until the helicopter splashed into the sea. Then they inflated a life raft and set the men adrift.

"I never saw men paddle so fast," MacDonald said.

Eventually all were picked up by the Navasota.

The Navy has begun an investigation to determine why the two Sikorsky Seaking helicopters crashed within hours of each other Feb. 5.

"As an old helicopter pilot, I'm convinced it was materiel failure," said MacDonald. "It couldn't be anything else."

But the Navy is withholding judgment. Meanwhile, the Seakings continue patrolling the Gulf of Tonkin, looking for other men to rescue.

FEB. 16, ABOARD CARRIER *RANGER* OFF NORTH VIET NAM

The Old Man is always alone. The final decisions are his.

Aboard the Ranger, the Old Man is Rear Adm. Maurice Weisner of Knoxville, Tenn., Commander of Carrier Division One.

Two of his big ships, the *Ranger* and the *Ticonderoga*, are on Yankee Station, off the coast of North Viet Nam. A third, the *Enterprise*, is on Dixie Station, farther south. The ships occasionally rotate. When they do, the Old Man shifts his flag. He stays permanently on Yankee Station.

It is 3 p.m., and one of his men—an A-4 jet pilot off the Tico— is in trouble.

The Old Man, with his staff, sits in his war room, listening, waiting, issuing orders.

Hit over Vinh, the youngster in the A-4 plane had tried to make it to the Gulf of Tonkin. There our destroyers would pick him up. Two miles from the coast, his aircraft burst into flames and crashed. The pilot ejected and his parachute opened. He landed in a shallow coastal stream.

A circling wingman reports he's alive. They have radio contact. The downed pilot says he's all right except for a broken arm.

"Get a SAR chopper (Sea-Air-Rescue helicopter) in there fast," the Old Man says.

289

"On the way, sir."

"Is he married?"

"Yes, sir."

"Family?"

"Yes, sir."

The Old Man closes his eyes and makes a pyramid with his fingertips.

Now the wingman reports a sampan is moving in. The pilot's parachute is a dead giveaway. He has waded to the far bank and disappeared into brush.

It is silent in the Ranger's war room as we get the word from hovering aircraft.

The pilot is seen coming out in a small clearing. Immediately he is surrounded. Some of those around him are in uniform. A rescue chopper moves in, but is driven off by gunfire. A second chopper tries. It comes out with six holes.

The kid is still down there.

"How many planes in the air?" asks the Old Man.

"Fourteen, sir."

"Get them over there."

They swarm in, firing their rockets and machine guns, careful to avoid hitting the downed pilot, trying desperately to create enough confusion so he can be rescued. Their ammo gone, some even drop their wing tanks. Planes are being launched off the Ranger and we're 90 miles out to sea.

A chopper moves in and is driven off.

Now the enemy troops are leading him away. We can't stop them. Another 15 minutes, and he's out of sight.

"Just like that," someone says.

The Old Man closes his eyes. There'll be other strikes this afternoon and throughout the night. In the air war against North Viet Nam there is no letup. He'll monitor those, too.

There are guests for dinner. The Old Man is an equable host. But he has no appetite.

"Thank you, steward," he says. "I'll just have a cup of tea."

After dinner, as always, there will be a movie in the Admiral's mess. It's billed as a comedy.

"If you gentlemen will excuse me—" the Old Man says and walks to his war room.

The man at the top is always alone.

FEB. 21, TRA VINH

The edge of a mangrove swamp is an awful place to die. But our young men are dying down there.

For two hours we have circled overhead helplessly, waiting for a signal to go in and bring them out. Minute by minute, we have watched the fuel gauge go down. Our tanks were full when we set out. But now if we don't go in soon, we'll have to turn back.

And young men are dying down there along the edge of a mangrove swamp. . .

"I have wounded," an American on the ground reports for the 12th time. "Some are critical. If you don't take them out soon, you needn't bother. I'll have dead men."

"We're working on it," our pilot replied. "As soon as we silence that machine gun we'll come in."

The machine gun is firing directly into the clearing where we'll have to land. Our jets and armed helicopters have been trying for two hours to knock it out. They've come close, but the guy is still there, still firing.

He must know that sooner or later we'll get him; that this is his last day on earth. But he knows too that he'll live longer by staying where he is. If he breaks and runs, he's a goner.

"If you can get that hootch (house) next to where you dropped the napalm," says the man on the ground, "you'll get a machine gun nest and 15 to 20 people. They're firing at you every time you come across."

"I'm doing my best," our pilot replies, "but we're just about out of ordnance up here."

"And I've got wounded down here!"

It's now or never. Lt. Col. Bill Maddox of Washington, D.C., put his helicopter into a steep dive, ducking behind trees and dunes. Three other helicopters follow. Maj. George Patterson of Atlanta, Ga., helps with the controls.

On the ground, Privates Jim Schatz of New Lancaster, Pa., and Dick Parrish of Peabody, Mass., toss out the ammunition we've brought in.

Then they gather the wounded. A machine gun chatters. But jets and armed choppers swarm in again, blasting the hut where the fire comes from. Rockets, napalm tear into the earth a few hundred yards away. The hootch catches fire and burns briskly.

Hurriedly the wounded are brought aboard. A boy with a bloody back-wound screams in pain. A kid with a shattered stump of a leg winces.

There are dead, too. But we leave them. They're beyond help.

The enemy's machine gun is silent as we take off. Maybe somebody finally got it.

The radio is on as we head back to Tra Vinh.

"Where I put that red smoke, requests an air strike," says an American adviser on the ground.

"I'll be dropping 1000-pounders," a Navy pilot overhead replies. "Are you at least a click [one kilometer] away?"

"I sure will be!"

Then: "Got anything smaller?"

"I have rockets, but they wouldn't be too effective."

The Navy pilot unloads his blockbusters, blasting huts and trees where the Communist Viet Cong are hiding.

"They're running toward the mangroves!" an American voice yells. "They're out in the open!"

Planes and armed Huey choppers swoop down on their prey. Now other men are dying. But they are the enemy.

Closer to Tra Vinh, other armed choppers swoop over a small canal. Their rockets blast a couple of sampans out of the water. This is Viet Cong country; anything back here is fair game.

It's dusk now. Our wounded have been evacuated. The battle is almost over. The enemy, what's left of him, is nearing his mangrove hideout. There he'll be safe for a while.

Someone says we've counted 77 dead Viet Cong so far.

"You can add two more," says Capt. George O'Grady of

Tacoma, Wash., an armed Huey leader. "They just ran out of a hut. One was foolish enough to carry his weapon. That was good enough for me. I shot them."

FEB. 22, AN CHOU THOI

It's war when they start shooting at you.

It's not war in Saigon—despite an occasional bomb outrage—where they have air conditioning, taxis, pizzas and bar hostesses. It's not war in Can Tho or Soc Trang where there are electric lights, fans and hot showers. It's not war in An Hiep, where we have our command post in the cool shade and Staff Sgt. Theodore Synowka of Sewickley, Pa., puts together a hot meal.

War is An Chou Thoi. What's left of it. The hamlet is on fire.

The Viet Cong were waiting for us. Fighters swarmed in right after daybreak to strafe, to bomb and to drop flaming napalm. Armed choppers followed with rockets. The Reds were dug in; a few got it, but most simply waited, knowing what was sure to follow.

Their machine guns opened up from foxholes 30 yards away the moment Lt. Gary Nelson of Clarinda, Ia., and WO Bill Ashley of Tacoma, Wash., touched down in an unarmed Huey. Our men hardly had time to insert their ammo clips. One was hit before he was out of Gary's helicopter. He fell back and was flown out. The battle of An Chou Thoi was over quickly for him.

Nearby, Lt. Sam Cannella, a Floridian, was hit in the leg when machine guns raked his chopper. It wobbled crazily and almost went out of control. Then he righted it and flew away without discharging his soldiers.

WO Dean Moorehouse's sleek Huey was hit through its plexiglass nose bubble. The rounds knocked out his compass and his radio. Dean, from Minot, N.D., said later stuff was "flying all over the cockpit." All we heard was, "I'm hit!" Then silence. We didn't know until later he'd made it back.

WO Bill Koshar of Pleasant Unity, Pa., had his chopper shot

up on his 21st birthday. His co-pilot, Pat McCullagh of County Tyrone, Ireland, was hit. McCullagh had 21 days left in Viet Nam.

A Huey irreverently dubbed "The Brat," flown by WO's Newton Pennington of Victoria, Tex., and Bailey Basinger of Pomona, Calif., got it worst. It limped back looking like a sieve. Miraculously, no one was hurt. And our men all fought back. Gerald Baltz of Orlando, Fla., door gunner, killed four Cong in the landing zone. Everybody saw them fall.

As battles go, it wasn't much. American advisers in the Mekong Delta are bitter these days; they say theirs is the forgotten war. Altogether we killed 112 Viet Cong. Our losses will be described in Saigon, 48 hours after the event, as light." They aren't "light" to those who get hit.

The Viet Cong were firing from the burning hamlet and the nearby trees. The villagers, as usual, had cleared out. They have their own grapevine.

Our little Vietnamese troopers have guts. They keep pushing ahead, running, dropping, getting up and running again. And always they're firing.

Others drop and don't get up again. Medics drag them back. Now the mortar shells come. They drop in unannounced, whoomping as they hit, tearing the soft earth.

Still the little guys push ahead.

Lt. Manuel Domingos of Gloucester, Mass., American adviser to the 11th Recon Company in the first wave, is on the radio.

"We're getting fire from a tree line to my front, a tree line to my right and a tree line to my left," he says. He seems amazingly calm.

More helicopters swarm in. But now they have an easier time. The Viet Cong are being driven back, and the landing zone—a wet paddy on the rim of a mangrove swamp—is relatively secure. Capt. Sherrill Brown of Wilkinsburg, Pa., is down on the ground now with his battalion. This is Brown's first operation and his voice cracks with the excitement.

We push ahead, nudging them out of the burning houses. We can see them running to new positions. Some apparently had been lying in the fields, waiting for us. They still wear their rice-straw camouflaged capes and hats. Others wear black pajamas.

Slowly we push them back. We have airpower, they don't. But as they retreat, they still shoot at us. A mortar crashes nearby and a man screams in hopeless agony. His screams gradually become a gurgle. Then he is quiet.

But the guns aren't. It's war as long as men shoot at each other.

FEB. 23, VI THANH

The loudspeaker on the side of the little Cessna plane could hardly be heard inside the cockpit. But we knew what it was saying:

"You! Viet Cong hiding behind that tree! We see you! Come out and surrender."

The answer was not long coming. A bullet plunked into the little plane's tail. This was not the first time it had been hit; it has patches on both sides. Air Force Capt. Robert C. Bogue of Portland, Ore., went for more altitude.

"You turn that speaker on," he said, "and every VC behind every tree for 10 miles really thinks you see him. They come out shooting."

This is a propaganda mission and some say nothing is more important. Speaker craft accompany every military drive. They usually fly over a battlefield days ahead, warning civilians to move out. I carried the little tape-recorder in my lap, turning it on and off at Bob Bogue's direction. The message was a few seconds long; the tape kept repeating itself.

We had landed at Vi Thanh soon after noon and Bogue had talked over his mission with Lt. Jim Oller of Cincinnati, the psy-war officer for Chung Thien Province. Chung Thien is one of the country's most heavily infested. There are Viet Cong everywhere. A couple of weeks ago they shot down a small plane carrying the Chung Thien province chief. The wreckage still lies there in the rice paddies a few hundred yards off the runway.

Oller had circled two areas on his map. One was the battlefield. The other was the Twin River area, an enemy stronghold.

Oller also had 70,000 leaflets. My job was to toss them out. There's science and technique in this. I sit on the right side of the cockpit, but toss them out with my left hand. Somehow, the wind is more apt to throw my right hand against the window. I forgot once and drew back bleeding knuckles.

One green pamphlet to be dropped over Twin Rivers simply warned the people to scram, that a battle soon would be fought there.

For emphasis, it included a sketch of a big bomb.

Others played on the homesickness of Viet Cong. It urged them to go home now that spring was here and the old folks needed them.

"Dear Countrymen," another read. "Having encountered heavy defeats, the Viet Cong in South Viet Nam are resorting to sabotage with the view of saving, to some extent, their lost prestige. The arrival of our troops is to assist you in fighting the Communist aggressors. Please don't listen to the distorting propaganda of the Viet Cong."

The pamphlets had floated earthward and the tape had played through twice. Navy and Air Force jets came in to strafe their targets. Their bombs set fires. Now a flight of sleek Huey helicopters brought in combat troops. We watched them dismount in the paddies below. Bob Bogue headed home to his base.

How much good does all this do?

There is some evidence it is quite effective. Viet Cong, in increasing numbers, have come in carrying safe-conduct passes dropped by our planes. Many Americans and Vietnamese are convinced propaganda missions are responsible for most of the enemy's desertions.

Bogue frankly doesn't know. He can only guess.

"Just once, I wish someone would give us a reading, show us this man surrendered because we did this thing at this time," he says. "But maybe that's too much to expect. So you just keep plugging."

FEB. 2, THOI HOA

We just landed in the middle of an inferno.

Vietnamese Air Force Lt. Nguyen Van Truong put his helicopter down in a small clearing. It had been cleared mainly by artillery and bombs. So the big H-34 simply came straight down. I'd never done that before. I realized I was holding my breath.

Thoi Hoa is 17 miles across the river from Can Tho. But it is another world. For six days we have tried to get in. For six days, we have been driven off.

The Viet Cong have tunneled into the schoolhouse. They know we won't bomb that. It's the only one in the district; its destruction would be a real propaganda victory for them. So they've turned it into a machine-gun nest. The kids and teachers stay home.

That's why Truong and his co-pilot, Lt. Buu Ngo, landed on the outskirts. For we had to get in. A kid named Pham Van De was there with a gaping hole in his stomach; a couple of hours could mean life or death.

Sgt. Vo Hon Cong spots Viet Cong in a cocoanut grove 40 yards away. He fires. They shoot back with .30-caliber. Sergeant Bao, the medic, and I have taken up positions on the other side within the helicopter. Our weapons are pointed out the windows. But there are friendly troops on our side, running, dropping, sloshing through a muddy canal to set up a perimeter defense. We might shoot into them.

There's a search-kill operation in the area. We flew over the armored cars while we circled. Capt. Gary Graves of Salem, Ind., is with them. One hit a mine at dawn; nine men were wounded. Vietnamese Skyraiders have plastered the area for an hour. Col. Stanley Irons of Oklahoma City, and Maj. Bud Richardson of Haddonfield, N.J., are up there now. They're still at it.

They bring the wounded boy out on a rough plank. He's

297

shoved aboard our chopper. A medic comes with him. Truong guns his rotors and we lift slowly. A mortar crunches into the earth where we had been. The craft trembles violently, but the pilots hold her steady. Slowly, we arch out of range.

❖   ❖   ❖

This is a story I am glad to write. I have been sharply critical of the Vietnamese Air Force (VNAF). I have accused it of refusing to pick up its own wounded. My last story was printed after I went home for Christmas. It caused quite a flap. Colonel Irons let me read his file.

"Reporter Lucas," one general wrote, "has a known anti-Air Force, anti-VNAF bias."

Irons invited me to "see for yourself," to fly with VNAF as long and as often as I wished. I accepted.

"I'd like to be able to eat my words," I told him. "God knows I'm not anti-Vietnamese."

VNAF pilots and their U.S. Air Force advisers tried hard to be polite, even cordial. It wasn't easy. They knew who I was. They'd read what I'd written. I was the guy who wrote, in effect, they were cowards. At first, I didn't feel exactly at home.

Whether or not my stories were responsible, I found considerable improvement. Two weeks ago a new group of chopper pilots, under Capt. Nguyen Van Hiep, came in from Bien Hoa. They now fly at night. The number of dead and wounded picked up in the Delta jumped from 97 in November to 407 in December. This was up to 487 in January, another slight increase.

❖   ❖   ❖

It was 9 p.m. when Captain Hiep and Lt. Lam Van Thanh walked briskly to their H-34. This was their first night-rescue mission. I went along. Sgts. Nguyen Van Thanh was the crew chief, and Nguyen Van Xa the medic. We flew to Vi Thanh in a heavily infested enemy area. There had been heavy fighting all day. Hiep put his chopper down beside a flare marker on the battlefield. Quickly five casualties came aboard. Two were stretcher cases. Their families flew out in a helicopter flown by VNAF lieutenants. It was a thoroughly professional job. And a breakthrough. Hiep, who flew for the French against the Viet Minh and later in Morocco, was elated.

The next morning, I flew with Lts. Truong and Ngo to the little outpost of Nghia Quan. A family of 10 was loaded aboard. They ranged from a nursing baby to an aged grandmother. All had been wounded, apparently by a mortar. One young girl was on a stretcher with a bad back wound. A child of four or five had a badly mangled leg. Again, the evacuation was accomplished without a hitch.

All day long it went that way. With a limited number of helicopters, the VNAF often ran behind, but it never quit working.

U.S. Air Force pilots are loyal to their Vietnamese colleagues. They believe they have been misunderstood and misrepresented not only by the press but by the Army.

"I am proud of these men," Colonel Irons says.

"One thing about flying with the Vietnamese, you get close to the war," said Maj. Robert Bennett of Lyons, Mich.

Bennett says the VNAF has removed armor plating and machine guns because this reduces the load by 800 pounds and lets them haul more patients. (Machine guns were put back for the trip to Thoi Hoa.)

I found too, that the VNAF has problems of which I was unaware. It has neither the maintenance capability nor the equipment to match ours. Of its 16 choppers, rarely are more than five flyable at one time.

I told Stanley Irons I thought he'd be happy with the next story I wrote about the VNAF—this one.

FEB. 28, BINH THUY

Capt. Nguyen Van Truong pushed a button and two 1000-pound bombs tumbled into the trees beneath his Skyraider's wingtips.

Moments later, they exploded, shaking his single-engine aircraft as it pulled out. Truong climbed back up to 3000 feet and prepared to make another run on the hamlet of Hoa Thuan. Another Vietnamese Air Force (VNAF) dive-bomber, piloted by

Capt. Nguyen Kim was already in its dive. Skyraiders flown by Lts. Nguyen Thanh Tri and Nguyen Van Xuan circled, awaiting their turns.

In the paddies below, elements of the 21st Division were searching for Viet Cong who had crept out of the U-Minh forest and occupied a number of hamlets. Hoa Thuan was one of those. Villagers had fled, and their homes had become enemy hideouts.

Captain Truong had flown low over our lumbering M-113 armored personnel carriers as they maneuvered through the paddies. They'd called back that anything in front of their position was a legitimate target.

These were not American imperialists bombing and strafing a helpless people. These were loyal Vietnamese bombing their own, destroying Vietnamese villages and hamlets to put down a rebellion against their government.

Truong, 30, studied at Saigon University to become a professor of government. He may yet realize that ambition; he wants, more than anything else, to teach. For the past six years, however, he has been a fighter pilot. He took his advanced training at Randolph Air Force Base in Texas.

Kim always wanted to be a commercial airline pilot; he came to the VNAF when war enveloped his country. Tri and Xuan are younger men, mere kids. Tri, from a wealthy Saigon family, went to flight school directly out of high school.

Hoa Thuan is enveloped by smoke now, and Truong has difficulty keeping his target in sight. The smoke rises up to meet his plane at 2500 feet as he circles for another run. He dives again and this time drops 100-pound white-phosphorous bombs. The phosphorous is almost impossible to extinguish. It clings to human flesh. It hugs the ground, seeping into the Viet Cong's holes and incinerating them.

Run after run the VNAF pilots make, until their bombs are gone. Then they open up with their machine guns, diving through the choking, mushrooming smoke, their wings spewing death.

Truong levels off and circles his target. The hamlets below

are in flames. Armored personnel carriers, with their troops, move in, guns barking. In the distance I see infantry troops following on the tracks of the lumbering cars.

We've been out an hour and this was to have been a two-hour flight. But our bombs and ammo are expended. Truong calls his base at Binh Thuy and gets permission to come in.

One by one the Skyraiders land at Binh Thuy.

In the ready room, Lieutenant Tri, the irrepressible, chortles.

"Twenty houses destroyed, three damaged, that's the count," he says. "Not bad."

Captain Kim, the flight leader, is not impressed. He eyes the youngsters balefully.

"Lousy mission," he grunts. "Lousy."

MARCH 2, AP BAC

It is 9:15 a.m., and one of our helicopters is going down.

A hit through the drive shaft at 1100 feet spun it out of control. Its tail rotor is gone. The craft has seven Vietnamese and four Americans aboard.

Warrant Officer Ed (Pappy) Reissinger, of Unalakleet, Alaska, and WO Larry Robinson of Sacramento, Calif., are flying this chopper—No. 12.

"Going down!" Pappy said, and there was surprise and anger in his voice. Surprise that his helicopter was capable of anything so unairworthy, anger that it should happen to an old-timer like him. At 42, you're an old man in this game, and Pappy is 42.

Lt. Carl Milko of Olmsted Falls, Ohio, saw what happened. Carl is flying the chopper which was directly behind Pappy. He saw the tail blade fly off and disappear beneath his own helicopter's steady nose.

Mike Masten of Cass Lake, Minn., also saw it. Mike is gunner in a chopper flown by Capt. Bobby Briggs of Hot Springs, Ark., and WO Billy Campbell of Jamestown, Tenn. For a moment, it looked to Masten as if Pappy could keep his ship under control. Then he lost sight of it and was too busy shooting at Viet Cong

301

within the landing zone to be sure of what really was occurring.

Losing his tail rotor is something every chopper man has nightmares about. It doesn't happen often. When it does, everyone instinctively knows what to do.

Carl Milko moved into Pappy's hole in the formation. Capt. Connie D. (Doug) Eady of Graham, Tex., and WO Mike Reithofer of Oak Lawn, Ill., his wingman, broke formation and followed him down. So did Lt. Col. Bill Maddox of Washington, D.C., and Lt. Wes Van Loon of Minneapolis in the control ship.

The others yell at Pappy to increase his air speed. If he can do that maybe he can float her down. As if Pappy Reissinger doesn't know! Yelling is simply a way to let him know they're with him.

The ship finally comes down along a small canal back of Ap Bac. This is hot country. In an ambush there three weeks ago we lost 76 men, with 100 wounded.

Doug Eady and Mike Reithofer follow Pappy in. Maddox is just behind. Pappy's helicopter is on fire. Most of the men have been thrown clear.

John Beliochio of New York City, and David Amason, Seadrift, Tex., Eady's crewmen, pull others from the flames. Beliochio and Amason recently pulled men from another burning wreckage at An Khe, home of the First Cavalry Division. Last week they were decorated with Soldiers' Medals. They'll be in line for another after this.

One Vietnamese soldier is dead, apparently from the concussion on landing. Others seem to be hurt internally. There is blood everywhere. The two pilots have hurt backs. Pappy was thrown forward and is spitting blood. Mike is trying to shout something, but he's incoherent. It's impossible to make it out. Sgt. Isaac Stuart of Dallas, Tex., the gunner, has a broken leg. Paul Martin of Newark, N.J., the crew chief, has a bloody nose.

Survivors and soldiers who had come in with Doug Eady fan out in a defensive position. More choppers come in. Armed helicopters and fighters circle overhead. Old No. 12 burns briskly. Mortars and machine-gun ammunition are on board. A mortar explodes and hurls itself skyward. Then another. And another.

Machine-gun ammunition pops like firecrackers. Some instinctively take cover. Others don't.

Pappy and Mike are loaded on Eady's helicopter and started to the hospital in Saigon. Pappy had about 60 days left in Viet Nam. Stuart and Martin go out on another. Wounded Vietnamese are loaded on others. Old No. 12 is smoldering now. All that's left is her nose cone and the outline of a helicopter in ashes.

We have two stretchers left, and they put the dead man on one. Bill Maddox says to take him off.

"The dead can wait," he says gruffly.

MARCH 8, IN A B-57 NIGHT INTRUDER OVER VIET NAM

Air Force Lt. Col. Dan Farr of Los Angeles puts his fighter-bomber into a steep dive.

The jungles rush up to meet us.

Here the Ho Chi Minh Trail snakes out of Laos, crossing the high ridge which marks the border, disappearing over the horizon into country that is all Viet Cong. Only occasionally does it show beneath the lush green of the mountains behind Da Nang, 12 minutes away by jet. That trail below is the Communists' lifeline, their main infiltration route. Without it there would be no war. Over it, daily in increasing volume, come the men and the supplies which keep the Viet Cong going.

Crossing out of Laos, it comes down the A Shau-A Luoi valley directly beneath us. In that valley 15 miles long, we have three Special Forces camps. For months it was touch-and-go whether we could hold them. Even now, though air strips have been carved from the jungle, they are difficult to defend. Each has been overrun. Each has taken casualties. They are frequently under fire.

Our present job is to protect three lumbering C-130's on a defoliation mission. The jungles on the rims of the triangular-shaped fortress astraddle the trail at A Shau have been sprayed with growth-killing chemicals for 800 yards in all directions. We intend to extend that to 2700 yards, to give its defenders a better field of fire and eliminate, if possible, the nightly threat of infiltration.

There's always trouble in this valley, Farr says. But they're less apt to get nasty if there are jets overhead. If they do, we'll take them on. If they don't, we'll drop our bombs, fire our guns in the foot hills along the coast. There, we suspect, the Communists are moving down to cut Route One, the Street Without Joy, between Hue and Da Nang. There were 17 cuts on the rail line between the two cities in February.

Our briefings had been terse, businesslike. Maj. Henry Bussell, of Seagoville, Tex., described our ordnance load. Sgt. John Mann of Lincoln, Neb., said the weather was marginal; with luck, we should find holes in the cloud cover. Lt. Bill Wilson, Philadelphia, told what he knew about the enemy's disposition, his strength and his weapons.

The transports with their outsized spray guns take off first. Capt. Dick Peshkin of Great Neck, N.Y., is in the lead. Capt. Joe Chalk of Tulsa, follows; then Capt. Paul Mitchell of Florence, Ala.

We follow. Air Force Maj. Lyle (Chuck) Palmer of Manitou Springs, Colo., and Capt. Wilbur Wright of Doylestown, Pa., are in the first ship. (That's his name, Wilbur Wright. And he has a brother, Orville, a helicopter pilot at the Naval Air Station at Patuxent, Md.) Dan Farr and I are in the second plane.

"We'll give you a call if we need you," Dick Peshkin said as he was airborne. And now he needs us. His voice just came over the air.

"We've taken hits from that hill with the clearing on it."

"Rolling in!" Farr answers.

We roll in. The Ho Chi Minh Trail comes up to meet us. Farr held his ship steady until I was sure we'd crash. He pulls out finally. Two 500-pound bombs drop into the jungle. They explode and smoke rises above the lush greenery. Now we're in the clouds, and mountains are on all sides.

The defoliation continues with the bombing. An Army Caribou lands at A Shau, discharges cargo. The C-130's finish their spraying and head home.

But Farr and Palmer still have ordnance. An Air Force Forward Air Controller (FAC) in a spotter plane out of Hue leads us to the Lang Ngai Valley, over the next ridge. There he has spotted people on the move. There are camouflaged structures beneath the trees. And this is a free-bomb zone; anything in it is hostile.

Again and again—23 times in all—we swoop down, bombing, shooting. Finally our bombs are gone, our guns silent. The FAC drops down to inspect. The jungles keep their secret. But the trail still echoes to the sounds of war.

Out on the Ho Chi Minh Trail tonight there undoubtedly will be trouble.

MARCH 14, HUE

The American Special Forces camp commander at A Shau said today many of its Vietnamese defenders were "Viet Cong" and turned their guns on his men.

A Shau was the outpost 51 miles north of Da Nang along the Ho Chi Minh Trail and only a few miles from the Laotian border. It was the place overrun last week by a large enemy force.

Evacuation of A Shau began Thursday but was not completed until Saturday. The post commander, Capt. John D. Blair IV of Atlanta, was one of the three last Americans to be flown out by Marine helicopter. He spent more than 36 hours dodging the Viet Cong in nearby jungles.

Blair was near tears and his voice was emotion-choked as he stepped from the rescue chopper at Phu Ba Air Base near here.

"A handful of Americans and Nungs made a last-ditch stand on the north wall of the fort," he said bitterly. (The Nungs are Vietnam-born Chinese. They are mercenaries, but Americans rate them top-notch fighters. The Nungs generally have little use for the Vietnamese.)

"But the CIDG were really Viet Cong," Blair charged.

(The CIDG—Civilian Indigenous Defense Group—are the Vietnamese Special Forces. These are Vietnamese who also work under contract. They can quit when they want to, and refuse orders they don't want to obey.)

A Shau was manned by several hundred CIDG and Nungs. It had 19 American Special Forces men. Twelve were rescued, many wounded. Blair said none was left in camp at noon Saturday.

There were only Nungs on the helicopter which brought out Blair and two other Americans. One Marine officer quoted Blair —I did not hear Blair make the statement—as saying there could be as many as 30 CIDG still loose in the jungle, but he did not recommend risking more lives to rescue them.

A Special Forces liaison officer who met Blair tried to pacify him. At an earlier press conference attended by top Special Forces officers in Da Nang, an enlisted survivor flown out earlier dutifully contended that both the Nungs and the CIDG fought bravely at A Shau.

Blair was too emotional to be calmed. "The 141st Company (a Vietnamese unit at A Shau) abandoned the south wall," he said loudly. "The unit went over to the Viet Cong and turned their guns on us. If I could get my hands on that Chung Wei (a lieutenant), I'd kill him!"

Blair's charges were supported by two Americans who came out of the jungle with him on the last helicopter out of A Shau.

"The CIDG laid down and died," said Sgt. Minter Hoover of Fayetteville, N.C. "It looked like they wanted to die."

Lt. Louis Mari of Folsom, Pa., also said the CIDG "went Viet Cong."

Told by a Marine crewman of a group of survivors he picked up, Mari said: "That's the company that abandoned the south wall. It went Viet Cong. We didn't think we would ever get out of there. We distributed them everything we had, before we realized what they were."

Marines and our Special Forces were forced to shoot some CIDG during the two-day evacuation so helicopters could get off the ground. One Marine said terrorized CIDG climbed aboard every aircraft that landed, clung to landing gear and tail sections and refused to be dislodged. The choppers were so heavily loaded they couldn't take off. At least two crashed trying to get airborne.

Marines said interpreters, flown in to assure CIDG all would get out, warned that no one could be rescued unless discipline was maintained. But this did no good.

As a last resort, orders were issued to shoot to kill.

One Marine said it was "either shoot them or join them."

One Nung survivor said A Shau's attackers were commanded by Chinese-speaking officers. Nungs understand and speak Chinese as well as Vietnamese. The survivor said he was able to anticipate Communist strategy because attackers apparently were unaware anyone present understood Chinese. On several occasions he learned of the plans to attack specific points and relayed this information to Blair and Capt. Tennis Carter, the Nung adviser.

In an earlier press conference at Da Nang, Sgt. Wayne Murray of Saginaw, Mich., said some attackers wore camouflaged jungle suits like those of the CIDG. Murray said it was impossible to tell friend from foe.

Murray, who was wounded three times, said he met three men in jungle dress near the ruined American team house during the peak of battle.

"I yelled, 'Nung?' and they shot at me.

"I shot back."

MARCH 15, PHU BAI

He doesn't look the part—The Skipper.

He's average-sized, with an unobtrusive way and a quizzical half-smile. But after A Shau fell last week, Marine Lt. Col. Charles A. House, 45, of Burlington, Ia., led 40-odd men three miles through a jungle night to high ground where they could defend themselves and be picked up by helicopters.

He saved their lives.

The Skipper is a Marine aviator. He flew B-52's off Midway and hunted submarines off Okinawa in World War II. He flew

307

fighter planes over the Pusan perimeter, over Inchon and the Chosen Reservoir in the Korean War.

He now commands a helicopter squadron in Viet Nam.

When the desperate decision was made to pull out of A Shau, The Skipper flew the first ship into that besieged outpost. He couldn't fly out. One of his crewmen who raced toward a nearby bunker was gunned down. The enemy held that bunker.

Later The Skipper got away, but we didn't know it at the time. Back in Da Nang, we wrote him off as gone. By that time A Shau's survivors who were not too seriously injured had gone over the wall into the jungle.

The Skipper joined up with them. There were Americans, Vietnamese and Nungs in the party.

The Skipper and our Special Forces officers with him were physically and emotionally exhausted after their ordeal. But Colonel House knew that the green beret was the only symbol of authority their Nungs would respect. So he borrowed a green beret and wore it. Then he took command.

House led his party through the jungle, up hill and down valley. Many men were wounded; the jungle was thick and the going slow. They stopped often to rest. When they reached a stream, House waded down into the water to throw pursuers off the trail.

At dawn he reached a small clearing. Three miles of jungle now lay between his party and the Viet Cong in A Shau. So House and his men took time to clear a landing pad.

Soon helicopters came in. The Skipper was one of the last to go out.

Now he is back here at Phu Bai where he started directing the last hours of the big rescue feat.

Seven teams were under his command. Maj. Lee Blankenship of Seattle and Lt. Ed Ressler of Bellmore, N.Y., were in the lead ship; Capts. Jay Davis of Molino, Fla., and Frank Walker of Blacksburg, Va., were in the second; Maj. Wyman Blakeman of Garden Grove, Calif., and Lt. Earl Bufton of Chicago were in the third; Capt. Wilbur (Mick) McMinn of Little Rock, Ark., and Lt. Sid Eilerston of Pensacola, Fla., were in the fourth.

The three additional teams comprised: Capt. Larry Polk of Greenville, Mo., and Lt. Denny Ferguson of Ames, Ia.; Lts. Don Byrnes of Chicago and Bob Morgan of Matthew, Va.; Capt. Tom Cowper of Schenectady, N.Y., and Lt. Don Farabough of Jamaica, N.Y.

When the Colonel got the order to send out this mission he figured he would lose half of his men and aircraft. His boss, Brig. Gen. Marion Carl, estimated losses would be one-fourth. The General was nearer the mark.

Among the rescued was popular Sgt. Gerald (Pappy) Balbert, 37, of Jacksonville, N.C. When Pappy arrived back his flight suit was torn and he was covered with leeches. He was both scornful and delighted.

Capt. Jim Leonardt of Silver Spring, Md., is on the phone. He barks that more planes have got to be sent to A Shau.

Major Blakeman is on the radio. His downed helicopter is on the A Shau runway, intact after three days. Should he destroy it?

He should, he is told.

"That takes care of that," the Captain says. "After three days you know it's booby-trapped."

This has been a "mandatory" operation. There's nothing worse.

Of those, Marine Lt. Jack Giessner of Cranston, R.I., says: "Usually you're scared later. I was still up, walking it off at 2 o'clock this morning."

Mick McMinn and Eilerston landed on the A Shau runway. Mortars crashed around them. Their rotors were riddled. The chopper's front engine doors were sprung. If they break loose and hit the tail, it's curtains!

"I figured we were done for," said crew chief Marine Cpl. Victor Casasanta of Columbus, Ohio.

A crippled chopper is in sight. Its flapping doors operate as a huge airbrake; its forward movement is painfully slow. Every man, The Skipper included, is out on the runway helping it down.

It lands, taxies, stops. McMinn, Vic Casasanta and Cpl. Walt Eagleson, of Wayne, Mich., hop out. The Skipper slaps them all on the back. "You rascals," he says proudly. "I believe we have now completed our mission. Men, I'm tired out."

The Skipper is quite a man.

MARCH 16, OBSERVATION POST NEAR DA NANG AIRFIELD

At dusk as the six young Marines began their vigil Pfc. Bob Mardis of Covington, Ky., had said:

"It gets scary. Man, I got scared last night!"

He had cause to be. Manning an observation post is frightening after dark—just listening and watching for an enemy attack that may or may not come.

If an attack does come, the job is to give the alarm and get back—if there's time—to the camp which is the base for India ('I') Company, Third Battalion, Ninth Marine Regiment.

After 8 p.m. anything that moves within sight of the observation post is fair game. But the moonlight along the coast of the South China Sea plays nerve-racking tricks. Stare at a tree or a bush long enough and it starts creeping up on you.

The six young Marines take up their watch. They've been together as a team only since December, but they've been through a lot, and the bond among them is close.

They're all single. They talk mostly about girls back home. But they aren't the lads who came to Viet Nam a few months ago. They've all lost buddies. It has aged them beyond their years. Sometimes they talk about it, hardly believing it happened.

Smitty, the fire-team leader, is the oldest, Cpl. Aaron Smith of Cleveland is 22. Pfc. Patrick Hannon of Littleton, Colo., is the youngest. He's 19.

Pfc. Mike Konieczki of Clinton, Ia., Cpl. Ed Gross of San Mateo, Calif., and Pfc. Forrest Flyte of Easton, Pa., round out the team with whom I spent a long night listening and watching—and sometimes talking in whispers about things that didn't matter too much to them before. Like the whole big world in which they live and will live in when all this is over and they go home.

Smitty, a big, shy Negro, starts it off.

"Sir," he whispers, "may I ask you a question?"

"Sure."

"What do you think about Viet Nam?"

It's a big order. I try to fill it.

"Myself," he whispers back, "I'm beginning to understand why we're here, and I think we're doing a good thing."

Words don't come easy to Smitty, but he goes on:

"If we'd done more for China when we could have, I guess it wouldn't have gone Communist so fast. But I don't think these people want us here.

"If they did, they wouldn't put their dogs out to give the alarm when we go on patrol. And they'd smile. Myself, I've never seen anyone smile yet."

Smitty's helmet cover bears the legend: "December, 1966." That's the date he goes home.

The talk is sporadic. There are interruptions. Mike Konieczki crawls close to warn of sniper fire. From time to time Ed Gross picks up his radio to report: "CP (Command Post), this is OP (Observation Post). All secure."

Once Forrest Flyte, napping between watches, begins to snore. Pat Hannon awakens him.

"I'm not responsible for what I do while I'm asleep," Forrest says with mild indignation.

"Nobody snores on my observation post," says Ed Gross, suddenly the stern commander.

After one long silence Pat's voice drifts out of the night:

"I guess being a writer is pretty cool."

I say it is, although I'm not too sure what he means.

"I like writing," says Pat, whose helmet cover identifies him as "The Colorado Kid."

"I used to write for my school paper. Mostly sports. They said I was pretty good. I keep a diary. Maybe I'll write a book."

Before he enlisted he had one year at Regis College in Denver, where he also attended high school. He was studying to be a dentist. Now he doesn't know. He'll be 23 when he gets out. And 23 is mighty old.

"I wrote a poem," he says. "I call it 'My Plea.' I'll show it to you in the morning."

"What's your plea, Pat? Peace?"

"I'll show you in the morning."

At one point I dozed off and was awakened by the shrill sound of voices coming from the hamlet of Ngon Cau, hardly more than a football field distant from our hilltop observation post.

Ngon Cau is ours by day. But at night the Viet Cong creep in and make it theirs. An angry, hysterical voice dominates all others in the hamlet.

"Viet Cong," Ed Gross whispers. "He's terrorizing the villagers. Telling them, probably, to come up with more chow, more places for his men to hide in the daytime."

"Somebody's talking back," says Pat. "Sounds like an old lady. It's usually the old ladies that talk back."

The frenzied harangue continues. "Sounds like Adolf Hitler, doesn't it?" says Bob Mardis.

"I was too young. But I've seen those old newsreels of Hitler at Munich, shrieking at the crowds."

The bullying voice is finally silent and the villagers turn in.

The Long night is over at last and at sun-up the people of Ngon Cau are working their rice paddies.

"Ask 'em if anything happened last night and every one of 'em would swear nothing did," Ed says.

"Poor devils. What else could they say?"

Morning brought the promised look at Pat Hannon's poem. I had guessed wrong about what Pat's plea is. Here's his poem.

MY PLEA

It's not a good feeling to have to kill,
But when your country's in need, you know you will.
We've been in Viet Nam for several months now,
And we're hardly ready to take our bow.
We've seen some fellow Marines go down,
But I'm sure each one is Heaven bound.

If my time is here to be,
I ask a favor from you to me.
Answer my one and only plea . . .
KEEP AMERICA FREE

MARCH 17, DA NANG

He weighed all of 80 pounds and he was 66 years old, his government identification card told us. His name was Vung Thao and he lived in Cam Se, just outside camp.

He was a bit scuffed up from being tackled when he tried to get away. He was scared, of course. He'd been wearing camouflaged brown rags to blend in with the sand, and he was trying to change into the white pajamas farmers wear around here in the daytime. He hadn't had time before the Marines were on top of him.

This frightened old man hardly looked like a threat to anybody. But he'd had a 1903 Springfield rifle. And there was Pvt. Leopoldo Gonzales, 18, shot in the abdomen, with part of his insides showing. Gonzales comes from Galveston, Tex. He was walking about 50 feet from his platoon leader, Marine Lt. Charlie Pyle of Floral Park, N.Y. They said Gonzales would survive and would go home—which is a break.

Vung Thao had shot him.

"Spread out!" shouted Capt. Dave Rilling of San Antonio, Tex., in command. "We're not going to a choir-sing!"

Gonzales and several others had been walking on a paddy dike, always dangerous, but also the easy thing to do.

Within five minutes a medical helicopter got him out. That made everybody feel better.

It was hot, but we stayed off the trail and the dikes. They mine those; booby-trap them, too. We stuck to the paddies, which made the going harder.

After Gonzales got it, a Second Platoon kid named McGonigle was wounded. It's the platoon of Lt. Pete Gotay of New York City. McGonigle had been hurt by a grenade, and his buddies

313

got the Viet Cong. A medical chopper moved McGonigle out, too, in five minutes.

Dave Rilling was angry. It showed in the way he walked. These were the first casualties he's had since he set up here.

Three Marines on flank security show up with another Vietnamese. This one doesn't seem scared; he's almost arrogant. We take him along. We list him as a VCS (Viet Cong Suspect). Old Vung Thao is a VCC (Viet Cong Captured). No doubt about him.

When we must cut through the patios around farmhouses, we're careful to mutter "Moon joy"—that's what it sounds like—which means "Greetings" or "How are you?" Most people don't even look at us. In one farmyard, however, a youngster "Moonjoyed" back.

The Viet Cong had been shooting at us steadily. Right at dusk we'd been bunched up on the skyline—we should have known better, and we did—when a shot rang out. Then another. Everybody took cover. Cpl. Tim Murphy of Plainsville, Conn., yelled he saw the sniper. He was in that village at the foot of the hill. He was running away. Now he was out in the paddies.

Lt. Mike Peterson of Coos Bay, Ore., the platoon leader, grabbed the phone.

"Captain!" he yelled, "we see that guy that fired those shots. Can we fire?" The Captain said yes. Everybody opened up.

Tim Murphy thought he got the guy. He and Cpl. Willie Johnson of Baton Rouge, La., strapped on their cartridge belts, picked up their weapons and went out to see. They came back empty-handed. If he was winged—and Murphy swore he was—he made it to one of those tunnels.

"They've only outfoxed us once," said Sgt. Clifford Dison of Bremorton, Wash. "Followed us back to our patrol base the other night. Peppered us all night."

MARCH 18, DA NANG

The tragedy of A Shau—where Americans were forced to shoot South Vietnamese—is that it need not have happened.

It wouldn't have happened if steps had been taken to implement a six-month-old staff study by the Saigon Defense Ministry recommending that the Civilian Irregular Defense Group (CIDG) be abolished or, as a bare minimum, be integrated into the nation's regular military establishment.

Official military investigation of the incident at A Shau is under way.

Washington is keeping the wires hot with demands for facts and explanations. It will be unfortunate and unfair if anyone is made the scapegoat. What happened at A Shau was a military necessity.

A Shau was manned principally by CIDG strikers—or helpers. Most of those killed in order to get our rescue helicopters off ground were CIDG. So were those who defected and turned their guns on their own people and on the handful of Americans in the doomed camp.

The CIDG are civilians. They work under contract at wages better than those paid to the Vietnamese soldiers. They can quit when they want to. They can refuse orders they do not want to obey.

On three successive nights last fall at a Special Forces camp along the Cambodian border I heard and saw a CIDG commander refuse to go on patrol. He offered no substantial reasons. His men were tired. They had no mosquito nets; they simply did not feel like going; they might be shot, and so on.

When we insist on aggressive patrolling, the CIDG men just quit and sign up again at some place where conditions are more to their liking. Which is a hell of a way to run a war.

The CIDG personnel at A Shau surrendered the south wall of the fort without a fight. They went over to the Viet Cong. They fled into the jungle and reappeared when our rescue helicopters arrived. They were told that unless they kept their discipline, none of them would be rescued. Yet they rushed every helicopter that landed and refused to get off.

Two choppers crashed trying to get airborne. So, as a last resort, orders were issued to shoot.

The Americans were not alone in shooting the mutineers. One

CIDG officer tossed a grenade at the mob, killing and wounding ten.

When Marine Lt. Col. Charles A. House, helicopter squadron commander, ordered his crewmen to shoot so his rescue craft could take off, one CIDG man aboard kissed his hand. Another embraced him. A third fell to his knees and grabbed the Colonel around the legs.

The CIDG is a military cancer. No one disputes this. I've talked to many about it, including Gen. William C. Westmoreland. As far back as I can remember, we and the Vietnamese have been "just about set" to take action.

The staff study completed in Saigon as early as last fall urges dissolution of the CIDG and incorporation of its men into the regular armed forces.

But I invariably have been told: "Just wait a while. We must proceed cautiously in these matters. Staff jobs are involved. We've got to be diplomatic and sell the Vietnamese on the idea, and let them think it's their own."

Meanwhile Americans and loyal Vietnamese must fight and die alongside the CIDG. Alongside men they are unable to trust or respect—men who refuse to go on patrols, who go over to the enemy, and turn their guns on their friends.

This is too much to ask of anyone.

It's time we quit being diplomatic.

It's high time we bust this thing and get the CIDG abolished.

A Shau needn't have happened. But there will be more A Shaus unless we act promptly.

MARCH 19, DA NANG

In his 29 years, James Turner, Jr., of Denver, Colo., has had a fairly full life.

He has acquired a wife and four children, spent nine years in the Air Force and risen to the rank of staff sergeant.

But now Turner—his left arm in a sling, the left side of his body full of shrapnel—says that in the jungles around A Shau he "lived a couple of lifetimes."

"Don't ask me how long we were there," he says. "I don't know. Don't ask me how long we were on the ground. I don't know that, either. It seems like a couple of lifetimes."

He says it quietly. It has all the more impact for that reason.

A Shau, the Special Forces camp astraddle the Ho Chi Minh Trail, was under such intense attack it had to be evacuated. Our casualties would officially be described as "heavy," one of the few times that term has been used. At mid-afternoon our men had been driven into a single bunker. The Viet Cong held the rest of the camp. They held the airfield, were between it and the camp, and there was hand-to-hand fighting.

Jim Turner's story began when his C-47 was ordered to A Shau. Jim, a Negro, is crew chief in a plane called "Puff, the Magic Dragon." It's a lumbering cargo ship, fitted out with Gatling guns. It's a fearsome thing in action.

It never had a chance to get into action this time. Jim's Puff was about 20 feet above the jungle when it was hit. He gives full credit to his dead pilot—who had to be left out there in the jungle—for getting them down. "If he hadn't reacted as he did," Turner said, "we'd all be dead."

The ship's gunner in the rear with Turner was badly hurt on the landing. Jim was flung the length of the plane, his arm badly hurt. He dismisses that as of little consequence.

As soon as they were down the Viet Cong attacked, coming toward the plane's tail section. The crew fought back, and for a while the enemy was stopped.

Jim's co-pilot started in their direction—firing as he went—apparently to see how many Viet Cong they were facing. But he never came back. And then the pilot was killed.

Turner was the only man of the crew who could still function. He got on the radio and called an aircraft overhead—getting contact only after several heartbreaking failures. He told them where the Viet Cong were firing from—and soon the fighter planes came in. They strafed the ground near the Puff's tail section.

When they ran out of ammunition, they told Turner to grab onto whatever was handy and keep his head down; they had to use their bombs. They did. They set fires. Turner got on the radio again.

"Get those choppers in fast," he said. "We've got a fire down here. If it reaches our fuel tanks, you can forget about us."

They told him the helicopters were six minutes out. Six minutes can be a long time.

It took less. Capt. Don Couture of Oak Harbor, Ohio, put his chopper in beside the stricken Puff. Turner, the flight mechanic and the navigator—half the crew still alive—climbed aboard. All were wounded. Their co-pilot was somewhere out in the jungle, if he was still alive. Two dead men were left in the fuselage.

Lt. Art Machado of New Bedford, Mass., came in next in another chopper. His crewmen, under fire, rushed to the plane. Machado was under the impression there were still wounded to be brought out. The crewmen came back to report all still on the ground were dead.

The Viet Cong, Machado said later, were so close at hand, "we could see a torn hole in one of their T-shirts."

Fighters then came in to bomb and burn the downed Puff. They had to.

Turner—he doesn't understand how or why—is alive. And grateful.

But he will not soon forget those two lifetimes he lived for 30 minutes in the jungles around A Shau.

MARCH 28, CHU LAI

"What is peace without freedom, or existence without future?

"Wave your banners of protest, student, and throw your paint and rotten eggs, demonstrator, while we die on a hill for that freedom you abuse.

"In 10 years his broken body could be yours, protesting unheard. A turned back invites only bullets, and cowardice buys fear."

Marine Cpl. Lester Wesighan of Branchville, N.J., wrote that before he died.

He did not mean for it to be prophetic though his buddies,

who found it in his locker, believe it turned out to be so. Nor did he write it for publication. It was the expression of an editorial judgment for civilians, not Marines.

Wesighan was a Marine Combat Correspondent—by all accounts, a good one. Certainly he was a brave and honorable one because he died trying to save another Marine. He was the first Marine Combat Correspondent to die in Viet Nam.

Les was 25. He attended a small college in New Jersey—biographical facts are hard to obtain about a dead man 10,000 miles from home—and was a Naval Aviation Cadet before he decided he would rather be a Marine Combat Correspondent.

He told his friends he had a newspaper job lined up in New York when he left service. That would be when the war was won.

He also left a poem. He wrote it last fall.

"Fighting men clash and die amidst gloryless pools of
. blood . . .
Raw trigger fingers sleep eternal for foes unseen,
As softer memories of distant homes bring lapses of mind at
time,
Following paths that never exist,
I ask, where is his glory?
Not here. But in the hopes of those who trust him dearly."

Marine Cpl. Ken Henderson of Imperial Beach, Calif., was Wesighan's partner and friend. They constituted a writer-photographer team. They were together on "Operation Utah."

Ken is 21. He came into the Marines out of high school. He is a baby-faced boy who looks even younger than he is.

He talks in the stilted phraseology of professional fighting men. He seldom leaves any place; he "exits" it. His account is terse, laconic. Emotion shows only in his eyes and an occasional break in his voice.

"We helo-ed in," he says. "Les and I were a team. One chopper was shot down. We had gone about 500 meters when we were hit. We moved up on a line. We were being hit with everything."

Now Ken was no longer just a professional Marine but also a frightened boy.

"We were having to fight for our lives," he said. "We didn't have time to take pictures or think about the story."

Wesighan and Henderson fought for a long time alongside other Marines. There were dead and dying all around.

A corporal named William Brown was hit behind the ear. Wesighan and John D. Rose of Chicago, another Marine photographer, dragged Brown to a Vietnamese burial mound. They burrowed into the grave. The battle still raged.

Rose started for help. Wesighan stayed with the wounded man. Then Wesighan stood up and waved his arms, yelling for a medical corpsman.

"That was foolish," Henderson said, "but it was brave. It was foolish because no corpsmen were available. We had six at the beginning—but three were dead and three were wounded. He was a perfect target."

Wesighan was shot in the back of the head.

"When I got to him," Henderson said, "he was lying on his face, moaning for a corpsman." Wesighan died minutes later.

Brown was still conscious, but out of his wits. Henderson had trouble keeping him down. He ordered Brown to "play dead" and said he would try to get him out.

Brown must have understood. He became quiet. But Henderson found it impossible to move. He lay there 50 minutes. Then:

"I saw this VC (Viet Cong) coming out of the bushes maybe 30 yards away. I whispered to Brown to be still. And then I shot the VC. I emptied half my magazine, and he fell. Those were the last rounds I had."

Henderson remained with Brown at least two more hours. He "could hear them talking all around us." Finally, he felt it was safe to move. He again told Brown to "play dead."

He'd gone only a few feet when he heard a shot. That was when he believes the Viet Cong finished off Brown.

"Our own mortars were coming in on us," he recalled. "I lay there shaking. Eventually, I went back to Brown. He and Les were both dead."

Darkness was coming on. Henderson and Rose, who had returned, were in tall grass. They were, as far as they could determine, the only living Marines around.

Just before dusk they heard someone shouting, "Hey, Marine!" They did not answer. The Viet Cong also use that call.

After a few minutes, they spotted five Marines and answered. The two groups joined up. They decided to make a break for it. Henderson and one other made it to a tree line.

"But," Henderson said, "the VC saw where we had come from and opened up. The awfulest part was having no ammo."

Rose and four others were pinned down. Eventually they crawled away—to safety. They had to. A mortar had hit nearby and set the grass on fire.

It was dark now. The party finally made it into our lines and there spent the night under sniper fire.

Rose discovered he had been nicked by shrapnel.

Robert Branham III of Artesea, Calif., another photographer, eventually showed up. He had carried a wounded Marine, shot through the stomach, for three hours. When our own or enemy mortars hit too close, he would lie on top of the wounded man.

Branham also was wounded by shrapnel.

Les Wesighan never got to write his story. That job in New York will be filled by someone else.

"I'll go out on the next one," Henderson says. "But it won't be the same. You don't expect it to happen to someone as close as Les."

These boys aren't amateurs. They're pros. And they're every bit as good as we were in the old days. Damn it, they're better!

MARCH 31, CHU LAI

The Marines from F Company stood on a bald knob of a hill, honoring their dead. The Chaplain spoke and then the Captain. A bugler sounded taps and they walked back to their bunkers, checked their weapons, and got ready for the night's patrols and ambushes.

Then the Padre drove down into the valley and across the

next rise to H Company, and it was the same all over again.

Foxtrot (F Company) went into Operation Utah with 160 men and came out with 80. Hotel (H Company) fared a little better; it took 60 casualties. A company is a lot like a man; it has a personality of its own. It can be brave or cowardly. It can stand and fight or it can break. It can be hurt, but it can mend.

Foxtrot and Hotel stood and fought. They fought with honor; their men died with honor. But the units were hurt. Badly. Now they have started to mend.

Replacements have begun to arrive. It isn't easy to replace a dead man, a man who has been your pal. No one knows that better than men like Ron Phillips of Hampton, Va., Don Hendrickson of Belleville, N.J., or Jim Martin of West Point, Ga. No one appreciates it more than Chumgali Ali of Brooklyn, a Russian Moslem, Bob Sweeney, who is 18 and from Mundlein, Ill., or Jerry Walters, 21, of Phoenix, Ariz. Or older men like Sgt. Jim Jewitt of Burton, S.C.

Nor can anyone understand it more clearly than Capt. Alex Lee of Oceanside, Calif., who commands Foxtrot, or Lt. Jim Lau, a Chinese-American who has Hotel. Lau had his company throughout. Lee crawled in to replace a wounded commander, a man who had shouted over his radio, "I'm hit, but I'm still commanding." Lee arrived in time to win his spurs. His men accepted him now. After the battle, headquarters wanted to pull him out. But Alex Lee and his men rebelled.

"We grew up together," he said, and they let him stay.

The new men hear and see all this. But they're not yet part of it. Bob Sweeney and Jerry Walters have been in Viet Nam one week. They've been with their outfit five days.

It hasn't been easy. It's the heat that bothers the new men most. It was snowing when Hendrickson left Newark. Viet Nam is hotter than they dreamed it could be. Captain Lee already has sent them out on an eight-mile hike. He sent them out at noon. He chose the roughest terrain in Viet Nam. He wanted them to know what it was like.

"I knew it would be tough," said Walters. "That's why I joined. I'm tough, too."

Ron Phillips was in the Dominican Republic. He's been under sniper fire. But this is different. Viet Nam is real war.

Jewitt was born in Cuba, of an American father and a Cuban mother. He has a score to settle with the Communists.

But, for the moment, the company belongs to the old-timers. There'll be an awards ceremony soon.

"You sit down to write these citations," Lee says, "and you run out of ways to describe it. You want to say the guy had guts. People who worry about our kids not measuring up just don't understand. Mine fought; they rose to every occasion. But they never lost their compassion."

Pfc. Clyde Martindale, 21, of Blythe, Calif., is an old-timer who came through. Clyde wears thick glasses. He's been a Marine 18 months. Clyde survived on his machine gun—picked it up with its 70 pounds of ammo, slung three rifles and a grenade-launcher across his back and loped 150 yards under fire to a new position. He set it up and began firing. His load weighed more than he did.

Pfc. Earl Morgan, a big Negro from Slidell, La., came through. When a white buddy, a man from the Deep South, was hit, it was Morgan he called for. "Come get me, Earl buddy!" he screamed, and Morgan went. Morgan pitched baseball in high school. He was so accurate with grenades, his men stacked theirs at his feet so Earl could pick off Viet Cong. He has no idea how many he got.

Cpl. George Kabeller, of Medina, Ohio, rushed an enemy bunker, tossed in a grenade and killed five. Fifteen more broke and ran. His men mowed them down.

Cpl. Glenn Hensley of Cromwell, Ind., was shot through the mouth. They flew him out to a hospital ship. Three days ago, he showed up again. He still isn't able to talk well.

APRIL 5, DA NANG

Survivors of the terrible A Shau battle and betrayal will be kept together as a team and reassigned to another outpost along the Laotian border.

A Shau was the Special Forces post overrun by a North Vietnamese regiment last month.

Army Capt. John D. Blair IV of Atlanta, Ga., said he and his men would replace a Special Forces team at Tien Phuoc—"as soon as we are all out of the hospital." After their ordeal at A Shau, Blair added, "We want to stay together."

When A Shau was lost, Blair escaped into the jungle and later was picked up by a Marine helicopter. He charged that Vietnamese irregulars in the little garrison went over to the Communists and some turned their guns on his men. Washington later confirmed his story.

After he and other survivors got out of the burning fort, Blair said, the Army notified their wives that they were "missing in action." Members of their families, he said, "already had buried us" before subsequent telegrams announced their rescue.

I encountered Captain Blair at the Da Nang airfield. Spruced up and in starched khakis, he bore no resemblance to the distraught survivor plucked from the jungle two weeks earlier. The shed-like terminal was jammed with servicemen waiting for aircraft to take them elsewhere in Viet Nam. None gave Blair a second glance. The Captain said he was en route to Special Forces headquarters in Nha Trang for another debriefing session.

"Refighting a battle takes longer than fighting one," he said. Blair revealed for the first time he asked for B-52's to bomb A Shau while he and his men were fighting for their lives inside. He was sure all would be killed if the big Guam-based bombers were employed but "we didn't expect to survive anyhow." He asked for B-52's, he said, "to take as many Viet Cong as we could with us."

The B-52's didn't come, he said, because it took too long to get the word to Guam through regular channels. However, B-52's since have bombed the now Red-held fort and its surrounding jungle.

The young captain, son of a career Army officer, was able to discuss his recent ordeal dispassionately, almost as if it had happened to someone else.

"I honestly did not expect them to try to pull us out," he said. "Of course, we were glad they did. But I was surprised when they made that decision. If I'd been in command, I might have decided differently. I don't know; it was a tough one. What I was hoping for was massive reinforcement. Not just piecemeal— that would have been murder—but a really big effort. We could have chopped at least two North Vietnamese regiments to pieces. But the weather was bad, and the aircraft just weren't available."

Blair paid tribute to the North Vietnamese who overran him.

"They were good soldiers," he said. "They were brave."

Blair "conservatively" estimated his men killed 500 North Vietnamese.

"Radio Hanoi—we always listen to it—admits 400," he said. "Of course, it also claims A Shau was manned by 1200 Americans and that we all were wiped out."

APRIL 8, DA NANG

Air Force CWO William Hartzler of El Paso, Tex., heads a 10-man Crash Recovery Crew at the airfield here.

The other day our planes had carried out a raid in North Viet Nam and 12 jets were coming back with minimum fuel loads. If everything went well, they'd just make it. Just.

Hartzler, 46, stood at his post and ticked them off. If any one cracked up, he'd have to get off the runway fast. The others wouldn't have enough fuel to circle. And Da Nang has only one runway. It's undoubtedly the world's busiest single runway operation.

It was one of Bill Hartzler's luckier days. All made it in safety. From his spot just off the runway, smack in the middle of the field, he breathed a sigh of relief.

Da Nang averages 35,000 landings and takeoffs every month. Its busiest day was Feb. 22 this year with 1799 landings and takeoffs. That averages one every 45 seconds.

About four times a day Hartzler and his men are called on to cope with an emergency. Sometimes it's Air Force, sometimes it's Navy, sometimes it's Marine. Any ship in trouble has standing orders to head for Da Nang. Hartzler will be there waiting for them.

The remarkable thing is that he had no prior crash rescue experience. At Biggs Air Force Base in El Paso, he was in charge of transient aircraft. All he had to do was refuel, clean and bed them down for the night. He was also scoutmaster of a Boy Scout troop sponsored by El Paso's well known Skyline Lions Club.

He invariably has plenty of unsolicited advice here, a lot of it from colonels and generals. It used to shake him up. Now as he has learned his job, he also has learned to tune out the static. Apparently, the kibitzers have got his message. Bill isn't bothered as much as he once was.

"Every man in my crew knows what he has to do," Chief Hartzler says. "I couldn't afford to listen to outsiders."

One recent morning, for instance, a Marine F-4 jet fighter came in riddled by hostile gunfire. It had lost all its hydraulic fluid. That meant it had no brakes and the pilot had lost much of his surface control. It landed, caught on the arresting wire— Da Nang uses many aircraft carrier techniques—and slowed to a halt. Bill's men were on it almost as soon as it stopped. Two minutes and 45 seconds later it was off the runway.

Their best record in cleaning a smash-up is eight and a half minutes.

To accomplish this, Chief Hartzler uses a 100,000-pound crane which also can hoist 100,000 pounds. He uses smaller equipment, too. His big problem has been the 40,000-pound B-57. He thinks he has solved that with a sling that ought to be able to lift 50,-000 pounds.

So far, he has had no occasion to use it.

Since July, however, his crews have picked up 17 jets which have crashed on Da Nang's concrete strip. One B-57 cracked up on takeoff with seven 750-pound bombs. One exploded on impact.

He's busiest during the wet season.

"Seems like they just can't stay on the runway," he says. "We're up all night pulling them out of the mud."

APRIL 12, DONG PHUOC

Marine casualties were light.

I looked at them and wondered if, when it happened, they understood why they had to die.

Probably not. Not in any words others would understand. Not in the high-flown terms the pundits use. They'd tell you, if they could speak, they had a job to do. They were Marines. There was one objective to be taken, a fortified hamlet to be cleaned out, a machine gun to be silenced. And that would be reason enough for them. That was why they had to die among the Cau Viet on a hot afternoon.

Death is our neighbor in Viet Nam. He's not a friend. We don't see him for days and we forget, almost, that he's around. Then he walks among us and we fall silent. We dislike him. We don't know how to act when he's around.

He shows up unexpectedly. Maybe while flying to Saigon, as Marine Col. Tom Fields was last week, and the plane stops in Qui Nhon. Forty-four bodies are put aboard. They're stacked in the middle in racks four high. The take-off is rough and they bounce in their racks.

For us, death showed up in a Marine helicopter which just landed at the foot of the hill. The pilot had promised to pick us up after he'd delivered a load of ammo in the valley. He kept his word. I rushed toward the open door, head down against the prop wash, and started to climb aboard. There was this pile of ponchos—that's what it looked like—and I almost sat down on it. Then I saw the feet sticking out, the rough-shod feet. I stepped back, embarrassed, wondering if the others saw, if they thought I was really that calloused. The pilot motioned me aboard and I stepped carefully over the stacked bodies and rode all the way to Da Nang.

I tried not to stare at them, but there was no place else to look. They were there. Their folks didn't know yet. They're

327

thinking about them, praying for them. But I know. And I don't even know their names.

The chopper lands at a hut hospital complex and the orderlies —one just out of the shower with a towel wrapped around him —grab the stretchers. They see what we have and, for a moment, step back. Then they carry off the bodies.

Our neighbor, death, can be cooperative, too. Sometimes we work with him. Charlie Harris did. He's the sniper that killed five Viet Cong in nine hours last night and this morning. Charlie's a 19-year-old Negro, a quiet, likable kid. He was born in Louisiana. He finished high school in Oakland at 17, and came into the Marines.

He sits on his helmet, sweating in the sun, and talks about it. He'd just completed two weeks' sniper training. He got the first one at 700 meters after the Viet Cong shot his first sergeant. Charlie was sighting on another "target" when he saw the sergeant go down. He also saw the flash. They train them in sniper school to watch for certain signs and movements. It depends, Charlie explains, on what kind of day, what kind of weather, you have. He shifted and got the guy who shot the sergeant. He was lying on a flat rock in a clearing and Charlie picked him off with one shot. Later, he walked by the body. He didn't bother to go look. Maybe he hadn't wanted to.

Charlie shot 12 times in nine hours and killed five men.

"I saw every man I shot," he says with a touch of pride. Professional pride. They teach in sniper school to fire only when there's something to shoot at.

Was this the first man he'd ever killed?

Yes, sir.

How did he feel?

"I felt nothing, sir. I just did my job."

The doctor comes by, a young white man from West Virginia, and shakes his hand.

"Go back and get some more," he says gruffly. "We got a lot of boys to make them pay for."

"Yes, sir, I will," Charlie Harris says. Then, embarrassed at all the attention:

"My buddy got more'n I did. He's real good."

"Charlie, you staying in?"

"No, sir. Soon as I can, I'm going back to school."

Death is our job in Viet Nam. But it isn't our career.

APRIL 20, CAM RANH BAY

For a half hour we had been darting around at 1400 miles an hour in a sleek F-4C Phantom at 30,000 feet altitude.

This Phantom is the fastest jet in our Vietnamese inventory. It flies at better than twice the speed of sound. It has a phenomenal rate of climb.

There were three Phantoms in our flight. I was in the back seat of the one flown by Air Force Capt. Al Schalk of Tacoma, Wash. Maj. Norman (Squeak) Watson of Austin, Tex., and Lt. Danny Layton of San Francisco were in the lead; Capt. Jim Grier of Wetumpka, Ala., and Lt. Dave Skartvedt of Seattle, in the third ship.

Sgt. Don Johnson of Baltimore and Airman John McDonald of Warren Point, N.J., had checked our ship out and it was "start engines" at 1 p.m. Ten minutes and 65 miles later we were over the designated area.

"You'll be flying in support of Korean Marines, Vietnamese Army and the 101st Airborne Division northwest of Tuy Hoa in the Operation Fillmore area," the briefing officer had said. "You are to expect some ground fire."

Layton registered disgust.

"All we'll see is trees," he said. "That's all we ever see. Trees."

The briefer stared at him coldly.

"There are," he said evenly, "two enemy regiments in the area."

"I'll bet you," Layton persisted, "we don't see anything but trees."

A Forward Air Controller (FAC) in a small spotter plane took over at Tuy Hoa.

"I have three targets for you," he said. "The first is in the open. The next two are up on the slope. In the trees."

We dive at the first. From 25,000 feet, Al Schalk brings his jet down to 10,000, then 5000, now to 2000, before he pulls out. There is a slight jolt as his 750-pound bomb is released. We circle and the smoke rises behind us.

Five times he does this. On the third run I almost blacked out. On the fourth I held my head down. That was a mistake. We were pulling five G's (or five times that of gravity), which meant that my own weight rose from 180 to 900 pounds. It seemed as if some giant had his hand on the nape of my neck.

On the fifth run, I blacked out completely for a while.

Then we were ready to strafe. Al likes this best of all. But the Controller said he had no target.

So we head for Pleiku, hoping they'll have one. But Pleiku has no target for strafers, either. It seems the bottom's fallen out of the strafing market.

In desperation we go back to Tuy Hoa. Situation's unchanged there. No strafing targets.

The others are luckier. One flight has been assigned an enemy hamlet. Huts with straw roofs. They burn easily; pilots love those. One boasts that he set four afire on one strafing pass.

Another flight is chasing Viet Cong in the First Cavalry Division zone. They're heading for the Cambodian border and the secure haven it represents.

"The name of the game," Col. W. C. McGlothlin of Washington said later, "is to get 'em before they get away. We got some."

But not our plane. Our missiles remain unfired, and we're heading home.

I land and Lt. Col. Jerry Beisner of Salina, Kan., commander of the 558th Tactical Fighter Squadron gives me a certificate attesting that I "did fly in combat against an armed enemy" aboard a Phantom.

APRIL 28, AN HOA

South Viet Nam's problems are exemplified in An Hoa.

The Vietnamese are trying to build a nation, establish

working political systems and create a viable economy while fighting for their existence. So it is with An Hoa.

An Hoa is about 25 miles inland from Da Nang along the Thu Bon River. Its area includes the country's only coal mine. It has the basis of a hydroelectric grid which some day can supply all of the populous First Corps Area. It has two fertilizer plants.

There is room here for other major industries. To fly in to An Hoa, set in the middle of nowhere, is to arrive in Shangri-La. There is a hard-surfaced landing strip with a decent terminal. There are roads, modern cottages for its engineers and supervisors, and housing for its workers. An Hoa has potable water and modern plumbing; also a fresh-water lake where men can fish, swim and ski.

But for defense it must be surrounded by a barbed-wire fence. A Vietnamese Army battalion is based here permanently. Its units are widely deployed, and often lose men. Nearby villages are dominated by the Viet Cong.

The railroad to Da Nang is useless; it was cut a year ago and its ties have been salvaged by both sides to build bunkers. The highway to the coast also has been cut; two-third of its bridges have been blown. A half-mile outside An Hoa an ambush can be expected. Two Vietnamese soldiers were killed and 12 wounded recently when a booby trap caught them as they crossed a stream.

The An Hoa industrial complex was begun three years ago with French and German participation. French and German engineers still are here. The Americans were deliberately excluded. French and German involvement is held to a minimum.

"Certainly the Americans could do overnight what we are trying to do," says Le Thuc Can, the young Vietnamese in charge, "but then it wouldn't be ours."

Can has an engineering degree from France. He spent six months in Ohio and Pennsylvania studying American strip mining. An Hoa is his life. He married six months ago and brought his bride to live here.

Throughout 1963 and 1964, An Hoa grew. At one time 3000

workers were here. Then in 1965 fate and the Viet Cong inter-vened. Floods devastated much of the valley. The Communists cut the railroad and the highway; ambushed and killed workers. The 3000-man work force dwindled to less than 1000. By February of this year, the Vietnamese were ready to throw in the sponge.

Then the Americans reluctantly moved in. Air Force C-123's brought supplies. They flew out An Hoa's coal and fertilizer. It is a thoroughly uneconomic operation; An Hoa's probably is the only coal in the world transported to market by plane. But it keeps An Hoa going. It keeps Engineer Can's dream alive.

We are here today, two battalions of U.S. Marines, to widen An Hoa's three-square-mile defense perimeter, give it more breathing space. We'd like, though this is unlikely in the time allowed, to reopen the highway.

Engineer Can is delighted. The Marines are happy, too. They're not used to running water, electric fans and roofs over their heads in the field. An Hoa's lake is tempting.

Outside that fence, however, there is trouble. A small hospital has been set up in the air terminal in anticipation of that trouble.

Maj. Gen. Wood B. Kyle of Pecos, Tex. and Arlington, Va., the Third Marine Division commander, flew in to see for himself how things are going.

"There is evidence they are watching every move we make," said Lt. Col. William Taylor of Birmingham, Ala., a battalion commander, briefing the General. "They may be getting jittery. Maybe I can aggravate them enough so they'll come out and fight."

So much could be accomplished if this unhappy land were at peace.

Epilogue

LONG KHANH

"Why do you do it?" the old man asked.

They made a strange pair, the old Vietnamese and his American visitor. The old man with his scraggly beard had lived in this village all of his years, and was its elder.

The young American had been twice wounded defending the village, and bears a silver plate in his head. Back from the hospital a second time, he had walked the half-mile into town to see his friend.

In Vietnamese, the old man's question was the equivalent of "What's in it for you?"

Capt. Ed Fricke of Paris, Ill., son of a coal miner, hesitated over a cup of steaming tea.

"I do not know that I have the knowledge or the words to tell," he said.

"Try, my son," the old man prompted. "We know you. We depend on you. But we do not understand you. Why does your body take these blows for us? Why do you risk your life for my country? You are not Vietnamese."

"I am not Vietnamese," the American agreed.

"Is it," the old man asked, "that you want to prevent us from becoming Communists?"

"I do not want you to become Communists," the young man replied, "unless you freely choose to."

The old man was puzzled.

"Why should we choose to become Communists?" he asked.

"I do not think you will," the Captain said. "No free man ever has. But if you chose, I would not prevent you. Do you understand me?"

333

The oldster was not sure he did.

"Do you say that Communism is evil?" he asked.

"I know it."

"You know it?"

The American nodded.

"There is much in the world that is bad," the old man countered. "There is much that is bad here."

"There is much that is bad in my country." the Captain said. "But we are free to change the bad to good as we acquire wisdom. Man must be free to grow."

"Do you think we are free in Long Khanh?" the old man asked.

"You can be," the young American replied. "I believe you will be. You asked me why I am here. That is my answer. I want you to be free."

The old man was pleased. Cackling, he called out to those who had clustered about and told them what the young American had said. Excitedly, they discussed it among themselves.

The old man smiled.

"My people remind me," he said, "that in our country we have an adage: Throw gold at the feet of a poor man and he will spit on it. Give him a cup of water with dignity and he will be your friend."

"I want to be your friend." The young Captain smiled and rose to go back to his camp.

The old man walked with him to the end of the village street.

"Good-by," he said. "Come again to see me, my friend."

THE RAILWAYMAN'S WIFE

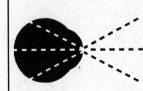

This Large Print Book carries the
Seal of Approval of N.A.V.H.

THE RAILWAYMAN'S WIFE

ASHLEY HAY

THORNDIKE PRESS
A part of Gale, Cengage Learning

GALE
CENGAGE Learning·

Farmington Hills, Mich • San Francisco • New York • Waterville, Maine
Meriden, Conn • Mason, Ohio • Chicago

LIBRARY OF CONGRESS CATALOGING-IN-PUBLICATION DATA

Names: Hay, Ashley, author.
Title: The railwayman's wife / Ashley Hay.
Description: Large print edition. | Waterville, Maine : Thorndike Press, 2016. | © 2013 | Series: Thorndike Press large print core
Identifiers: LCCN 2016010643 | ISBN 9781410490025 (hardback) | ISBN 1410490025 (hardcover)
Subjects: LCSH: Widows—Fiction. | Loss (Psychology)—Fiction. | Triangles (Interpersonal relations)—Fiction. | Thirroul (N.S.W.)—Social life and customs—20th century—Fiction. | Large type books. | BISAC: FICTION / Historical. | GSAFD: Love stories. | Historical fiction.
Classification: LCC PR9619.4.H38 R35 2016b | DDC 823/.92—dc23
LC record available at http://lccn.loc.gov/2016010643

Published in 2016 by arrangement with Atria Books, an imprint of Simon & Schuster, Inc.

Printed in the United States of America
1 2 3 4 5 6 7 20 19 18 17 16

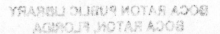

For Les Hay

It's not what we forget
But what was never known we
most regret
Discovery of.

— STEPHEN EDGAR

I, who had always thought of Paradise
In form and image as a library
— JORGE LUIS BORGES
(TRANSLATED BY ALASTAIR REID)

1

She sits, her legs folded beneath her. The fingers of one hand trace the upholstery's pattern while the other hand holds the pages of the book.

It could be any day, any year: call it 1935, 1938, 1945, or somewhere decades away in her future. Perhaps it's the day after her wedding, the day after her daughter's birth, the last day of the war, the last day of her life. Whenever it is, Anikka Lachlan is reading, swallowed by the shapes and spaces made by rows of dark letters on pale paper. She wets one finger, not slowly, but absently, and moves it to turn the next page.

From outside, across the roofs of this small town, comes a sharp line of noise — a train's brakes and the squeal of wheel on rail, metal on metal. Ani looks up from the page but at nothing, and at nowhere, as if the room she's sitting in and the rest of this whole cacophonous world do not, at this

moment, quite exist.

The sound fades. The silence holds. She looks down, and finds the next word.

2

These are the sort of people they are, Ani Lachlan and her husband, Mac. They are people who make a fuss of birthdays, people for whom no effort is too great in search of the perfect present, the perfect tribute, the perfect experience. Even during the war, when their daughter, Isabel, had asked — impossibly — for a bicycle, Mac found the bits and pieces to craft a tiny ornamental one, to see her through until a proper one could be sourced, and saved for, and procured.

And so in late 1948, on the weekend before Isabel's tenth birthday, Ani and Mac take the train up the coast to Sydney to find her next birthday present — she's asked for something magical. All morning they rummage in dusty shops near Central, until they find — in the last quarter hour before their train — a dull cylinder with an eyehole at one end and a round dome of

11

glass at the other.

Mac holds it up to one eye, the other eye closed, and the kaleidoscope transforms the overfull shop into a series of mosaics. Now it's a stained-glass window; now a fan of Arabic tiles. Now it flares into brightness as he angles the tube towards the shop's open door. He hands it to his wife, smiling. "You'll love it," he says, watching her turn the tube, watching her transform the busy mess of the shop. Its drab brass looks heavy against the glow of her skin.

"Yes," she says, turning the tube to make another image. "Yes, she'll want this. She can make everything she looks at into something beautiful with this." No better present for their Bella. Mac pushes the coins across the counter to the old lady who stands there, wrapping the gift in a thick sheet of paper the color of a pale-yellow dawn.

"For a present?" the shopkeeper asks, tucking the parcel's ends neatly into themselves.

"For our daughter," says Mac.

"Turning ten," says Ani.

The old lady smiles. "So many ways of seeing things," she says, patting the paper. "I hope they are all beautiful, the things your little girl sees." And she wraps the tube

again in heavy brown paper, tying its ends with string, like a bonbon.

Ani smiles in return. "You should see where we live," she says, touching Mac's arm while he packs the parcel into his bag. "Most beautiful place in the world."

Mac blushes, partly at the extremity of his wife's words, and partly because he loves it when she says this. Because he was the person who took her there, the person responsible for delivering her to this beauty. In a scratched and spotted mirror behind the counter, he sees them standing together, Ani a little taller, and fine, like the saplings that grow down by the beach. The paleness of her hair is so uniform that she looks as if she's been lit from above. And there he is, Mackenzie Lachlan, solid next to her, his head thick with hair that looks blond next to any but hers. Her reflection smiles, and he turns to catch the end of the real thing. That's what illuminates him, that right there.

In the shop's darkness, a clock chimes, and he grabs her hand again. "Train, love."

The shopkeeper comes around the counter, bows her head with her hands pressed together like a prayer. "Then a safe journey back to your home and your little girl," she says, standing by the door. They fly out to

the street, past shop fronts, across roads, around corners, up stairs, and onto their platform. As they swing into an empty compartment, the engine gathers steam and lets out one perfect cloud of white, one perfect trumpet of sound, and begins to move off.

"We've got a good loco in front of us," says Mac, leaning over to watch the big green engine take a curve. "Home in no time — it's a thirty-six; nice run down the line."

Most beautiful place in the world. He feels Ani tuck herself between his body and the angular edge of the train's wooden window frame. The warmth of her arm brushes his own as he turns the pages of his newspaper and mutters the names of the countries in the news — Burma, Ceylon, Israel, South Africa, two new Germanys. By the end of the second page, he feels her heavy against him and knows she's going to sleep through this patchwork of suburban backyards, their clotheslines, their veggie patches, their hemorrhaging sheds. She'll sleep through to the slice of the journey she loves best, when the train surges through one long black tunnel and delivers her onto the coast, the northern tip of Ani Lachlan's most beautiful place in the world.

"I'll wake you up when we get there," says Mac. And she nods, squeezing his hand. She sleeps quickly, deeply, on trains, as if their rhythms and noise were a lullaby. He watches her breathing, feels the air from her mouth on his shoulder.

They cross the Cooks River, then the Georges, pushing south. Through the window now, thick bush rushes by, transformed into fragments and segments of trees, palms, grasses, birds, and sky as if they'd been poured through the kaleidoscope too. His eyes flicker and dart, trying to isolate a single eucalypt, the fan of a palm, and then they close. His newspaper drops to the floor as the landscape changes from eucalypt forest to something more like a meadow — almost at Otford; almost at the head of the tunnel — and her fingers, light, begin to pat his arm.

"Not often I get to wake you." She smiles.

"Almost there," he says. The engine is puffing and blowing, pulling hard, and the train presses on towards the archway that's been carved to open up the mountain. "Now," says Mac, taking his wife's hand. "Now," his mouth so close to her ear. They're in darkness, the sound monumental, the speed somehow faster when there's only blackness beyond the windows. And

then they're out, in the light, in the space, in the relative quiet.

And there's the ocean, the sand, the beginnings of this tiny plain that has insinuated itself, tenuous, between the wet and the dry.

It's a still and sunny day, the water flat and inky, the escarpment colored golden and orange, pink and brown. As the train takes the curves and bends of its line, the mountain's rock faces become great stone monoliths that might have come from Easter Island, and then the geometric edges of some desert temple. Here are the hellish-red gashes of coke ovens; here is the thin space where there's only room, it seems, for a narrow road, a narrow track, between the demands of sea and stone. And here is the disparate medley of place-names — simple description, fancy foreign, and older, more original words: Coalcliff, Scarborough, Wombarra, Austinmer. And then Thirroul.

They pass the big glass-and-wooden roundhouse in Thirroul's railway yards — *Ani's favorite building* is how he thinks of it, although it's where his every working day begins. As the train slows, they're almost home.

The engine lets out a long whistle and pulls into Thirroul's station, its low waiting

16

rooms set back from the platform's edge and the Railway Institute and its library on the opposite side of the tracks. Ani reaches for Mac's hand, and steps out of the carriage. The air is thick with salt and ozone from the unseen ocean nearby. Arranging their bags, they begin their slow walk home, east towards the water, south up the hill, east towards the water again, and halfway along Surfers Parade. From the steps to the front door, the view is all mountain and water, while behind the back fence, and maybe a mile farther south, a headland rules off the space she's told him she regards as the edge of their world.

"A mile south of that pine tree, sitting in our yard like a pin in a map for X marks the spot."

"Then I leave the world on any train run to Wollongong," he protested once. "I go out of your world in the course of every day."

"Out of our world, yes, but you're very good about coming home."

When they first came, newly married and more than twelve years ago now, they'd climbed the mountain too, straight up the cliff face to the summit of the scarp, where they turned and stood, gazing east over the limitless blue.

"Nothing there," said Mac quietly, "nothing at all — until you hit Chile." The tops of the trees below looked like crazy paving, and among the grey-green of the gums were the odd cabbage-tree palm, the odd cedar, the odd tree fern an almost luminous green among the eucalypts, the turpentines. In late spring came extra punctuation — the fiery scarlet of the native flame tree; the incandescent purple of the exotic jacaranda.

They'd watched a storm come up the coast that day, clambering down the track in its noisy wetness, and arriving wild and muddy at the bottom. "I've got you." Mac had laughed, wrapping his wet arms around her. Then closer, quieter — "I've got you now" — and he held her fast with a kiss. She'd squirmed then, anxious at the embrace in the open air, and he'd laughed at her for it, hanging on. Hanging on.

Now, as Ani makes a pot of tea and hides the precious present, Mac watches the sun set, remembering that kiss, that discomfort, and the messy embraces that came next. The shapes of the shadows, the colors of the world begin to shift and change towards nightfall and he longs for the gloaming, for one more walk in the wide dusk of a Scottish summer and an unexpected kiss in the braw open air. But it's too far away, the

other side of the world, and too many years since he left. Kisses now tend towards the perfunctory, the habitual, with the occasional moment of surprise, spontaneous or remembered. It's just life, he knows, rather than anything particular or sinister. Still, he's glad for recollections, and the privacy of imagination.

From the corner of his eye, he sees a flash of color against the growing dark, and it's Isabel coming home from a friend's house by the shore. He whistles three times, twice low and once high and long, so that the sound slides back to the pitch of the first two notes. Even through the gloom, he sees her stop and steady herself before she whistles in reply. *It's power, to whistle your girl home,* he thinks, opening the gate and feeling her hug hard against his body.

The next weekend, on Isabel's birthday, after breakfast and the present, Ani slides the birthday cake into the oven and the family walks to the beach with the kaleidoscope. It's a clear morning, the sky very high and light, with a band of clouds, thin and white, tucked in beyond the ridge of the mountain. Isabel stands with the brass tube of her gift, changing the world with the smallest movement of her hand. "Like magic," she says,

19

and Ani and Mac smile. She loves birthdays; the present, the cake, and always an excursion — a milkshake in Wollongong, she wants, and they've promised to take her after school, one day in the coming week.

"Maybe chocolate," she calls now, "or maybe chocolate malted. Or would it be more grown-up, now I'm ten, after all, to have caramel?" She dances circles in the sand around her parents, looking at this, at that, with her precious new spyglass while they head towards the silvery smooth pylons, the fractured segments of joists, that are all that remain of the old jetty, pushing inland above the line of the low tide and out to sea the other way.

"We should've given you a telescope, love," Mac calls to his daughter. Then: "Looks like there's someone sitting up there on one of the poles." And the three of them pause, peering ahead, the sun warm on their backs as they separate the shape of a man from the shape of the weathered wood.

"You know, I reckon that's Iris McKinnon's brother," says Mac at last. "One of the drivers said he was home. You remember, love — he's the one published the poem during the war. We took it round for Iris, do you remember?" He shades his eyes, more a salute than anything to do with glare.

"Wonder what he'll do now he's back here? Not much call for a poet in the pits or on the trains."

Offshore, a pod of dolphins appears in the face of a wave, curling and diving as the smooth wall of water curls, and breaks, and surges in to the shore. Isabel laughs, and the dolphins rise up and jump and dive again.

"They look like they're on a loop," says Mac, "like something at a carnival, spinning round and round. And another!" he cries, as a dolphin leaps clear of the sea. "Always there's dolphins for you, my girl, but still no sign of my great white bird." Mac's fantasy, on every coast he'd been on: to look out towards the horizon and see an albatross, bobbing gently and at rest.

"Maybe for *your* next birthday, Dad," Isabel calls, whooping as another dolphin somersaults from a wave's sheer face.

On the top of his pylon, the poet has seen the creatures too, leaning forward towards their movement, leaning back as they plunge down into the blue.

"There's got to be a poem in that," says Ani. "If I was going to write a poem, I'd write about dolphins. They always look so happy — and it's always such a surprise to see them."

21

Mac laughs, grabbing her hand with one of his, Isabel's with the other, and skipping them all along the sand. "It's a grand omen for Bella's tenth birthday — that's what it is. Now, I want to pop home and try a slice of that lovely cake." And he starts to run, his two girls — as he calls to them through the wind — hanging on to him and flying across the sand like his coattails.

But as they reach the rocks and begin to climb up to the street, he pauses, looking back along the stretch of sand. What does a poet look like, up close? he wonders. Would he look different to how he looked before the war? Would you be able to see some trace of his occupation about him somewhere, like loose words tucked into his coat pocket? Mac strains to pick out the shape of the man's hat, his head, his body way off down the beach. *And how will he get down?* The incoming tide is roiling around the bottom of the uprights, white flecks of spray bursting as the water breaks.

"Do you not want your cake then?" Ani teases from the top of the cliff, hurrying him up. And Mac takes the stairs two at a time, breathless when he reaches the grass.

3

He'd remembered as soon as he reached the beach. Way down at the southern end, tucked under the line of Sandon Point, there was the old jetty, its boardwalk fractured here, disappeared there, and its pylons polished to smooth silver wood by the coming and going of the sea. He remembered, too, that when he and Iris were kids there were trains running along it, across the ocean's waves, ferrying loads of coal to waiting ships. They would watch from the northern end of the sand, the distance reducing the engines and their carriages to tiny, shiny toys. That was years ago; by the time he went to the war, nine years back, the jetty was already heading towards the piecemeal forest of trunks and planes that he sees now. By the time he went to war, it was already a relic, a ruin.

This morning, it had come to him all of a sudden, the urge to shinny up the trunk of

one of those pylons along the waterline and watch the tide ebb and flow from above. Back then, he'd never tried, but he's lighter now, for sure, and sprier too. He's seen the calligraphic dash of his own shadow as it runs alongside him and its narrow elongation across the sand seems dangerously accurate.

All right, he'd thought, *come on* — pelting along so that the hard sand reverberated with his footsteps. *St. Simeon of Thirroul, will you be, Roy McKinnon? Perch yourself on your pole and wait for inspiration?* And he'd set his foot against the vertical surface and pulled himself up, light as a feather.

"But there's nothing of you," Iris had said again and again over the first meal she made for him. And he explained how little eating he found he did now, how little eating, and how little sleeping. People used to tell him he looked like Fred Astaire, slender, and kind — although it was his friend Frank Draper who could dance like a dream. Now they used words like "scrawny" and "gaunt." And no one hummed "Top Hat, White Tie and Tails" when they saw him.

"We'll soon have you sorted now you're here," Iris had said, plying him with potatoes and gravy, which he arranged on his plate, and then left.

Balancing now on the pole's narrow top, he wishes he could believe her. Or, better yet, that the midday sun might somehow transform him into an extension of this tall, thin trunk, taller and thinner and subsumed into its top. And if he never came down? Surely that would be no less daft, in his sister's opinion, than opting into a war in the first place, or fancying yourself a poet in the middle of it, or taking three years after discharge to come home.

Where he sits now, up in the air, hoping to disappear into the clear light of noon.

From the top of the pylon, Roy McKinnon watches dolphins surface and dive like wooden cutouts in a carnival shooting gallery. Up and down; above, then below. He raises his right arm, steadies it, and points his finger. He could take a clear shot from up here.

How many men did you kill, Roy? How many times did you raise that gun and fire?

Out on the horizon, he sees a ship making for Melbourne, retracing the route that brought him to Sydney and here, at last, just the week before. For the better part of three years, since the war's end, he'd mooched around the farthest parts of the country, staying out of the way of people he knew, staying out of the way of his sister,

her questions. There was a strange consolation in his parents' dying while he'd been overseas — if his father had faced him down and asked about numbers, he could never have refused to answer.

Coming back in '45, he'd bounced from Sydney out west to the unknown emptiness of a sheep farm, then down to Melbourne for a disastrous spell back working as a teacher. He'd known from the first day that he'd lost his place in any classroom. Everything he'd loved about the children — their optimism, their noise, and their unbridled curiosity — now rankled and pinched at his skin and his nerves, poking him into impatience and frustration and a final, awful fury. *The things I could tell you,* he wanted to shout above their perceived uninterest, or disrespect. *The things I have seen.* He'd walked out of that school yard and never gone back.

In Adelaide, then, he'd worked peaceably with a bunch of Germans making wine, thinking about the oddness of history. Then he went farther west, across the whole body of the continent, until he landed in the Western Australian wheat fields as a harvest was coming in.

He'd carried a notebook in his left breast pocket, the exact size and shape of the

metal-plated New Testament Iris had made him carry through the war. But for all the things he saw, all the people he met, all the places he visited and the things that he did, he could never tease out a single line or observation to write down.

Messed up then, aren't you, buster, he thinks now, taking another shot at a dolphin with his cocked fingers, *if you can come up with poetry in the middle of some muddy bridgehead and not find a single sentence here?* He'd almost put his name down for one of the farm schemes for soldiers — it would be something, he'd thought, to have someone else etch out a plot of land somewhere and tell you you had to make do with it. But in the end, he'd traced the edge of Australia from Fremantle around to Sydney, and caught the train down here, to Thirroul, to his sister's place — the closest thing to a home he had now, he supposed.

Back along the beach, on a verge thick with lantana, D. H. Lawrence once sat still awhile and wrote a book — Roy nods to the low bungalow every time he passes it. If Lawrence could write here, he figures, maybe he can too. *If it's not fancying yourself to put yourself with* Lady Chatterley, *mate.*

A wave surges up around the pylon, drenching his feet, his shins, his knees —

it'll be a wet dismount, if he's going to make it home for lunch. He shades his eyes and looks north along the beach, past the place where Lawrence worked, past a sculptural outcrop of rocks, and beyond to where his sister lives, across from the council pool's pump house. He can almost see her, worrying along the edge of the sand, wondering what silly place he's walked to now. There are dozens more pylons stretching away from him and out to sea, some still topped with wide, wooden girders and the last of the railway line's rails; others bare and uncapped, pointing straight to the sky. *One day,* he thinks, *one day I'll run along here and dive out through the horizon.*

"And will you go for a job with the trains, then, Roy? Or will you try for a job in the mines? Though I suppose there's the ice works, or the ice cream factory, if you wanted something" — she had pawed at the air, perhaps looking for a kind word — "sweeter." That was with his dinner too, the first night he arrived. The anxiety stretched across her elfin face, making it sharper, more judgmental. He'd forgotten how inappropriate his sister could make him feel — so short, she made him loom large; so fine, his own thinness did slip towards scraggy; so dark, his own brown hair looked mottled.

He'd forgotten how different they were.

"I don't know, Iris, I don't know what I'm doing. That's why I came home — here. That's what I want to find out." His fingers fiddled with the salt cellar until she reached across to settle it, perfect, in the middle of the table again.

"I just always think it's best to be busy."

Another wave surges up and he looks at his watch — midday, which he should have known, of course, from the sun. *Perhaps I don't pay enough attention anymore.* And perhaps that's the problem with trying to write, if he's walking around with his eyes shut.

He snorts: *In for a penny.* He's sure his sister thinks him mad — a seawater suit is only going to confirm it.

And it feels so good, so good to plunge down into the foamy surf — it's only just lapping his neck when he touches the bottom. The way his suit, his shirt, his underclothes press in around him as if he could feel the edges of himself more clearly.

Back on the shore, he's laughing with exhilaration, feeling in his coat pockets for the miracle of a shell or a barnacle to take home as a souvenir. If he were a cartoon, he thinks, he'd have a seahorse poking through his lapel like a boutonniere and wreaths of

seaweed looping around his waist for a belt. And he laughs again, this tall, lean man made taller and leaner again by the tight wet fit of his clothes.

4

The next week, on the afternoon set for Isabel's milkshake, Ani walks up through the village towards the station — past the grocer's, the co-op, the haberdasher's and the hairdresser's, the café that sells fancy china, the two rival shoe shops. She glances along the side street towards the railways' roundhouse, her view of its windows — glittering like a rich chandelier — cut by a passing engine, 3621: she registers its number, its pedigree, as Mac would say, and takes a deep breath of the thick cokey air.

This place. Down the coast from Sydney, there's a point where the border of Australia's sheer sandstone cliffs pulls inland a little, and a tiny sliver of plain opens up. This is the bluff at Stanwell Tops where the trains' tunnel emerges. This is the bluff where Hargrave flew his famous box kites, more than fifty years ago now. Ani's always wished she could have seen one, soaring

high and free.

The ridge heads inland, forming a line that sometimes mirrors, sometimes offsets and counteracts, the shape of the coast. And between these two lines, the water on one hand, the vast spread of the rest of the country on the other, a web of streets and avenues, groves and drives lace across the available land, held firm by the one road that feeds in from the north and out to the south.

And then there's the air, the nor'easters that play along the shoreline; the westerlies that dump fractious moods over the edge of the escarpment; the smoky drafts in late spring and summer that telegraph bushfires and then spur them on. There are soft sea breezes that tease and tickle with the lightest scent of salty water. There are southerly busters, powerful fronts that push up the coast to break open the heat of the day — they smell clean and crisp, and Ani pushes her nose hungrily into hot afternoons in search of their coming.

Reaching the bridge over the railway line, she pulls up short. A hearse is carrying a coffin up to the Anglican church, and Ani ducks her head quickly, her eyes down as the funeral procession passes. Don't turn to look at a hearse; don't count the number of

cars following in its wake; touch a button after the hearse has gone by: her father trained her in these superstitions in the wake of her mother's early death — Ani was only four. Now, she touches her finger to the button of her dress, and runs across the road towards the station, where Isabel stands with her nose in a book.

My lovely little thing, thinks Ani fiercely, pulling her into a hug. She's quiet, Isabel, and careful — when she bounds along the beach with Mac, her blond hair flying, or follows his leap from a high board down into the pool, Ani can see the way she works at this playfulness, this exuberance, because she knows her father loves it. With Ani, just the two of them, Isabel has a stillness that Ani knows is not usual in a ten-year-old. And she knows this because she remembers it in herself.

Isabel smiles up at her, then down at the page, as Ani scans the width of the sky, the line of the escarpment against its blue. It's a happy thing to stand and to gaze — she reaches out without looking and pats down Isabel's end-of-the-day hair, and her daughter catches her hand and squeezes it without looking up.

The train is late.

"What flavor milkshake today, Bella?"

"Chocolate malted" — without a glance.

"Chocolate malted," Ani repeats, smiling — it's the full stretch of her daughter's available luxury.

Across the tracks a pane of glass rattles. Ani glances towards the sound and sees a window open in the Railway Institute's library. Such fascinating things, libraries. She closes her eyes. She could walk inside and step into a murder, a love story, a complete account of somebody else's life, or mutiny on the high seas. Such potential; such adventure — there's a shimmer of malfeasance in trying other ways of being.

She loves their trips to the library, loves the sight of their three separate piles stacked on Miss Fadden's desk — the family's collection of daydreams and instruction. Isabel always arrives with a list, filling it as best she can and asking for the librarian's assurances of happily ever after. But Mac loves to graze, weighing up the attractions and merits of different books as if he had really to choose between fighting off Mormons with Zane Grey's spry heroine or undertaking a secret mission with Hornblower in Central America. She loves watching him make his selection, as if it might open up new ways into his curiosity, his imagination.

"What if I kept some books at work, well

away from your eyes," he teased her once in a while, "for a little bit of privacy?" Yet whenever she went to the library with him, she couldn't resist watching his hand move along the shelves, choosing an adventure with airplanes and jungles, dismissing another with cowboys and wagons. She'd seen him pause at *Gone with the Wind,* and move on to *Sons and Lovers.*

"What you looking at, Ani?" he'd asked, without turning towards her. "You know where my loyalties lie."

Next to the railway was a field, with men and youths playing football for their lives. When Mac brought her to the coast, she'd carried *Kangaroo* like a literary Baedeker, trawling its pages for identifiable spots, even recognizable people — against Mac's protestations that it was a novel, "a novel, love, that's made up, you know, made up, and years ago to boot." But even now, she shrugs. Here is the railway; behind her is the football — just like the book. This place belongs to Lawrence; she is living the next chapter of a famous story.

From the football field now comes a surge of chants and cheers, and Ani turns towards the noise. It makes her shiver sometimes, that open stretch of grass: effigies were burned there in the war — Hitler first, and

then rough approximations of the nameless Japanese men who were thought to be coming to invade. A high whistle rises up and Ani remembers the air-raid sirens, the dark stuffiness of the shelter Mac dug in the backyard.

"Like being buried alive while you're waiting to be bombed," he always said, insisting on sitting aboveground, in the garden, so he could see if any planes came close. He'd been so certain of his own survival — his immortality — that she'd worked hard not to be anxious for him, out there and exposed.

Now, a short, sharp siren comes from the north — *Probably the roundhouse,* thinks Ani — and she turns away from remembering the war, and football, and Mr. Lawrence. Above the ridge, the clouds are inching towards sunset, morphing from puffy, fluffy white shapes that Isabel might place at the top of a drawing to something longer and more elegant. It will be a glorious show, firing the clouds with color while the greens and browns in the scarp and its trees drain towards darkness.

"You're for town, Mrs. Lachlan?" Luddy, the young stationmaster, is at her elbow. But as Ani nods, he shakes his head. "Sounds like there's a problem with the

trains coming through — an accident along the line and they're not letting anything pass. Do you want to wait a while, or will I try to get a message to Mac, let him know you're not coming?"

Isabel looks up, her finger marking her place on the page: "My birthday treat, my milkshake . . ."

Ani frowns, tucking Isabel's hair back into its bunches again. She's been looking forward to it too — walking down Crown Street, looking at the shops, sipping her own tall, cold drink. She hates problems she can't solve, but: "I suppose you'd better, Luddy. Tell Mac we'll see him at home?"

And he smiles at her, nodding and tweaking Isabel's neater hair.

"Can we go to the beach then, Mum? Can we go to the beach on the way home?"

"We can, Bella. Still a bit of a treat. We'll go down to the rock pool, see if we can find a pretty shell." She holds her hand out to her daughter, who makes a great show of smiling and waving to Luddy.

The sun has almost left the sand by the time they reach its edge, Isabel flying towards the water while Ani bundles up shoes, socks, and bags and picks her way across to the rock shelf. Almost every day, she comes down to the beach, but nothing

has ever taken away the surprise of seeing it. A country girl, grown up on the Hay Plains in the far west of New South Wales, the first time she saw the ocean was the first time she'd seen anything so big and so blue that wasn't a vast, dry sky. When she was married; when she'd moved to the coast.

Leaning against Mac, back then, on her first day in Thirroul, she'd had no sense that the sea would be so enormous. She could hear it; she could smell it. And she could taste it — it was salty, which she had expected, but it was sticky too, which she hadn't. And all of this had seemed so much bigger, so much more impressive than the wide stretch of its color, the vast stretch of its space.

"I didn't think," she'd said softly to her new husband, "I didn't think it would be so many things all at once."

He'd squeezed her hand, kissed her shoulder. "At home," he said, "it's mostly grey, but I like this color, this thick and briny blue." A wave roared at the edge of the rocks, and Ani had jumped back, startled at how high, how near, it reared. "It just wants to meet you," said Mac, laughing, "just wants to see who you are."

Now, in this late afternoon, Ani watches Isabel run across the rocks to the very lip of

the land. A surging wave would no longer make her jump, and the tide is a long way out in any case, pushing a low burst of white water against the rocks once in a while. A crab scurries beneath a heap of seaweed that smells of pure salt; another scuttles under a rock at the bottom of a shallow pool. There are purple barnacles and tiny orange conches, striped shells and smooth rocks.

Overhead, two seagulls swoop against the blue sky, making their barking calls. Isabel barks back from the shore and the birds settle on the sand at a safe distance as Ani laughs, leaning forward at the edge of one deep rock pool. There's a clamshell down there, a beautiful thing, pearly silver inside and gold and rose-pink outside — colors that belong to pretty dresses, rich taffeta, and swirling dances. She pushes up her sleeve, dips in her arm, shivering. It will feel warm in just a moment. The strange tricks of distance and perspective — her fingers feel for the shell as deep as she thinks it is, but still wave uselessly above it. She inches forward and grasps the pretty shape.

The number of rocks she's taken from this beach in those twelve years; the number of days she's combed along its shore; the number of nights she's come down here with Mac. She closes her eyes and sees the

two of them dancing along the sand in the weeks after the war, their eyes closed to the barbed wire that still looped its indecipherable script along the waterline. On those nights, if there'd been enough moon, she was sure they could have danced out across the ocean's marbled surface, and said so.

"You make me romantical," her husband had said then, and she'd laughed at the frolic of his words. He was many things, Mackenzie Lachlan, strong, and true, and hers. But he was purpose, and he was pragmatism — the moments of sentiment, of soft sweetness or high emotion, were exceptions, and she treasured them for that.

"What about this, Isabel?" she calls across to her daughter. "Treasure enough?"

She loves her daughter's careful attention — the paragraphs in her book; the shell cupped in the palm of her hand; completely considered.

"It looks like something precious," says Isabel.

"Like an evening dress?"

"Maybe, but a listening-to-music one, not a dancing one."

"I thought dancing and swirling," says Ani gravely, "but you might be right." She rubs at the colors, brushing the tiniest specks of sand from the shell's dents and pocks.

"Home then?" And her daughter surges back again, butting in at her side.

"How long will it take Dad, if the trains are stopped?"

Ani shakes her head, the opalescent shell heavy in her pocket.

"Let's see," she says. "You finish your book, and we'll see how long it is before he's coming along the street." She holds out her hand to her daughter and they climb the stairs cut into the cliff two at a time.

The house is quiet and Ani, cutting vegetables in the kitchen, can hear the drumming of Isabel's fingers on the windowsill in the next room as she sits and waits for her father. She smiles, singing a soft lullaby in her father's old language in time to the gentle beat, its angular syllables studded with *t*'s and *k*'s and *n*'s. There are still no trains, and the silence is starting to ring.

Then: "Mum?" There's a tightness in her daughter's voice. "There's a car at the gate." Ani hears her daughter shift, can sense her stiffen.

"Mum?" Isabel's voice is less certain again. "There's a big black car."

In the kitchen, Ani tries to stop the movement of the knife but the end of the blade nicks her thumb. She stares at the skin; just

dented, she thinks at first, but then the blood comes and she hears Isabel say again, "Mum?" — and feels her pressing in at her side, against the table.

There's a black car at the gate. She's almost thirty-seven years old. Here is her daughter. Where is her husband? Her thumb is starting to bleed. The kitchen is very quiet and very bright, and Ani hears herself say: "Now, Bella, run next door to Mrs. May and I'll get you when it — when I —"

"But I want to wait for Da—" Isabel begins, and Ani hears her own voice, uncharacteristically harsh: "Isabel — so help me — I will not tell you again." The words scrape the walls like sharpness against glass and she squeezes her eyes tight as her daughter throws the shell hard against the linoleum floor — it shatters into five sharp pieces — and slams the door.

So this is what happens, thinks Ani as the front gate unlatches, the footfalls hit the stairs, a knuckle taps the wooden frame of the screen door, and the minister calls, "Mrs. Lachlan?"

She closes her eyes and sees herself lying next to Mac, nine years ago now, the day Australia's war was declared. "But what does it mean, 'Australia is also at war'? What does that mean for us?"

"Needn't mean anything," Mac had said. "They'll need the railways to keep running, so I should be all right."

"But would you want to go? Would you rather?" She remembered her father's friends trading stories from the Great War, teasing him for missing the fun, the adventure, and being stuck behind the ramshackle fence of some internment camp instead.

"Don't be daft, Ani love; leave you and Isabel and go off to be killed? They'll need the trains, so they'll be after us to stay — and I'm not the heroic type, now, am I?" He tickled above her hip bone so that she giggled and squirmed. "I intend to go on living — always have, and always will."

She'd grabbed his fingers, pushing them away. "But if Australia's at war, then we're at war, aren't we, you and me? Our melancholy duty, like Mr. Menzies said? We'd have to fight, if the war came here. We'd have to be able to kill an enemy. And there'll be dying, so much dying."

Keep us safe, she'd thought, over and over, *keep us safe,* through the next six years. As she watched women becoming wives without husbands, mothers without sons, Ani had an image of a searchlight sweeping around, illuminating this woman:

widowed; that one: her son on a drowned ship.

Now that searchlight has found her, catching her in its sweep and pinning her, arbitrary and irrevocable.

So this is what happens, she thinks again — so distinctly that she wonders if she says it aloud. She presses a tea towel onto her thumb and walks towards the front door, the men, the news that the car has brought. The house has never seemed so long and at each step she thinks, *This is how I will remember this.*

The door at the end of the hall is her last hope: Ani on one side and the men, and the night, and the news on the other. *If I keep my eyes closed,* she thinks, shutting them fast, *perhaps I'll open them and find I've been asleep this whole time. Fast asleep and dreaming.*

"Mrs. Lachlan?" says the minister again. "Can we come in?"

5

First came the knock on the window, and then the boy's voice: "Mr. Lachlan? Mackenzie Lachlan? Early shift."

Ani opened her eyes as Mac replied, "I'm here, I'm coming," and felt the bed pitch a little as he stood up. "Go back to sleep, love," he said then, without turning towards her. He always knew when her eyes had opened.

She smiled and rolled onto his side of the bed, feeling its warmth and reaching out to touch him as he pulled on his trousers, his undershirt, his shirt, and his coat.

"I'll stay awake till I hear your train, you know that," she said, her palm resting against his back as he sat to tie his boots. "And I'll see you at the end of your day."

And he leaned back then, turning so that she could feel his weight pressed down on her as he kissed her mouth, her forehead, the top of her bright, light hair. "The end of

my day is when I come back to you," he said, kissing her with the last word. "Now go back to sleep — there's not even a bird awake out there."

She listened as he opened the front door and closed it again gently, listened as his boots made the front stairs creak, as he stepped over the last one, which was loudest of all. She listened as he went out through the gate and onto the road. And she tried to picture how far he walked before his footsteps faded.

It was early spring, 1945, and the war was over. The war was finally done. The night before, at the movies, they'd seen a newsreel of the celebrations in Sydney — images of a man dancing through Martin Place, spinning round and round. When the film had ended, and the lights came up, Mac had grabbed her waist and danced her out into the street — past everyone, past their smiles and their laughter. And on they'd spun, twirling and laughing, in and out of the puddles of streetlight, and all the way back home.

Now, in the darkness, she heard the train's whistle — there he was; off he went. And as she settled into sleep again, she reached out towards the place where he'd slept not a half hour before and sensed the sure shape

46

of Mac's body against her own as clearly as if he were still there. Bright against her closed eyes, she saw that dancing man, spinning and leaping, an evocation of happiness, spinning into a line of light.

6

Slowly, carefully, Ani opens her eyes, but the men are still there, their hats in front of them like shields: Reverend Forrest, the minister; Luddy Oliver, the stationmaster; and a pale man in a dark suit who she knows, without asking, will be from the railways. She unlatches the door and holds it open, nodding at all three as they walk into her house.

"I'm sorry," she says, gesturing towards the shell, "I haven't had a chance to sweep that up. I'm just trying to get a meal ready for Mac." His name falls hard in the quiet room, and the men smile; three small, uneasy smiles. She says, "Of course you should sit down," sitting down herself. The brightness of that searchlight is unbearable.

"My dear," says Reverend Forrest, disconcertingly familiar. "I'm so sorry, but there's been an accident."

She says, "Of course." She says, "Do you

need to tell me what happened?" Because whatever has happened, Mac clearly isn't coming home.

The room stretches as if her armchair has pushed itself miles back — a suburb, a desert, a continent away — so that she can barely hear the men's voices. An accident, an engine shunting — she concentrates on the shorthand of "engine"; Mac would have told her its full number, its every particular, rivet, and plate.

An engine shunting, and Mac had jumped down and gone round to check the coupling. They think. They're not sure yet — no one is sure. But there'll be an inquiry later, and the coroner, they say. The coroner.

What they are sure of is that an engine coupling with something — well, an engine coupling with *anything* — it exerts a powerful lot of force. And.

Their voices fall away to nothing. Ani doesn't move. She thinks, *How dare they bring this into my house? Mac would never have allowed this sort of thing to be said, out of the blue, all of a sudden, and at dinnertime.* She thinks, *If we'd arranged to meet him earlier, this would never have happened. We'd have had our milkshakes and come home together.* She thinks, *I did not keep him alive through six years of war for this.* She thinks,

There's been a mistake — it's someone else's man, someone else's husband, anyone's. She thinks, *This throbbing in my thumb, I can feel it in my throat, in my forehead, in my stomach.* She thinks, *I yelled at Isabel, I said "so help me." I don't* say *things like that.*

She says, "I should make you some tea," and the minister stands up, touching her shoulder lightly, and saying, "No, no, let me — the kitchen through here? And what's this blood?" He peels the towel away from her thumb and stares at it a moment as if this might stem the flow. And it works. "You have to be brave, Anikka," he says.

Her Christian name — she's surprised he even knows it. *But perhaps,* she thinks, *you can no longer be called Mrs. Something when there is no Mr. Something. Perhaps you stop being Mrs. Someone when Mr. Someone stops being.*

The man from the railways is talking again. About the accident, about the injuries sustained, he doesn't want her to think of these, of course, but under the circumstances they will arrange for a cremation as soon as possible — it can be arranged for tomorrow, and he tells her this as if the arrangement is already in train. And, "You do not need to see the body, Mrs. Lachlan. You do not need to see the body."

From the kitchen, she hears the kettle clatter against the edge of the sink, its bottom sizzling a moment later as the minister puts it onto the stove. She hears the scrape of it sliding in towards the middle of the hot plate, hears the stove door creak as the minister opens it to add a little more kindling, a little more coal. She closes her eyes and sees the leap of the flames, and their lick.

"What a strange thing," she says at last, "when my husband can walk down to work one morning and be taken for cremation the next. It seems very —" She shakes her head. The rush of it; the rank implausibility.

"This is what we do, Mrs. Lachlan." The railways man leans forward a little, reaching out to stop her words. "The inquiry will happen later, but we organize the cremation as quickly as possible. I'll be there, and Reverend Forrest. But you do not need to see the body." And as he says this again, Ani finds that she cannot disagree with him, is not sure if she wants to, or even if she should. There is something hypnotic about the phrase.

"I'll be with him, Mrs. Lachlan." The minister is passing her tea in a chipped cup she would never offer a guest, very milky and, when she puts it up to her lips, very

51

sweet. "I'll say his prayers." And she swallows, wondering about the pale-black tea, no sugar, which she usually drinks. Perhaps she isn't supposed to drink that anymore either. And this tastes surprisingly good.

Through the wall behind her, Ani hears the kitchen fire spit again in its box and closes her eyes against the image of her husband's body — muscular, burly, familiar — set among its flames.

"Tomorrow, then," she says. "Yes, I see. Tomorrow."

Of course they will organize the notices, the railways man goes on, and the minister will be ready to talk with her, whenever she is ready, about a memorial service in the place of a funeral. "Whenever you're ready, Mrs. Lachlan, just whenever you're ready."

And as they sit and watch her drink her tea, she tries to remember Mac's voice and fails. *Is that it? Has it gone?* And how long will these three men now sit here, watching the rise and the fall of her cup?

"We don't want you to feel that things will be hard now," the railways man says then, patting his hands against the air as if he is trying to soften his own words. "You won't be on your own with this."

"Of course I won't be on my own. My daughter will be with me." Ani wonders that

52

the words can fit through her tightly clenched teeth. "Thank you for the tea." It's peculiar to be sitting in her own armchair, staring, wondering what she's supposed to do, wondering if there's anything she can say that will make it all a mistake that can be swept away, and Mac just home late for his supper.

Now Luddy is crouching in front of her, balancing himself with one hand on the arm of her chair — so close she can smell the sooty steam on him. She draws in a huge breath and the room rushes in across the continents, the deserts, the suburbs, and back to its normal size.

"This afternoon," Luddy begins. "I'm sorry, Mrs. Lachlan, I had no idea this afternoon. I did call through the message that you'd gone home. But of course he wasn't, of course he didn't . . ." He means to comfort her, to say something big and warm — she can see that. But his tears drip onto the carpet while she stares at her thumb, and then her hand's solidity dissolves somehow so she sees only the wet drops he's leaving on the ground.

"Thank you," she says. There are a thousand alternatives, a thousand other possibilities for what else might be happening in the world this night. And Mac is at the center

of them all, walking along the street, whistling to Isabel, coming through the gate, food on the table, calling her name — "Ani." She smiles: *There's his voice.*

A sweetness, then, and she sniffs the air. "I've left the chops," she says. The smell of burning flesh is close and enormous; the stationmaster on his feet, the minister into the kitchen to pull the meat away from the heat almost before she's finished the sentence.

The railways man looks into the middle distance, his hands fiddling with the hat in his lap.

As long as I keep them here, thinks Ani wildly, *they can't tell anyone else what's happened. As long as I keep them here, as far as anybody knows, my husband is safely alive.* And so she sits, and she waits, until she can bear the waiting no longer.

"I'm sorry," she says then, "I'm sure there are all sorts of things that I should be asking and you should be telling me, but I think I need you to leave."

"Mrs. Lachlan." The railways man stands up, extends his hand — it's formal, like a presentation, or an introduction. "I'm so sorry to have been the bearer of this news. If there's anything we can do . . ."

But she shakes her head, follows them all

to the door, and even thinks to send her wishes to the minister's wife, and the stationmaster's. From the corner of her eye, she sees Mrs. May framed in her own doorway, imagines Isabel pressed in behind her, wanting to look but not sure if she wants to see.

But where is his body now — right now? Anikka thinks suddenly. *And who will drive it up the mountain to be burned tomorrow?* Her mouth almost opens to call this last, terrible question across her front yard but then she sees the shape its words would make against the quiet night.

Impossible.

The noise of the car, its engine idling, is too round and warm to have brought such cold, hard news. Next door, Mrs. May's screen door opens slowly and Ani hears her call softly, "Are you there, love? Are you there, Ani?" But Ani's voice has gone and she doesn't know if she could have cried out, or stopped herself from falling, if Mrs. May hadn't come through the gate then to put her arms around her and hold her up. Saying, "Shhh," saying, "There," saying, "It's all right — Bella's inside."

"Shhhh, love. Shhhhh."

Across the rooftops, across the backyards, across the grass and the sand and the

shoreline, the sound of the ocean is rolling and turning; for the first time in as long as she can remember — as long as she's been on the coast — Ani can't think whether the tide is coming in or going out. She feels a saltiness in her mouth, like a great gulp of the sea, and realizes she's crying. Quiet and awful crying in the dark, as regular as breathing.

This is how it will be, she thinks.

In the darkness, then, she sees something move against the flowers on Mrs. May's side of the fence, and she calls out, "Bella?" The girl is so thin against the night, slipping around, slipping through the gate, wedging herself in between her mother and the wall of the house. "I'm sorry I yelled before, Bella, but . . ." She shudders, appalled that she doesn't even know what to say to her own little girl, and can only let her head nod slightly as her daughter pushes close and asks one small, scared question.

"My dadda? My dad?"

The ocean rolls and turns, and there are stars above now, and a mopoke somewhere close in a tree, calling its own name. *I don't know what to say,* Ani thinks again. And then, *I've got to get the smell of that meat out of the house.* The awfulness of wasted food.

She stands up, Mrs. May holding her left

hand, Isabel holding her right. "All right, let's go in then," says Ani. "Let's go in and see what happens next."

And as she pulls the wire door out towards herself, she hears the rumble, the growl of a train moving along its tracks.

At the end of it all, she stands awhile in her daughter's room, watching her quiet oblivion. Every night for ten years, she's done this. *All those years,* she thinks now, *all those benedictions I made for your safety and your health, I was concentrating on the wrong person. I was protecting the wrong one.*

It's a nasty thought. She pushes hard at the side of her head to dislodge it.

"Beautiful Bella," she whispers, leaning down to kiss her shoulder. *You and me. You and me. You and me.*

From some deep crevasse in her mind, she retrieves her father's story about a rainbow bridge that spans the world of the mortals and the world of the gods. If she could find the right rainbow, her father had told her when she was young, she might skip along it to see her mother. But even in the wide space of the southwest, the beginnings of rainbows had been hard to catch.

"You only need one dream to slip along, Ani," her father had said, "one moment,

and you're up one side of the rainbow and sliding down the other for the briefest visit, the shortest glimpse — but it's enough. It can be enough."

She smoothes Isabel's blanket, the next thought so strong, so vehement, that her hand shakes and her daughter stirs against the movement. *How could I not have known, not have felt it when it happened? I was on the platform. I was at the beach. I was slicing stupid carrots.*

"Mac?" she says at last, climbing into her own bed. "Where are you?" Outside, a few crickets are calling, and the waves are turning, gently and lengthily, below the staccato beat of the insects' sound. A world with no Mac.

The worst of it is how normal, how usual, how familiar the house feels — *But perhaps this is shock,* she thinks, *and some pummeling comes later.* It would be easier if some part of the house had collapsed, if there was some destruction to see.

In the corner of the room, she sees his socks, an undershirt, crumpled on top of the laundry basket, and is puzzled by the idea of washing them. His feet will never fill out that wool again; his torso will never stretch that cotton to capacity. She makes herself think these things, wondering how

58

she should feel. She recites his name over and over in her mind, wondering how she might manage to close her eyes — or open them again in the morning.

"Mackenzie Lachlan," she says aloud at last, "I can't sleep; can you tell me a story?" The way she used to say it, when he was home, when he was here.

It's the darkest, coldest time of night, and her only answer is three dogs passing mournful barks between them as the night's breezes drop away. Aching with tiredness, her hands rub at her arms, creep across to her belly, up to her breasts, and she is thinking about the last time her husband touched her. Against any other memory she might find, here is this thing that was only the two of them — and she hadn't realized it was happening for the very last time.

She stills her hands, her body uninterested in their cold, tiny touch. *Never again,* she thinks. *Never again.* Somewhere deep in the center of herself, she senses that the decisions she will make tonight, tomorrow, in the world's next days, will govern and dictate what happens in what is left of her own life — she's never thought of that as a finite stretch before.

"No matter," she says, too loud and reckless. As if she will ever care what anything is

or isn't again.

A car turns into the street and crawls past the window, its lights stirring up another dog and then the dog's owner, who yells, harshly, for the little bugger to shut up. Ani flinches, as if the command was a response to her noise, her words.

Rolling fast into the empty space in the bed, she presses herself — facedown and hard — into the space where Mac should be and can almost feel his firm, strong shape. A mattress spring twists unexpectedly beneath her sudden movement, poking so sharply into the softness of her belly that she recoils fast onto the other side of the bed, her tears distracting her from the urgent surge of desire she feels and doesn't want to.

The car's headlights move back along the street, the dog silent this time, and as they turn and head down the hill it's as if a little of their shine stays on, stuck in the tongue and groove of Ani's bedroom walls. There are birds then, here and there, and then one massed and raucous outburst.

The dawn is coming, a new day; the next day. She sighs, turns her pillow over, and is suddenly asleep.

Ani Lachlan sleeps through the washes of the morning's colors and the warm bril-

liance of sunrise. She sleeps in a world where she remembers, perfectly, every detail about her husband, this day, that sentence, another touch. She will remember it all in the deepest sleep, and lose it again the moment her eyes open and she wonders how late it must be for the sun to already be so high and then remembers, in the next instant, what happened the day before.

7

On the nights when he can't sleep, which is most nights, Roy McKinnon breaks out of his sister's shut-up house, silent as a thief, and continues the walks with which he fills his days. He's used to the tiredness by now — years without proper sleep will do that for you, and he can't remember having had a decent rest since he shipped out in 1940. He's used to the strange pliability of the time when most people sleep — the way nocturnal minutes can drag out like hours; the way nocturnal hours can collapse into seconds. If war was good for anything, it was good training for boredom; God, the waiting — the noise and the waiting. These things were never what you expected them to be.

He slides the bolt in the lower half of the back door — the half that creaks less — and pushes open its panel, ducking underneath and shushing the hens as they stir and mut-

ter in their coop. It's too quiet tonight; he hasn't heard a train for hours, and as he thinks this, he hears an engine puffing up the line. What is it — nine o'clock? Maybe ten? Iris has been in bed an hour or more already, and most of the lights in the village's houses are already switched off. Roy shakes his head: do people really need so much time to dream?

Stretching up towards the stars, he leaps the fence and pads over to the council baths. He'll stay close tonight, he thinks; his legs don't have the power to stride for miles.

The surface of the pool rocks a little as if it's trying to level itself. It was beautiful here, before the war; its glorious underwater lighting turned the water into a pond of gold. No way they'd put that back — such extravagance, such luxury.

A cormorant raises its head from its perch on the lamppost, but nothing else stirs, and Roy settles himself cross-legged by the water's edge, trailing his fingers through the cool, salty water, and letting them hang, dripping, above the concrete beside him. Once, a couple of nights ago, he was certain he saw the letter *A* in one of these wet splodges on the pavement, and he'd walked through the hours till sunrise calling out every word he could think of that began

with *A,* in case one of them sparked some inspiration. On the top of the hill in Austinmer, someone's window had rattled open and a man called, "For pity's sake, mate." Farther down, in the hollow below the station, he called, "Ascendant. Anastrophe. Atlantes" — and a cat called back in reply.

"Adumbrate. Aurora." Those two were particularly beautiful, he'd thought, shouting them as he passed the Presbyterian manse and imagined the minister and his wife sleeping peaceably inside. "Abatis. Ablation. Abulia." It was like the dictionary game he'd played in his classrooms, declaiming words, suggesting meanings, watching the younger kids struggle with the spellings, the older ones puzzle at the definitions. "Abulia: I think it's a flower, sir." And, "I don't. I think it's a country." In the dark night of some battle somewhere, he'd remembered a classroom of voices learning how to spell "accommodation," the way the letters came out naturally as a sweet and lilting song. A-double-c, o-double-m, o-d-a-t-i-o-n. He'd felt the beat, the rhythm, at the center of himself, and he'd sung the phrase out, over and over like a salve, until the firing stopped at last and his world settled into another temporary peace.

He'd known that night, known that he'd

never be able to teach a child a thing again, the weight of too many terrible stories pressing against his teeth, wanting to spill out across some innocent imagination, and too much fury and shock stored up in the muscles that used to guide children's pens across their first pages, or kick balls as far as a lunchtime field allowed.

Now, he brushes his fingers across the pool's surface and lets the water fall. Nothing. He stands, puffing out a mouthful of air as he looks across Thirroul's scattered houses. Maybe he will walk a little after all, and he sets off past the pump house and up the hill; he'll just nip round to Lawrence's place, he thinks, and then head home. But every light in the usually dark bungalow is blazing and Roy scoots away from the illumination. What could the matter be? Something wrong? Someone ill?

Why do you always suspect the worst, Roy McKinnon? There must be other people who don't sleep too — or maybe they're having a party. People must still have parties, he expects, although he can't recall having been to one since 1939.

He'd like to set up a fraternity for his fellow insomniacs. There were doctors in the war who said that the worst cases of shock and hysteria could be cured by nothing

more than a good night's sleep. He remembers reading about it — it sounded so improbable. Exhausted air-raid and fire wardens were hypnotized into a restful sleep, he'd read, from which they awoke the next day *refreshed and able to carry on.*

He'd spent the next dozen nights or so swinging his own watch in front of his eyes.

He turns along Surfers Parade and a gust of wind buffets him from behind; he imagines himself for a moment surfing along this aptly named street, carried forward over its topography, floating and free. He always meant to try surfing when he was a kid — there must be such freedom, such poetry in gliding across the water's surface on a big, wooden board. But the boys who surfed all knew what they were doing — there were competitions and carnivals — and Roy could never get up the courage to walk into the water and fail in front of their experience.

He surges forward, running now, with his arms out like he remembers a surfer's stance to be. Maybe his missing words are etched farther out on the deeper water — he'll hunt around for a board to borrow tomorrow, old enough now not to care how he looks.

The wind pushes him again and he leaps,

stumbling as he hears a woman's voice, low and dreadful, coming out of one of the darkened houses. He stops, counts along. Was this the Mays' place or the Lachlans' place? He remembers Mackenzie Lachlan from the railways, from the football. Must ask Iris if they still live there — or if his counting, like his memory, is out.

Standing in the shadow of an oleander, he leans in towards the noise, its despair, its totality. *If it is the Lachlans', is that Mrs. Lachlan?* He has a faint memory of someone tall and slender, standing very still beyond the rush of a game, with blond hair, he thinks, that lit up under the sun. Someone quiet, contained; it's not an image he can match to this terrific noise.

The sobbing breaks off; there's a cough, then the rattle of a window sash. Roy sees the backlit shape of someone for an instant and senses a pair of hands tearing at hair, perhaps even at skin, it seems, before he darts on past the front of the house and along the street. Not wanting to be caught spying on whatever enormity is playing out inside.

Glancing up at the stars as he turns down the hill, he sees one shoot straight from the west towards the ocean. And he watches it fade, wishing that whoever is crying like a

demon in the weatherboard house behind him might sleep long, and sleep well, and sleep soon.

8

"Mum?" Isabel's voice sounds far away, but urgent. "Mum? The car's back — those men have come again. Reverend Forrest and the man from the railways. Mum?"

It's three days, maybe four, beyond the accident — Ani has trouble distinguishing them — and as she pushes herself up out of sleep, the memory of Mac hauling himself over the edge of the swimming pool comes to her through her own movement. All the strength, all the push of his arms as he levered himself out of the water, back into his body's weight, and up onto the concrete ledge of the wall; her own wrists feel thin enough to snap.

"Bella? Are you all right? I'm sorry, darling, I must have been sleeping." She takes Isabel's hand and pulls herself up, surprised to find she's been asleep, surprised to find herself outside, in the backyard, on the grass.

"Reverend Forrest's here again, Mum, and I think it must be that railways man. They're on the porch — I didn't know if I should ask them in. But I can make some tea, if you like, if you wanted."

Ani nods, rubbing the grass from her hair. "You do the tea, Bella, that would be lovely. And I'll see what they want this time." She leans down to kiss the top of her daughter's head.

But it's strange, sitting in the dim space of the living room — Ani wonders if she's awake at all, or still dreaming outside, as she catches at fragments of her visitors' words. As the minister talks about a memorial service, how many people would like to pay their respects, she hears her own voice ask if it might be better not to have one, if she'd rather not be able to remember what her husband's memorial was like.

"Just a hymn or two, Mrs. Lachlan, and perhaps a reading," says Reverend Forrest. "It needn't be long. But I think you will regret this if you don't do it. So many of the ladies in the village have asked if they might provide flowers."

And she hears herself demur and say she'll think about it, she'll see.

The other man speaks then, as Isabel comes in with the teapot. "Whatever you

decide, Mrs. Lachlan," he says gently, "the railways are very concerned that you know you needn't worry about your future. There's a compensation payment for the accident, of course — and also in this instance it's been suggested that you might take a particular job with us: perhaps you know the library of the Railway Institute, down at the station? Our librarian is about to retire, and it's been suggested that you would be ideal for the position." And he recites the hours, morning and evening, the pay, the facilities — a heater, a piano — the duties and tasks she'd need to fulfill.

She watches Isabel stir the leaves in the pot. An evening shift would change their meal, their bedtime. An evening shift would change the way their family worked. *So everything changes when one thing goes,* she thinks, reaching for a teacup to pass to the minister and hissing as a drop of the hot liquid sizzles against her skin.

The idea of a job: she'd asked once at the pictures if they ever had an opening for someone selling tickets or ice creams, but the manager had laughed and said he'd a brace of daughters and his own wife for such a thing, and couldn't see he'd want anyone else's. As for any of the other places she might have approached — the rubber

factory, the nicer ice cream one down south, or an office job with the brickworks, or a shop — it was all shifts and lines and tasks she couldn't quite imagine.

"What do you want that bother for, Ani?" Mac had said. "We're all right as we are — bit of care, now and then, with the shillings, but we come through each month."

The more capable she felt in her own house, her own world, the more she wondered if she'd be any good in the wider space of anyone else's. And so she'd made her home and nurtured her family, polishing the good fortune of her circumstances in her mind as she crafted a pretty quilt, folded a clean sheet, kneaded a good dough, or planted out a garden bed in spring. It was, she told herself, enough, and she relished her life's small pleasures.

But: "It would be nice to have books coming in boxes again," she says at last, reaching for the cup again and steadying its saucer against her hand's unexpected shake. "When I was growing up, out west, our books came in boxes from the city. My father ordered them and they came in consignments. So that would be nice. The piano . . . I don't . . ."

"No, no — it's just part of the institute's facilities," the railways man interrupts her

as if he can countenance any objection. "Nothing for you to worry about other than taking the occasional booking for people who'd like to use it."

Ani nods. "All right," she says, with what she hopes is a reassuring smile for Isabel. "But I might not be very good at it — I've never done anything like this before." She passes the biscuits to the two men, to her daughter, letting the rush of the job's details wash over her — who she needs to meet at the institute's library in Sydney; how opportune it is that the local librarian will be retiring in just a week or two's time.

"What about after school?" says Isabel quietly. "What about my dinner?"

"We'll work something out, Bella, we'll have to. This is how things have to be now." Ani's fingers are clenched so tight around the handle of her cup that she expects it to break in two. She feels Isabel press in against her side and hug hard as the men stand to leave.

"And we'll see you back in Sunday school soon, little one?" says Reverend Forrest, patting Isabel's hair.

"I'm ten now," she says, "ten last week. I'll be able to get my own job soon."

"It's all right, Bella," says Ani, holding her close as the men drive away. "We'll work

this out. Maybe you can come with me, or have tea with Mrs. May. There's always a way. Come on now," she soothes with a calmness, a certainty she doesn't feel.

There isn't any other way it can be.

Isabel rubs her eyes, stepping back. "I think I spilled tea on your birthday card," she says at last. "I was making it on the kitchen table this morning and I couldn't get the teapot lid to go in properly."

"Shh," says Ani, pulling her in again. "You're lovely for even remembering my birthday." They stand a moment, swaying back and forth. "I'd forgotten it myself."

From inside the hug, she hears Isabel say, "The trouble is, Dad was in charge of the present — and I don't know where he's hidden it, or even what it is. I wanted . . . I wanted . . . I thought I could use my Christmas money and ask Mrs. May to get you something, but I couldn't get the stopper out of my money box, and . . ."

And Ani starts to laugh — the first time she's laughed in days. "You're lovely, Isabel Lachlan," she says, squeezing her so it almost hurts. "And a card is all I need, even if it is a bit splotchy. But come on, let's see if we can think where your dad might hide a mystery present."

Because it must be here, somewhere in

74

the house; maybe already wrapped, and tucked into or under something that Ani would never think of disturbing. Isabel darts into corners and cupboards — the back of the chiffonier where the special glasses are kept; under the sofa; behind the horsehair couch.

"I know!" she calls, running towards her parents' bedroom, but Ani is already there. The tallboy's doors make a squeaky protest, the drawers, always stiff, a little stiffer for not having been opened for a few days. She pulls out piles of underwear, socks, but there's nothing in the first drawer, or the second; nothing tucked into the shelves; nothing pushed to the back under the rack of hanging shirts.

She tries the closet, the nightstand, the low table beside the bed that still holds the book Mac was reading, its pages pried apart by the larger yellow-bordered shape of a *National Geographic*. A layer of dust has settled around them already: Ani watches as Isabel makes a line with her finger, then another perpendicular to the first, so that the two stripes form an X. But there's nothing in the little table either.

"No X marks the spot," Ani says. "Never mind. Maybe we'll have an epiphany about it tomorrow. Now, we should have some-

thing to eat."

But she finds herself standing still and purposeless in the middle of the kitchen, her fingers patting the cover of her husband's last book.

"Will everybody know, Mum?" says Isabel, breaking her reverie. "When I go back to school, will everyone know what's happened? Will I have to talk about it?"

Ani props the book against the teapot, like a marker or a shrine, and sits down with her daughter, taking her hands. "Of course people know — you know that, Bell. That's why they're bringing us all those stews, all that soup." The endless provisioning of their doorstep. "But mostly they'll just want to say they're sorry. Or they might ask you what happened, and you can say you don't really know."

Opposite her, Bella pulls her hands free and picks up her pencil, working hard at the blue sky of her picture, her mother's name spelled out in letters made of clouds. "I was thinking," she says at last, "how all the dads who died in the war will get their names carved into the war memorial. And I was wondering where my dad's name will be carved."

"I think it's up to us to remember your dad's name, love," says Ani, reaching over

76

for her daughter's blunt blue pencil and whittling its end back to sharpness with a knife. "We're his memorial, I suppose."

And Ani's gone again, into that silent, timeless space of inertia, of loss, of dislocation.

"Mum," says Isabel quietly. Ani has no idea how much time has passed. "Mum! You'll hurt yourself — you're chewing your lip."

And Ani feels herself blush, like a naughty child caught out.

"Ah, Bella," she says then, "I shouldn't be watching you make this card — it should be a surprise for the morning." She kisses her daughter once more on the top of her head and goes back into the yard, to lie on the grass, and to wait.

9

"What will it be for your birthday then, lass?" The two of them, at work in the garden, on a warm spring afternoon.

"Oh, nothing, Mac. Nothing now." October 1945, two months of peace. What could you ask for on top of that?

"There must be something we can get you, something we can try to find now that the world's supposedly back to normal." Mac laughed at the hollowness of it.

"There is one thing I'd like," said Ani at last, twisting at the tight root of a dandelion, "but I think it will stump even you, Mackenzie Lachlan."

"Try me."

"I'd like to see snow, like my father talks about. I'd like to see white mountains and I'd like to feel their cold." And she wiped the sweat from her forehead, laughing.

Mac leaned on the shovel. "No challenge at all," he said promptly. "I know just the

thing — and Bella's going to love it."

Look at her, Anikka Lachlan, swirling around on the silky-smooth ice of the Glacarium, her husband surging ahead of her holding one hand, her daughter behind her, holding the other. The air was cold from the ice on the floor and the great ice works in the basement below. And at the front of the giant hall, the walls were bright with a huge mural — an Alpine scene, high craggy mountains, vast cerulean sky.

Around and around, gliding and gliding; wanting to put her arms out to fly. Her husband in front of her, her daughter behind. Around and around through a whole afternoon.

At the end, as they stood on the street with cups of hot chocolate, the air exploded with the sound of bells — "The carillon, at the university, I think, up along Broadway," said Mac.

And Ani laughed. "There should always be bells." Bells for celebration; bells for jubilation. "Happy birthday to me."

Happy birthday.

10

The morning of Mackenzie Lachlan's memorial is clear and bright, capped by an impossibly vast sky. The ocean is calm, its blue as consistent as a wide watercolor wash. A breeze plays with the shapes of the grass, of petals and leaves, and it must be up on the mountain too, because when Ani tries to focus on the trees that mark the escarpment's edge, they're blurred, furry, as if they'd been drawn by a thick lead pencil and then half rubbed out. Yet the air feels still, *stable,* she thinks, like something against which she might test her weight. Her hand moves for milk, for sugar, as it has these past days, to add to her tea, but she draws it back and so takes her tea black, weak and black, the way she used to drink it. The way Mac would know to make it. This morning, for the first time, she woke facing the window, her body turned towards the light, as she always used to, rather than

facing the empty space in the bed beside her. This morning, she thought about staying away from the service, as if avoiding its memorial might make Mac more alive.

"You could borrow this, Mum." Isabel is at her side, offering her the brass tube of her birthday kaleidoscope. "You said it was good for seeing things differently."

And Ani smiles, taking it from her and training it on the view over Thirroul. "Perhaps we can share it," she says as the view she's been studying rearranges itself into repeated lozenges of color. She knows she's looking for Mac in the corners of its movement.

And what would Isabel think of staying away from the church?

"What was the last thing Dadda saw before he left Scotland? What was the first thing he saw when he came here?" Isabel asks her questions without pause, and Ani smiles again, but faintly. These are not things she ever thought to ask, and now, of course, she can't.

"Your dad said good-bye to his grannie up in the Highlands and walked away without turning back to wave — he'd promised her that. He took a ship from Glasgow and went through the canal at Suez. Do you remember the stories he used to tell when

you were tiny and sitting on the beach together? He'd bank the sand up along one side of you, fold up a little paper boat, and sail it through the sand. That was Suez, he said. Do you remember that?"

Isabel shakes her head, picking at a scab on her knee. "I remember he said he was seasick for a week and that the first night he went up onto the deck he nearly keeled over from the number of stars. And that he sat there and tried to count them all."

This is not a story Ani has heard. "Did he say how many he counted?" She herself has sat with Mackenzie Lachlan, counting the stars, and it feels strange to feel jealous, now, at the thought that he might have counted more on his own, somewhere earlier, somewhere else.

"Two thousand and fourteen," says Isabel. "More than Dad and I counted when it was the war and all the lights had to be off. Remember that, Mum? Remember how late I was allowed to stay up?" Ani shakes her head as Isabel frowns. "But you were there — you must have forgotten. You did have that horrible cold." She takes the kaleidoscope from her mother and points it at her scabby knee, grimacing at the repeat of its image.

"There's an anxious space," says Ani, still-

ing her daughter's fingers as they worry again at the scab, "between not knowing if you've forgotten something or if you never knew." They will eat their breakfast, put on their best clothes. They will go to this service for a husband, a father. *I do not want to be fifty or eighty or a hundred, wondering if I've forgotten my husband's memorial or if I never knew about it.* "Come on, Bell. Let's have some porridge — 'It'll stick to the ribs,' as Dad would say. Let's get ready to face the day."

The white wooden church is mostly full and the organ is wheezing when Ani and Isabel arrive. The two Lachlan women, their blond heads caught by sun as they walk along the aisle towards the space where a coffin should be but isn't. It hasn't occurred to Anikka, until now, how awful that emptiness will be. *He has been cremated a week.* She makes herself think it as flatly as she can. *His body is burned, his self gone.* They're injurious statements, like Isabel picking at her scab to keep it weeping.

Walking between the rows of pews, Ani feels the tight freeze of her face's expression, somewhere above a smile, she hopes, but she's tricked herself into thinking she was smiling before and seen her mouth set

hard and unwelcoming in a mirror or a window. She looks through the women she passes: Mrs. Padman, Mrs. Bower, Mrs. Floyd — all war widows. Ani remembers how Marjorie Floyd had howled when the news of her husband's death came, howled in the darkness, and then rocked, back and forth, singing him a lullaby. *How strange,* thinks Ani, *that we're here together to mourn my husband.*

She has met each woman, and many others, in the village in the past days, required each time to deliver a telling of Mac's accident, of hearing its news. Three, she discovered, three was the magic number: by the third telling each day she could hear the phrases that worked, the ones that moved the narrative fastest. By the third telling the story felt more like a story, rather than something she was being required to live.

On the end, sitting slightly apart, Iris McKinnon, whose brother, the poet, was the man on the pylon. "It's never what you think," she says, reaching up to touch Ani's arm as if to brush at a speck of dust. "But the living goes on, it always does." And she smiles as Ani ducks her head and blinks.

Once, long ago, she'd described her mother's death to Iris McKinnon — described herself as four years old, uncertain of why

her mother had gone away, or where, or for how long. And Iris had leaned forward and patted her arm. *Time heals all wounds,* she'd whispered, and Ani had found herself pulling away so fast her body almost shuddered. *No,* she'd thought, so loud she wondered she hadn't shouted it. *No no no.* Not all of them, not always. There were some things you carried and carried, and now, she is willing this to be one of them.

The organ's notes rearrange themselves from the Twenty-Third Psalm to "Rock of Ages" as Ani follows Isabel into the front pew, thinking about the supposed balm of Iris McKinnon's time. She feels a hand on her shoulder and glances around: the stationmaster, Luddy. She sees shopkeepers, train drivers and engineers, and firemen — even Bella's teacher, tucked away at the back. There's a man sitting next to him, obscured as he reaches down for his hymnbook. But as he straightens up, Ani catches a glimpse of strong shoulders in a dark suit, a ruddy cheek, and speckled-blond hair. *It's Mac,* she thinks quickly, and, *so good that he could get away from work and be here after all.* And her mind lets her hold the illusion for almost a second before she realizes where she is, and why, and that the man she can see is nothing more than a random ap-

proximation of familiar shapes and colors. She tries again to smile.

Along the church's north-facing wall its windows are set with panels of colored glass — rose, blue, yellow — alternating along the length of the building. And as the minister speaks, as the readings are read, as the hymns are sung, as heads are bowed and raised again with *Amen,* Ani keeps her eyes on a patch of sunlight coming in through one yellow pane. It inches closer and closer to the place where the coffin should stand, solid and definite. She registers her own name, and Isabel's, in the minister's eulogy. She registers the reading from Corinthians that she loves — *For now we see through a glass, darkly; but then face to face.* She registers the thin-sounding congregation voices that sing, never quite coming into a hymn at the right moment, and with one female voice always rising above the others, trying for a descant. In all her years of sitting with Mac and Bella in this church, she's never identified that aspirant soprano.

The sun inches forward, marking out a perfect rectangle on the carpet. *There he is; there's his resting place.* She swallows hard. *I should have gone to see the flames and the smoke. I should have insisted they take me.* She winces at this and feels Isabel's hand

on her knee.

". . . And may the grace of the Lord Jesus Christ, the love of God, and the fellowship . . ."

And then she is a little girl, four years old, watching her father watch her mother's coffin being lowered into the ground. She will never forget the hollow sound of dirt hitting wood when her mother was buried, the look of shock, of distaste and revulsion, that shot across her father's face.

Somewhere close by, she hears Mrs. May talking quietly to Isabel as her daughter moves up the aisle with their neighbor. She hears voices on the porch, and outside, which fade a little as people take their leave or move over to the hall. She hears the rustle of the minister in the vestry. She hears a bus rattle past on the road. Standing carefully, she kneels down and touches the floor's wood where the sun has warmed it.

"Mrs. Lachlan?" The minister is crouching beside her. "Anikka?"

She nods, her fingers moving slowly across the wood as if she were picking out a scale on a piano or counting a clock's chime.

"There are refreshments in the hall, when you . . ."

"Thank you," she says. "I think Mrs. May has already taken Isabel." She looks up care-

fully. "I will come — I just wanted . . ."

"Take your time, Mrs. Lachlan. No rush, there's no rush at all," he says, patting her lightly on the shoulder as the stationmaster had.

This is how you touch grief, she thinks, watching as a single tear hits the floor and sits domed on its shiny surface. *How long before it soaks in? How long before it disappears?* She has no idea how long she stays there, wondering. She has no idea how often such stillness will come.

"Ani, love? I've brought you this." Mrs. May is holding a cup of tea, a huge scone wedged onto its saucer. "You don't have to do this all on your own."

Ani takes the tea, staring at the size of the floury scone. "Thanks for taking Bella," she says. "I'll come in a minute — I just . . ." She shrugs.

"You take your time, love; I'll keep her busy with the sausage rolls. Always good to have something hot after a funeral — I'll try to keep a couple by for you."

Breaking the edge off the scone, Ani winces at the flurry of crumbs that fall like snowflakes on the pew and the floor beyond. She eats a little — it's still fresh from someone's oven — and then a little more. Mrs. May is right about hot food. Gulping

the tea, she tries to sweep up her mess, kneeling down on the floor in front of the pew and brushing at the crumbs with her hanky. Her other hand touches the sunlit space again, and she feels its warmth against her skin, wiggling her fingers in its brilliance.

The magic of light through glass: when Mac got his job on the railways they sat with his guard's lamp lit between them on the table in her father's kitchen, flicking the lens from red to green and back again.

"A shame you can't get other colors," Ani had said. "Blue would be nice — it's how I imagine looking up through the ocean to the sky."

He'd flicked the light back to green so the room glowed with strange, arboreal shadows. "That's how it is, lass, that's how it is," he'd said. "And now I've a beacon for you to find me by."

In the church, remembering this, Ani watches as the sunlight traces the earth's turn to fold over the altar steps, across the communion rail, and on towards the pulpit.

"Where are you, Mackenzie Lachlan?" she whispers. "Where can I find you now?"

11

"What's the last thing you see before you sleep at night?"

Ani's voice wavered as a sheet of lightning breached the room's curtains and lit its furniture into stark shapes — the pub's bed, the pub's wardrobe, the pub's washstand, the pub's chair. In the morning, they'd leave the wide Hay Plains and take a train away to the coast together — the first time Ani would see coast or ocean. In the morning, they'd take a train, the new Mr. and Mrs. Lachlan, away from this place where Ani had lived all her life, its grasses as blond as her hair. Now, in the night, their faces close, noses almost touching, her right hand held his left. Here they were, lying with their heads on the same pillow, in the same bed, for the first time.

"The last thing I see?" Mac spoke so quietly that his voice thickened and slurred around its consonants. "It's the ceiling, I

guess, or the wall — it's the room where I'm sleeping. Is that what you mean?"

She shook her head, and the gesture made her hair glimmer against the pillow.

"No. I mean, sometimes just before I go to sleep, or when I begin to dream, I see somebody — a figure, a person — caught in a beam of light. Sometimes they're dancing. Sometimes they're just standing there, still, in the brightness. And I watch them for a while, and then the light drops down, and then I'm asleep." At the other end of the bed, her toes brushed against his, and she flinched at the unexpected proximity of another person's flesh in her bed — another person.

"It's all right," he said. "It's going to be all right."

The clock on the mantelpiece chimed once, and Mac frowned; he'd lost track of the time, even the day — was it one o'clock? Two? A Saturday? A Sunday? At least he knew it was almost summer, late November 1935. And there she was, just inches away, his bride, staring into his eyes as he studied hers. There were so many colors in them: grey and gold and a green that was almost metallic. In the center, near the pupil, was a flash of ocher so bright it was almost red.

"Your eyelashes are different colors," she

said at last.

"Different how?"

"Different to each other — you've got blond ones and ginger ones and brown ones. Like in your beard. I've never noticed that before."

"Would it have changed your mind about marrying me, my motley eyelashes?" He smiled, squeezing her hand tight, and his legs hugged her feet, her toes. This time, she didn't react.

"Nothing would have done that." Beyond the room, the sky cracked open with thunder and lightning that had been menacing all day, and inside, safe and together, Ani and Mac Lachlan both jumped a little, and laughed. "Some omen, some portent, my dadda would say," said Ani. "Some message from his old northern gods."

"Maybe that's what your people are, dancing and running before you sleep." His accent made the "maybe" *mebbe;* his accent made "before" *afore.* His accent thickened "are" and "running" into rich, fudgy sounds. "Maybe they're messengers from your old country." Tucked this close to her mouth, he could smell her breath as she spoke, and wondered if he might get a little drunk on the perfume of her words.

"That's what my father says — Thialfi or

the Valkyrie."

"My gran would say it's the second sight." His eyebrows rose slightly, his lips making the smallest smile. "She'd swear she'd seen any number of happenings before they happened — I'm counting on it that she's seen us married now without waiting for my letter."

She looked so young in this flickering half-light, but they had fifty years of life between them. Because he thought of them as added together now, he realized, rather than two separate tallies of time. It made him feel sure, more secure than he had in years.

Here they were.

"Nice to be inside with you, Mackenzie Lachlan," said Ani as the thunder rumbled.

"Nice to be anywhere with you, Anikka Kalm — no," he corrected himself, "Anikka Lachlan." This new combination of words.

Outside, the thunder collided with the sound of a train; one noise all air and movement, the other all weight and metal. "They're late in with that loco." Mac's eyes focused on the window, as if he might see the reason for the engine's delay from where he lay, warm in his bed. "A good night to be indoors. A good night to be with you, Mrs. Anikka Lachlan."

She leaned forward, kissing his smile.

"Thank you."

And later, when she was asleep, he watched the occasional flicker of her eyelids, the rise and fall of her breath. Touching his fingers lightly against her wrist, he felt its pulse. Touching his fingers to her hair, he felt its silk. She was beautiful, without a doubt, and bright too. "She's well able, lad," he imagined his grandmother saying. "And she'll smart you up, my blatherskite." He wasn't wanting for sharpness himself — Mac smiled against the darkness — but he did stretch the truth of things now and then, not an outright lie, but perhaps a rearrangement of a story's dimensions to skate across an ignorance or an elision.

An' look what it gets you — tracing the curl of Ani's hair against the pillow — *a fine, bonny ferlie.*

She'd been ready to love him — he'd seen that — and he her. So what if he talked up the places he'd show her, the prospects he had, the things that he may have dreamed of doing? So what if he claimed her own favorite books for himself? If a man made the right guess at the right time, what harm of it, if it made his girl smile? He could read fast enough to make good the deception, and he'd sort out the settlement of any other promises later on.

The pale fabric of Ani's wedding dress picked up a chink or two of the lightning beyond the drawn drapes, so that one sleeve and a strip around the waist seemed to float above the rest of the dress's material, as if animated by another bride's body. Then the curtains flicked a little in the breeze and re-arranged the dress's highlighted illumination, now more, now less, now a whole panel, now a tiny speck.

Her fine clothes, and how fine she'd looked. He'd felt his breath catch when she'd stepped up to him at the altar and let go of her father's hand to take his. No matter a little thing about a fancy novel; a man only gasped at the sight of his true sweet-heart.

Beside him, Ani stirred, her free hand moving against his skin. "Sweet dreams," he whispered, feeling certain, feeling foolish. He closed his own eyes at last, while Ani, nestled against the unusual warmth and weight of someone else in her bed, headed deeper into sleep.

And it was Mac she saw this night, Mac in his fine suit, dancing and twirling as he had earlier in the pale lamplight of the pub's dining room downstairs.

Maybe, she thought as the light around him dimmed, *or mebbe it always was.*

12

In the vast quiet of the Railway Institute's central library, set at the end of Sydney's Central Station, Anikka walks through the rows of shelving, watching as books are selected and sorted, packed and returned. They pride themselves, these real librarians — that's how Ani thinks of them — on being able to source almost anything for anyone, dispatching volumes all over the state to their various and voracious readers.

"I'm looking forward to all the reading I'll be able to do," Ani says at last, and they smile at her benignly. A common misperception — everyone thinks they'll have that time.

When the meeting is over, Ani stands on the curb outside taking great breaths of the steamy air pushed out by the nearby trains. Her mind is a fug of hours and requirements, this new busyness jumbled against the disappearing rhythms of her days.

Before, she marked her hours around Isabel's going to school and coming home, around the changeable pattern of Mac's shifts. Before, she could watch the light move around the house as the day passed, around the garden as she watered here and weeded there. Before, she was the person who had time to think about what was happening to other people — to arrive on their doorstep with a cake or a stew when domestic disaster struck.

When disaster struck elsewhere.

She registers the hands of the station's clock and moves automatically towards her platform, her train, her mind distracted by remembering her father's voice, his anxiety about her money: "I took a boarder in when your mother first died — you might not remember. Another carpenter lived with us awhile. The money was good. And the company. You could think about that — move Isabel in with you and rent out the room." Telephoning from the post office with condolences and suggestions.

Just once, Ani has convinced her father to visit them on the coast, to come away from the plains, to come and see Isabel. When Isabel was just over a year old, he came and slept in the baby's room, while the baby slept in her little crib at the end of Ani and

Mac's bed. "I don't like to be away, An-ikka," her father had confessed at last.

"I don't like to be far away from where your mother was — I still think of her sleeping there, under the feather quilt my mother sent us when we were married. I miss my bed, Ani; I've never told that to a living soul. But I miss my bed — I feel too far away from my wife." He blew his nose loudly, startling Isabel as she kicked on a rug in front of his feet. "Such closeness to a person, keeping watch as they sleep."

Ani bit her tongue against saying, *More than twenty years, Dadda; she's been dead more than twenty years.* And instead made him his favorite breakfast of porridge with butter and jam — ignoring her Scottish husband's disapproval.

That night, when Mac was asleep, when Isabel was asleep, when her father's snores were shaking the hallway, Ani had crept into his room, turning on the lamp she'd set there when the baby was born. He was tall, still, but stooped a little now, and all the gold and red had finally bleached out of his hair, his beard, leaving him with silvers and the palest white-greys. But his skin was tanned and smooth, and his hands were still busy, even as he slept, flicking and fidgeting on the bedclothes as if he were trying to

solve a problem of joinery somewhere.

She'd never thought of it before, about keeping watch over someone, although she'd watched Mac while he slept, and she could not go to bed herself without sitting a moment with Isabel, just looking, just checking, just making sure her sleep was calm and sound. Mac laughed at this ritual — "Do you think she'll have climbed out the window and escaped?" — but Ani knew that he did it too, awake early for a shift, or on the rare nights when she was away from home, or asleep first. She'd laid her hand gently across her father's busy fingers, and they curled around her palm in response, holding her there.

More than twenty years, she'd thought, and his friends' daft ideas of finding him some spinster or widow he could marry. *They mustn't know, they mustn't know the way he carries her still.*

Easing her fingers from his grip, she had pulled down the blind and pulled up the blanket. This inversion of roles, the parent and the child; she kissed his forehead. *"Hyvää yöta ja kauniita unia"* — good night and sweet dreams — as he had wished her every night of her childhood that she could remember. She loved the lilt of those words, the way they swayed.

She opens her eyes, disoriented to find herself in some deep darkness. She doesn't remember boarding the train, let alone the trip away from Sydney, through its suburbs, through the thick bush of the national park, and into her talismanic tunnel. It's the tunnel's dark that presses against her now, as if she was unexpectedly blind or somehow sleeping. She soaks in the noise of the train's progress: she loves the rattles, the thuds, the almost visceral percussion the carriages make, pulled unrelentingly along with the steam engine's exertion.

For thirty years now her father has carried her mother — *forsaking all others,* thinks Ani, almost smiling at the old-fashioned and nuptial phrase. She never questioned that he did, or wondered at his being alone. It hadn't occurred to her that he might have had a choice about it. For herself, she thinks, there will be no boarder, no extra body in the quiet space of her home, no new and unknown being in her bathroom, her kitchen, or triggering the intimate creak of her floorboards, her front stairs. There can be no more change.

Which is — she almost smiles again — *the one thing there must be.* This job, this library, this new, widowed life. Idiotic to believe she can control any of it.

Opening her mouth, she takes in the tunnel's thick, sooty air — she can taste the cleaner steam on its edges — and pushes her nose as far through the open window as she dares to make the noise louder, the taste stronger, the risk (how far away *is* the tunnel's wall?) more precarious.

The carriage rocks and tilts and Ani braces her hands against the hard leather seat, steadying herself above its unpredictability. Once, a long time ago, Mac had told her a story he'd had from his grannie about sending her own daughter — Mac's aunt — down to Glasgow for work. There were strange hazards to beware of, Grannie Lachlan had said. Don't talk to young men. Lift your skirt on only one side when you prepare to cross a road; to lift it on both would reveal too much of your ankles. And when entering a tunnel in a train, put a pin in your mouth to stop any bold young man from kissing you. *And we laughed and we laughed and we laughed.*

"Might I be so bold?" Mac had said then, quiet against the train's roar, although Ani was sure the whole train could have heard him. He was a broad man, and sturdy, and the way he pushed against her sometimes, it was as if she could feel the full weight and

momentum of his railwayman's job behind him.

Her mouth opens against the memory of it, and as she swallows a sob, the train bursts out of the darkness and onto the coast.

The ocean is bright and sharp and the sky above echoes the water's deep navy in its own thick color. There is light in the leaves of the trees, blasting them into different greens, shiny and almost metallic, that might belong properly to jewels. There's so much brightness it's as if every light in the world has been thrown on: every flare, every candle, every beacon.

Above the sound of the train, Ani catches the screech of cockatoos with their improperly loud voices. There are cars on the road below too, people walking on the beach, and wreaths of smoke winding up from chimneys, tracing illegible messages across the sky. Color and movement and noise and bustle everywhere and it's life, it's life. *All these stories going on,* thinks Ani, *while I sit in the dark and open my mouth for a kiss I can't feel anymore.* She looks up to the sky, down to the shore, out through the air — looking for kite men; looking for seabirds — and across the face of the escarpment. The beauty of it all, the changing combinations of its shapes and its shades and its shadows:

it's as if she's been delivered into the barrel of Isabel's kaleidoscope.

Come away, her father has written again and again, and she lets the sobs come now, thinking of this. *Never never never never.* To lose this moment, this moment in every journey from north back to south. To walk away from this place she had found with her husband. Well, now it will be her shifts that fold around the working of the house, where it used to be Mac's. Now it will be her job that marks the comings and goings in the days. Now it will be her job to sleep alone in her bed and explain to her father that she cannot leave.

Up ahead, the engine sounds its call and the train draws into Stanwell Park. Ani leans back, the brilliance of her realization draining away to an ordinary day as the carriage shudders and slows. She wipes her eyes. She blows her nose. There are other tunnels, she knows, between her and home, but none of them give you this moment, this arrival, this bursting out like magic.

The train pushes south, its line counterpoised between the ocean and the cliffs. Along the horizon, a trick of sunlight turns the water to the color of metal, glistening like treasure or a fine, thin blade.

Alighting at Thirroul, Ani stands a moment with her eyes closed against the departing carriages — it's bad luck to count how many there are. As the guard's van leaves the platform, she opens her eyes and catches sight of the guard's arm and the distinct shape — not much more than a dangling trinket at this distance — of his lamp.

Directly opposite, across the tracks, sits the library, a pale, boarded box of a building rising straight up from the platform with one window open and — as Ani watches — the other pushed up to frame the shape of Miss Fadden, the librarian she is about to replace.

"Hello, dear," Miss Fadden calls, waving across the tracks. "I thought I'd let in some air for you." And Ani waves in reply, crossing the tracks to enter her new world, this library.

It's a nice place, not too large, and with big windows that look beyond the railway lines towards the sea. Inside, its floors are oiled up sometimes for a dance, and there's a faint smell of cedar from the shelves, the librarian's desk.

Coming around to its front door, Ani

pauses at the porch, raised just half a step up off the ground. Such a strange thing: on the building's eastern side, where it abuts the platform, it sits hard on the gravel, as if the library had been set down on top of it like a child's block. But this porch wants to make a distinction between itself and the ground; the porch wants to hold itself up a little. Ani takes the awkward step, rocking her weight back and forth to gauge its height.

As she rocks, she notices for the first time that the four columns supporting the porch's awning are decorated with pieces of dark black stone, sharply angular. They jut out from the smooth surface with jagged points, and when she presses the soft flesh of her palm into them, she's sure she feels tiny pricks of blood on her skin. Is it basalt? Some sort of schist? Or coal? Can coal look this shiny, this sharp? She's never paid attention to its shape as she's shoveled it into her stove. Coal would make sense: all the mines running back through the wall of the mountain; all the men deep underground, hauling it out. *Call it coal, then,* she thinks, and she steps inside, calling the librarian's name.

Miss Fadden is crouched on the floor, trying to fit a pile of books into a large box

like the pieces of a complex jigsaw.

"I've never got any better at this," she says, smiling as she stands to shake Ani's hand. "Perhaps you'll have a gift for it." And she holds out two Zane Grey adventures and a copy of *Kangaroo.*

"Must that one go back?" asks Ani, taking the Lawrence. "I'd like to find it here when I start."

The older lady nods. "There's always someone wanting to read it," she says. "Looking for things they recognize, I expect — and finding them. You can find anything in a story if you look hard enough." She sets it square in the middle of the wide table, straightens her glasses and a pretty little fan just off to one side. "I'll leave it here then, on your desk," she says, and it takes Ani a moment to register the designation.

It comes from the south; a huge surge of noise and movement and the train bound for Sydney is suddenly in the station, its sound amplified by the room. Carriage doors open and close; feet scuffle across the gravel. And then a sharp toot, an acceleration, and it's gone.

Ani looks up to find the older woman's gaze fixed on her, pensive. "I did wonder," Miss Fadden says quietly, "if it was indeli-

cate of them, somehow, to ask you to work alongside such a noise as that all day. When, you know, it was a train that . . ." And she waves her hand, so that it brushes along Ani's sleeve once, twice.

"I hadn't thought of it," says Ani. "I'd rather not . . ."

"Very sensible, dear. Now, perhaps you'd like to have a look at the shelving while I sort out this box." She's through the door and into the smaller room, rustling through paper, before she's finished speaking.

Ani turns carefully, staring across a row of paperback romances — *Bella's happy endings,* she thinks — and other reassuring fictions, while the room sparkles with silence.

13

From the kitchen window of his sister's house, on the corner of Ocean Street, Roy McKinnon stands with his hands in the warm, soapy washing-up water, looking at the ocean itself. There's some trick of perspective in this place, as if the house, the road, the grassy verge beyond were set below the level of the water, as if the sea curved up, the horizon above the line of sight and the water, at any moment, about to cascade down.

A seagull cuts across the window, and Roy jumps, shocked at his own shock — *A bird, buster, it was just a bird.* He checks the clock on Iris's mantelpiece against the time on his wristwatch on the sill — as if to say, *How long is it going to take, to get used to being back in the world?* Behind him, on the kitchen table, is the slender rectangle of an anthology of poems, including his own from the war, with the publisher's polite note

about when they might see something new. *What's next, Roy McKinnon?* the man had written. *You know we're all waiting to hear.*

As am I, mate, he thinks. *As am I.*

Pulling the book from its envelope this morning, he'd been unsure where to place it in Iris's neat house — not so much for fear of disturbing any of her possessions but because it was a house almost entirely free of books. There was a family Bible in the hall cupboard, he knew, and three well-thumbed romances tucked under the leg of the settee — he'd found them when he bent down to retrieve a shilling on the night he'd arrived, laughing as his sister whisked them away again like some illicit material.

He smacks at his forehead with his hand, surprised by the wet suds against his skin: the library at the station — Iris had said something about the librarian retiring, and even that hadn't reminded him of its existence, its potential cornucopia. *Sink down into the words of others,* he thinks, plunging his hands back into the warm wetness and feeling around for loose flatware. That poor young widow was starting next week, Iris said. Roy tilted his head, trying again to remember something more of the Lachlans than long-ago football, a quiet spectator. He'd met the man once or twice, he thought

— a drink, maybe, or a rack of snooker. But there isn't much to his repository of prewar memories. Sometimes he distrusts that there ever had been times, or places, before the war. Pretty, his sister had said of the widow — "You'll remember her when you see her" — and Scottish, of the husband. "You'd have seen them at the dances," she'd said, "before they had their little girl. It was Ani Lachlan who brought me your poem when it came out in that magazine."

Still, even then, he'd stood wondering what she'd made of it, whether she'd read it. And still, even then, he'd found no way to ask — caught instead by the memory of overhearing Anikka Lachlan's grief.

"Roy? Are you here?" His sister struggles through the door, her basket heavy — he should have gone to help her with the shopping.

A useful thing, you could've done a useful thing, mate. And he lunges so quickly to take the basket from her that he knocks it, sending a paper bag of apples, a bottle of milk, a precious packet of tea spilling out across the floor.

"Oh, Roy." A sharp intake of breath, as if she's trying not to reprimand a child. "Don't worry, don't worry." She takes the dishcloth from him, watching the milk soak

into the still-rationed leaves. "Set the kettle on if you want something to do — I think there's enough tea in the caddy for us to have a pot. I'll go back and see what I can sort out."

It's her house that makes him nervous, he realizes, not just its want of books, but it's too neat and too ordered. *There's no living done here,* he thinks, *just Iris and her opinions.* She should have married; she should have had her own children to reprimand, not just take that tone with him.

"I saw Mrs. Lacey today when I was coming along the beach," he says, following his own train of thought. "She said they've got the replacement doctor lined up at last — and you'll never guess, Iris, you'll never guess who she said is coming."

His sister's hand, wiping the cloth across the floor, stops, leaving a wide, white slick on the lino.

"Well, of course it's Frank Draper; I was sure you'd know," says Roy, trying to position the tea caddy exactly as he had found it. "Did you hear from Frank, these past years? I always thought, you and he —"

"Could you get me that towel, Roy, or must I do everything myself? That's a whole pint of milk, you know, a whole pint of milk gone to waste. And no, I didn't hear from

Frank Draper. He said it was a lottery, if he'd come back from the war or not, and he told me not to bet on its odds." Her voice is pinched with a fury she's sustained for years.

Roy passes her the towel, wincing at her words as he tries to collect the scattered apples and wipe them clean and dry. Of course he should have known this of her — it's so brutal, clearly, so close to the neatness of her surface. And he remembers suddenly that he loves this about his sister, that she will say things, expose them, with no thought of the cost to herself. There's something clean about her, and something ferocious. He admires that; he even envies it.

"Be good to see Frank," he says slowly, rubbing a piece of the fruit against the front of his shirt and distracted from Iris by the shine it takes on, its freshness, its existence.

"It will be easier to give it a good mop." And Iris is through the back door and away from the conversation. He can see her standing in the tiny square of garden that opens out behind the house, hardly big enough for the outhouse and the chicken run. He can see her standing there, holding the mop as if it were the mast of a ship in a storm. He can see her shoulders, rising and

falling, rising and falling, and her dark hair a shadow against the day's light.

Who knows what really happened, he thinks, pouring the boiling water into the teapot, setting it precisely on the mat she keeps precisely in the middle of her kitchen table. *But maybe there's a chance for living yet.*

"I'll leave your tea here, then, dear," he calls, setting it next to the pristine anthology. "And I might take a walk along the beach." Heading through the front door, clamping on his hat, he turns to see her come in at the back with the mop, the bucket, and her sticky, wet face.

"When will you be back?" she calls, although he knows her real question is what could he possibly be doing out there, walking around, or gazing at the water, all these days and nights. He knows she distrusts his freedom, his idleness. And if anyone had told her they'd seen him perched up on one of the pylons around by the old jetty . . . He shakes his head.

Few poems in the middle of a war, mate, and you call yourself a poet.

At least his friend Frank Draper has made something of himself — has a job, an occupation, a profession. Dr. Draper, coming back to the coast to tend to the sick. Roy

113

laughs: *Neither of us with anywhere else to be in the end but here.*

The plans they'd made when they were younger men. "And you'll be a poet, Roy, my friend," Frank would say, ordering up another drink and slapping his friend on the back. The doctor and the poet; the grandeur of young men's dreams, while Frank learned his anatomy and Roy taught spelling and math in forgotten country schools.

Then there was the war, and they'd both gone — Frank to England, Roy all over the place, Europe, and then the Pacific. *Where's Frank been to only just get home?* Roy wonders, recasting his own aimless itinerary.

He pulls up in the shadow of the pool's boxy pump house. Farther down the coast, farther south, he can see heavy grey clouds and rolling banks of squall. There's a storm coming. He turns and waves back towards Iris's house — she'll be watching, through the window, worrying about rain and wind, and him. But it's a while away yet, he's sure of it. And he jams his hat down farther over his eyes and sets off into the teeth of the gale, ignoring the lines of lightning beginning to shatter along the horizon.

14

"This is how it was. I was a wee boy, away with my gran in the north, waiting for the lights."

Mac as a boy, at the top of Scotland with his grandmother; the stories he told were thick with words like "gloaming" and "baffies" and "puddocks." Around the turn of autumn, the turn of spring, the sky might light up with the aurora, sheets of grand brilliance, he called it, all purples and greens and bright shiny whites — sometimes reds and oranges too.

"Better than any of that phosphorescent beach stuff you hanker after," he'd say. "Imagine it, Ani, out across the whole sky."

Once, he told her, he thought he'd seen it in Australia too, taking an engine through a heavy summer night and seeing the sky bristle and shimmer.

But, "A bushfire coming over the plains," the driver had said. "We're all right; we'll

push on through," leaving Mac at the locomotive's open doorway, staring at the color, wishing it belonged to something less destructive.

"I dream of a trip to the old country one day," he'd say to Ani. "One more trip, and the skies all brilliant." *His trip,* he always spoke of it as *his trip,* while she worked to carve out her own space in his fantasy by talking about herself meeting Grannie Lachlan or traveling on again to her father's country in that higher European north. It was a daydream, of course: as if the world would ever shrink itself for a railwayman and his wife.

Out to sea now, towards the horizon, the sky lights up with bands of white and yellow: there's a storm out there, and coming on. Ani settles herself against the wall of the porch, watching. Another flare — she strains to hear its thunder. Her father used to tell her stories about the gods and their thunder and lightning. It was their hammer, thrown hard, that caused the brightness; it was their horses, riding fast, that caused the noise.

Ani starts: there is a horse coming along the street, drawing a little trap. She squints, her hand up to block out the rest of the world. The trap's driver raises her own hand in return.

"Mrs. Lacey," Ani calls. "I thought you were my father's thunder god, riding out towards that lightning."

"There's more storm coming up the coast, Mrs. Lachlan. You can see it from our veranda." The Laceys' dairy farm, where Isabel collects their milk, looks south from the back of the hill from which Ani and her house look north. "But I look to be beating it home." She pauses. "I was sorry —"

Ani raises her hand again. "Thank you," she says. She gets her acknowledgments in so quickly now that no one gets past three or four words of condolence. "I can smell the edge of that rain," she says then, changing the subject.

Mrs. Lacey nods, pulling her coat around her. "I was down to meet the new doctor," she says, steadying and readying her horse, "but he wasn't on the train. Frank Draper — do you remember him? They say he's just back from overseas, been on war business all this time. He used to come to the dances down here, before the war. I expect we'll find him much changed after all of this. He was a beautiful dancer — made me feel like Ginger Rogers. Of course that was years ago now."

Ani smiles; she can't imagine anyone making Mrs. Lacey feel like Ginger Rogers. The

doctor must have been a magician. "I probably met him once or twice — I think I remember him dancing with Iris McKinnon." She rubs her hands against the suddenly cooler air. "Maybe he'll come tomorrow."

Mrs. Lacey waves again, giving her horse a giddyup, and Ani listens as the percussion of its steps disappears along the street. A new doctor, whose war has gone on three years longer than everyone else's. That will give the village something new to talk about. Yes, she thinks she remembers him, dancing with Iris McKinnon sometimes, and sometimes laughing with her brother. He lived up in the city and came down for weekends and holidays, just as he had when he was a boy — they all did, the three of them. Then there was the war, and Iris came to stay. And perhaps, thinks Ani, she's been waiting all this time; one for Bella's happy endings. But it feels too hard to wish such things, even for other people.

Out at sea, the slabs of sheet lightning are overlaid with sharp forks of other brightness. The wind is picking up, the rain almost here. She's read somewhere that lightning smells like salty air — would the aurora have that smell too?

A swerve, a little skid, and Luddy's car

comes up the hill and into the street, his arm through the open window to wave at Ani as he passes, and a man, tall, dark-haired, in the passenger seat. The doctor, Ani assumes, somehow missed in the train's arrival, and being driven round to the Laceys' for the night. The rain begins to fall as the two men pass her fence, its heavy wetness immediately washing away any hint of the car's journey.

Out on the horizon, miles of light break out and hover, luminous, for just a little longer than Ani expects. Her breath catches with their flare — there's something triumphant, magnificent, in it, like a loud chorus or a blast of angels. *For he shall give his angels charge over thee; they shall bear thee up in their hands:* she remembers the psalm from nowhere, and in the instant of thinking of it, the light flares again and she's sure she sees the whole surface of the land and the water rising up a little with its blaze.

"My angel," Mac had called her — twice, maybe three times, in all their years together. She'd liked the nickname, had wished he'd use it more, but it felt presumptuous to ask if he would. It was too much, and in the end, even she hadn't been able to bear him high enough to be safe.

15

"Outside, Luddy, outside." The two teams surged along the grass, Luddy with the ball tight against his chest, and Mac just behind him, calling for it, and calling again.

"Here, Luddy, here, over here," watching the stationmaster swing the other way and pass — directly to his opponent. "Help ma boab!" called Mac, pulling to a halt and bending to catch his breath. It was extremities that threw him back into his dialect — in bed with Ani, or when this baby was finally born, he suspected, or when his *dreich team wouldnae play.* He wasn't sure how long he stood like that, stooped and panting, but when he looked up, he felt he was looking at a painting, or a photograph, as if everything from the trees and the people down to single blades of grass had been snapped into stillness. The world was quiet, and he stumbled, his breath thick, almost scared he'd been transplanted into

the backdrop, the staged busyness, of someone else's story.

The whistle blew for halftime, piercing whatever moment held Mac fast, and he shook himself back into the world and jogged to the side of the field, reaching for an orange. "What you doin' out there, Luddy? M'a on yer deaf side, mon?" His accent thickened again through exasperation and the fruit, and as he shook his head in disbelief, great drops of juice flew out from his face.

"There's half a game to go yet, Mac," muttered one of the younger blokes. "We're only a point behind."

Mac shook his head again and threw himself down on the grass. "C'mon, lads, I need a win today — last match before the bairn comes, I'd wager." And made a great show of stretching and pulling.

"Wondered where Mrs. Lachlan was," said Luddy through his own mouthful of orange. "Maybe we just play better when we've got her cheering us on."

"Well, Mac plays fiercer when she's not here to see, that's for sure," said the grocer. "You're like a great engine, running us all down on the grass — and that's us on your own team, mate. The way you take off, you'll plow someone into the turf."

"Away w'ye," said Mac with a laugh, standing up and ruffling Luddy's hair. "Daft buggers, the lot of you. There's no danger of me hurting anyone — you know me, lads, couldn't hurt a fly." And they laughed at his heft, his bulk, his wide shoulders and his fast legs.

"Do your worst, Mac," called someone from the opposition. "We've got our own doctor on the sidelines . . ." He gestured towards Frank Draper. "Do your worst; he'll fix us up."

Shading his eyes, Mac looked over to the western edge of the field, saw two men standing, talking, their hats tipped onto the backs of their heads. Draper, the doctor, and Iris McKinnon's brother. He tried to think of the last time he'd seen them — they both worked away, he knew; came down for weekends here and there — but couldn't place it. He frowned: no, it was an odd meeting, somewhere odd, or something odd about it. *Whisht, I dinnae ken, I dinnae ken.* He frowned again at his memory's lapse into old words, and took a step towards the two men as if an extra yard or so of proximity might free a recollection.

Behind them, on the railway line, an engine chugged southwards, hauling a line of freight trucks. *That's a saddle tank,*

122

thought Mac. *What's that doing out of the shunting yard and up here on the lines?* He watched its belch of smoke trace a line above the platforms, watched the clean, round lines of its tank and light disappear around the corner, dragging its load behind it. The doctor and his companion slipped into another crevice in his mind, and he reached for another orange, wondering how Ani was, sitting at home instead of here, waiting through the last days before the birth of their child. *A girl for sure,* thought Mac. *And I'll call her Isabel, for my mum.* Ani, he knew, favored Elise as a name, but it was the only immortality Mac could think of to pass his mother's name on to his daughter; the mother who'd been dead precisely as long as he'd been alive. He just had to make Ani think "Isabel" was her idea.

And I'll know you this time, Isabel. I'll spend the rest of my life knowing you.

"All right, my men. Who's for it? Who's for it?" Mac was halfway across the field, keeping pace with the referee, as the rest of his team pulled up their socks and gulped at their water jars. "C'mon, hurry up, hurry up — it's a braw day for a win."

The whistle blew, the man with the ball paused for the smallest sliver of a second,

suspending the world and its time again. And then the game went on.

16

Opening the library door on her first morning, Ani watches the room reveal itself. There's no sign of Miss Fadden, her presence recalled by only the slightest imprint of her glasses and her fan in the desk's dust. Ani opens the windows, first one, then the other, craning her head to see the first train so as not to be surprised by its noise. If she learns when to expect their great loud rush, she reasons, they won't catch her off guard, won't surprise her into thinking about Mac, about shunting, about the solidity of a train against the soft give of a body.

She stands a long time, holding off this last thought, mesmerized by its awfulness. *This is how it is,* she thinks. *Two shifts, morning and evening, and Mrs. May heating up Bella's supper.* Another breath. *All right, all right, this will be all right.* The clock on the wall ticks loudly, and for as long as Ani stares at it, neither of its hands appears to

move. Which would be worse, she wonders, a day in which no one came — or a day in which people came and talked with her, at her, about finding her there, about how she is, about the circumstances of her employment?

She had never appreciated before the lovely anonymity of an unremarkable life.

The minute hand scrapes slowly around from five past to ten past. She would take any conversation.

Pushing herself out of her reverie, she begins a circuit of the shelves. *Of course, if no one comes, I really can spend my time reading — what could be better?* And she reaches for *Kangaroo,* left, as Miss Fadden had promised, in its rightful place. But the words blur and merge, her eyes unable to decipher the text. Replacing the book, she tries another and another. It's so quiet, so sepulchral, that she fears for a moment the world has stopped — or perhaps just the world of this one room.

Frozen, here, with time stood still. And if I can't read, if I can't read — the wave of panic that has been building in her since Mac's death finally crests and breaks, and she sits gasping and crying until a northbound train clamors into the platform outside, its noise jolting her back into herself.

A scant quarter hour has passed. She wipes her nose, her cheeks, her eyes, stretching her face into as many contortions as she can manage as if to confuse its memory of her weakness.

She thumbs at the ledgers then, the card files, the neat stacks of paper ranged in the neat wooden trays — a strange topography for her to learn; where things are recorded, how things are traced. She glances at the names of the library's borrowers, names from church, from Isabel's school, from conversations in the street. The lady who owns the dress shop has been borrowing Penguin classics. Mrs. Padman, Mrs. Bower, Mrs. Floyd — their husbands all crossed out of the register; probably Mac has been crossed out like that now too. The two owners of the rival shoe shops had both requested a manual of railway signs — how peculiar is that? Her fingers flick towards L for Lachlan: Ani, Isabel — and Mac. And there it is, the list of every book he's ever borrowed, the line now through his name, the terrible sense of a thing reckoned complete and unalterable.

The northbound train pushes out of the station as Ani turns and opens the window farther, catching the last of its sound, its steam. She does love that smell, slightly

heavy, slightly mechanical. She loves the way it tastes. And as she tastes it now, she runs her hand along the piano, tucked to the side of the window, and slowly opens its lid. She's slightly scared of pianos, as if someone might expect her to know how to play if she's standing near one. And she did take a couple of lessons from one of the shoe-shop owners when she first came to the coast — he played piano for the Saturday-night dances — but gave up in embarrassment. The only thing she knows how to play is the treble part of "Für Elise" — her father had taught her by rote, numbering the keys so she could remember their sequence, when she and Mac visited before Isabel was born. Ani can still feel the way Isabel kicked and squirmed as she destroyed Beethoven's lovely tune over and over again.

"We could call it Elise, if it's a girl," she remembers Mac saying, standing behind her. "Maybe the baby's trying to tell us that it already recognizes its name."

"Elise or Ludwig." Ani laughed. Mac was always so sure the baby was going to be a girl — *and she was,* thinks Ani now. *There she was.*

She pauses halfway through a bar, goes back to the beginning. Why didn't they call Isabel Elise? It was a lovely name — al-

though Isabel is too, of course, and for Mac's mother, which seems to matter more. She's glad she insisted on that. She hums the melody, a note or two out from the version she's picking out with the index finger of her right hand. *"Für Elise" — imagine being able to hum a tune you knew someone had written for you, and such a beautiful one, so beautiful.* She tries the opening again, and again. Perhaps she could teach herself the piano here — or at least learn this one melody so that it sounds as graceful, as easy, as it should.

Elise Lachlan: that would have been a lovely name. But then perhaps it would have made Isabel a different person. *And what would I change of her? What tiny piece would I want to be different?* Her thumb and little finger pick out an octave, pulsing from higher to lower and back again, louder and louder, until she hears a sound at the door and turns to see Mrs. Lacey, her arms full of paperbacks.

"Mrs. Lacey."

"Mrs. Lachlan, I thought you must have started — I saw Miss Fadden in her garden as I came down the hill."

"You're my first borrower," Ani says, making a great show of taking the books and finding the card.

"You'll get used to it," the other woman assures her as Ani falters then, casting around for what to do next. "Miss Fadden always had a deck of cards in the drawer — she used to play Patience when there was no one around."

Ani slides out the drawer, and there's a deck of cards, the colors garish, with caricatures of Uncle Sam as the kings, and the Statue of Liberty as the queens, Hitler and Mussolini faced off as the jokers. She laughs. "I would never have expected this — I should return them to her; they look like some sort of souvenir."

"We did mark that victory however we could." Mrs. Lacey moves around the shelves, pausing here and there. "I read this when I was a child — always wanted to read it again. Always wanted a daughter that I could call Anne." She pats *Anne of Green Gables'* cover, placing it carefully on Ani's desk. "You won't tell anyone if I borrow it?"

Ani smiles, shakes her head. "I loved these books when I was little. Bella's reading them now — she reads me sentences and I can almost remember what dress I was wearing when I first read it myself, or whereabouts I was sitting in our garden. Such strange particulars, and yet other memories are gone in a minute." She smiles again. "Which

is a blessing, I suppose."

But Mrs. Lacey has moved away, scanning across titles. *This is better,* thinks Ani. *Quite nice — quite a nice way to pass the time.* She brushes nonexistent dust from the cover of Mrs. Lacey's book, smoothes her ledger for its entry, readies the library's card.

"And these two," says her borrower. "Iris McKinnon told me this *Timeless Land* was very good, so I'll give it a go."

"I enjoyed it" — Ani nods — "and there was supposed to be a sequel coming — I'll let you know if it comes in — if it's any good." She breathes, feeling her way back towards inconsequential conversations. "Did I see Iris's brother on the beach a while ago?" Proud of being able to shape such pleasantries.

"Yes, he's home — with poor Iris wondering how long for and what he intends to do. Iris says he's no idea about teaching anymore, just talks about wanting to write, and doesn't. I imagine you'll see him in here before long; she never was much of a reader and if you were a poet, well, you must need to read all the time, mustn't you?"

Ani transcribes the titles carefully, not looking up. "I don't know anything of poets, Mrs. Lacey. I'll see if I can get any hints if he comes in here for books." And they smile

at each other — *easy; pleasant.* "I was thinking about Iris when you mentioned Dr. Draper coming. I'm afraid I don't remember your dancing like Ginger Rogers, but I remember Frank and Iris — she wore such beautiful dresses then."

Mrs. Lacey settles the books in the crook of her arm and taps the side of her nose. "That's a story still in progress, Mrs. Lachlan. But I know she's lonely, even with her brother home." And she turns towards the door, pausing on its step. "It was lovely to be your first borrower, dear. I hope you like it here — it seemed such a fine idea when Luddy told me. I could imagine you being happy somehow." The words are unexpectedly expansive — Ani bows her head underneath them, and when she looks up again, Mrs. Lacey is making her way across the gravel.

But Mrs. Lacey is right; she does love a library. She remembers once, during the war, getting out of the rain in Sydney — she can't place why she was there or what she was doing, but a great spring storm had come on and she'd run up the stairs of the nearest building to find herself at the new public reading rooms, pushing the heavy doors open with her shoulder.

It was dim inside, dim and quiet, like a

church, and then she saw it: a great map made in mosaic, a whole ocean laid out across the floor, with grand ships and blue waves and angels blowing the wind from the southwest, the northeast.

"It's beautiful," she'd said softly as the door eased shut behind her. "Beautiful." In the middle was an old outline of Australia from centuries before when the west coast was mostly rumor and the east coast a single, unvarying straight line — the cartographers' graceful guess at filling a blank. There was no hint of her beach, her coast, her part of the world. It was funny to think that where she lived had been invisible, or missing.

She patted a whale, traced out the accurate shape of Tasmania, and then stood up, moving slowly forward through the next set of doors and into a huge room with the soft light of a pale blue glass roof, and bright stained-glass panels illuminating its walls.

The hush was magnificent, sullied only by the occasional scrape of a chair, the shuffle of paper, and once or twice the sound of a catalog drawer tugged open against its will. Standing very still and quiet, Ani felt like a child in an adult's room from which she knew she should be barred.

She scanned the banks of shelves, the

pretty stairs that ran up to higher shelves again, the wide desks nested on the floor. What was this paradise, this sanctuary? And the light through the delicate roof — it was shimmering, and it was gorgeous. Around the walls, the stained-glass windows glowed with images of newspaper presses, of old, old books, of scenes from Chaucer — the pilgrims leaving Southwark, the pilgrims arriving in Canterbury. She tilted her head: was that a koala on the bottom? Were there koalas in Chaucer? Then again, what did she know about Chaucer? Epigrams, really, that was all. *Love is blind. The life so short, the crafts so long to learn.* And, *People can die of mere imagination,* a line that had terrified her when she was at school.

"Can I help you with anything?" There was a tall man at her elbow, a librarian, she supposed. "Was there something in particular you were wanting?"

Ani shook her head. "No, thank you, it was raining, I came in. But it's lovely, lovely to see this."

And the man smiled: "There's something about a room for thoughts and words." It was a statement, simple and direct, but it rang for Ani with the sharpness of revealed truth. "I've always wondered if paradise might not be a little like a library," the man

said then. "But that's probably a sacrilegious thing to suggest."

Ani blushed, as if it was, and at the grandness and the intimacy of the words. Her eyes flicked along the rows of men, some women, who sat with their books, their pencils, and their notes.

"It was raining, I came in," she said again. But what would it be like to come somewhere like this for a day's work, instead of the trains or the mines or any of the other noisy, messy places where most of the people she knew went to work? She glanced at the librarian and saw his hands smooth where Mac's were rough and grained with dirt. His shoulders, too, were stooped, and thinner than the straight broadness she was used to. But to come here to work; to sit in that silence, and that light.

She'd told Mac about it that night, as if she'd discovered a new world or uncovered a treasure, and she'd blushed when he laughed at her, at the power she'd invested in the idea of just sitting, sitting and reading. "Well, I do, I do think it sounds like heaven. And I do think about the things other people do, the other people I might be." Which had silenced him, and made him say something sharp about regretting he could make her no more than a railway-

man's wife, and made her wish she had never said any of it, never talked about this new and beautiful place. They were rare, these dissonances and petty tiffs. Ani would have walked a thousand miles rather than have had one.

"And how would I have found you, hidden away in a great library?" he'd wanted to know. "There's nowt of adventures and explorers on shelves like those." The stories he loved; the stories, she suspected, he dreamed about living when he dreamed of being someone, or somewhere, else.

There's another footfall on the gravel and Ani looks up, startled out of the loop of that thought — startled, somehow, to find herself in the realization of this library that's suddenly, unexpectedly, her domain. A shadow changes the light in the doorway, and then a man comes in, dark-suited, dark-haired, and rubbing his hands together as if he's come in from the coldest winter.

"You're the widow, then," he says, taking off his hat and drumming his fingers across its crown. "I heard they'd given you this job out of pity."

Ani watches his fingers play over the fabric, beating a tattoo that matches the rise and fall of her stomach. There she is, mired back in the one story by which she might

now be defined; she hates him, whoever this is.

"I'm Draper," he says. "The doctor. Come to minister to your sick and your dying, and bring all your new people into the world."

He coughs, and Ani tries to fit his shape to some memory of dancing — but all she can imagine is Mrs. Lacey in a fine frock she saw Ginger Rogers wear once in a film, all swan's down and chiffon, and that image is too ridiculous to belong to anything real. She waits for whatever he will say next, rubbing her own hands together as if to ward off his chill.

"And they've given you all this." He gestures so flamboyantly that there's no doubting how little he thinks of the place. "Which is generous, when not so many women have been able to stay in work since the war." He sets his hat down on the desk — her desk, she thinks, proprietorial for the first time. "Still, there's an argument, I suppose, that it will be better to keep your mind busy than to let it stretch and twist at leisure."

"Dr. Draper," she says at last, "you're not at all how I remembered. But I heard you were coming. And of course I have a daughter to support, and a house to keep." She's blushing, wishing to sound cool and sure.

This isn't anyone she can remember; this isn't anyone who would dance or laugh.

"As so many do, losing their men to war — so many women, all over the world, and now the world is supposed to be back to normal, and the men are back to take their jobs, and what happens to those widows who haven't rushed back to the altar with some new man? What happens to their daughters, to their houses?"

Ani feels her teeth clench. "There's Legacy," she says slowly: it feels like an interrogation, an exam. "There are provisions for helping war widows. And as for me, everyone has been very kind. I'm neither ungrateful for this compensation nor" — her voice narrows to a tight spit like his — "unaware of its privilege." She pauses at the squeal of a train's wheels on the tracks outside. "But it's an odd gift, perhaps, to work by the sound of the thing that killed your husband. Not even your war widows have had to endure that." They're unsayable words; she is almost sneering as she watches the doctor's face crease with distaste, but she feels strangely powerful. *What now?* she thinks, defiant. *What will you say to me now?* She's never felt so sharp before.

But the distaste, it seems, is for himself. "My apologies, Mrs. Lachlan." The brash

gaze is gone, his eyes focused on his own fingers as they worry at a knot tied in the corner of his handkerchief. "I lost many things in those years abroad, and among them were my social graces. Psychoneurosis, our American friends call it, if you want to be learned about it. People always like to have a label — for a newcomer, an outsider, or a widow. Still" — he straightens up, drawing a random shape on the brim of his hat with one finger — "the nuances of widowhood must be different, of course, when they aren't marked out by the weight of a war — I wonder whether people will regard you as more, or less, available."

Ani stares, wondering how it would feel to slap his face. She's never wished to do anything like that to anyone before. "My husband is barely dead." There's ice in her voice, and as she looks down to make the calculation by the calendar, she sees the date of her wedding anniversary, a few weeks ahead, and tastes something sharp and metallic in her mouth, unsure if its bile is for the nearness of a date that now feels purposeless or the fact that she didn't know, immediate and certain, precisely how many weeks, days, and hours had passed since Mac stopped being in the world.

The train pulls out, and as the room falls

silent again, the doctor turns, his gaze panning the rows of shelves. "I expect there's nothing here that I require, but I will come and look another day."

"The hours are pasted by the door," says Ani, wishing she could think of something more cutting or retaliatory. "I'm sorry I don't remember you much from before the war, Dr. Draper. Mrs. Lacey tells me you were a fine dancer — and I think I remember you dancing with Iris McKinnon and laughing with her brother. It would have been lovely to have met you more properly then."

And it is satisfying, she thinks, to watch the color drain from his face, to watch his fingers reach again for his wrinkled handkerchief. "That was a long time ago, Mrs. Lachlan, a long time ago now." In the room's quietness, they regard each other, level. "I don't think I'm much good for dancing or laughter these days."

"Do come, if you think the library might have anything you need. The hours, as I said, are pasted up." And she watches as he walks away towards the platform, disconcerted to hear him whistle, and wishing she could rinse his conversation out of her mouth.

Glancing up at the clock, she sees that its

hands have finally reached the end of her first shift. Pulling the windows down and the door closed — the lock checked twice, three times — she realizes she's never felt more tired in her life. And she hasn't read a single page.

17

She recognizes him at once, the man who balanced on the high, weathered pole, his gaze fixed beyond the white line of breakers, the wavy line of horizon. Roy McKinnon, Iris's brother, the man who wrote the poem during the war. He is tall, she sees, taller than his sister, and his hair is greyer than the color she took it for outside, from a distance, on the beach. Inside, closer up, he looks a little more stooped and weathered. She is scanning the lines on his forehead, around his eyes, and when she realizes he is studying her in turn, she blushes.

"I'm so sorry — was there something . . ."

"Do you keep a poetry section, Mrs. Lachlan?" As soon as he begins to speak, he looks away from her, studying his shirt cuffs, his shoes.

She shakes her head, startled by his directness and fearing another conversation like the doctor's the day before.

"No, no, I don't think we get a lot of poetry through the shelves. Is there something I can request for you?"

He draws in such a deep breath she expects the papers on her desk to shift a little towards him.

"No, perhaps, I don't know. I'm sorry. I just thought there might be something I could take with me now." He's pulled a pen from his pocket and is fiddling with its cap, snapping it on and off, on and off, as he gazes at the shelves. "I'd take *Kangaroo* if you had it."

"For poetry?" she asks, stepping around the barrier of the table, pulling D. H. Lawrence from his place.

"No, just for something that comes from here. Can I use my sister's card?"

She nods. "I admired your poem very much, Mr. McKinnon," she says, opening the ledger to Iris McKinnon's record. "And your sister was thrilled when she saw it in the magazine." She knows this is a stretch, perhaps even a lie. Iris McKinnon had never even acknowledged the verse as far as Ani knew — it's one clear memory she has, handing the cutout sheet to her through her front doorway, watching her take it without so much as a glance, put it on the table beside her, and say that if there was nothing

143

else, she had things to get back to, and close the door. Ani wonders, watching him, if her brother knows any of this.

He says, "You're very kind," and smiles at her, a warm and proper smile.

She wants to say she's never met a poet before, wants to say she saw him perched on the old jetty's pylon, and to ask how he jumped down without drenching himself, or whether he sat through a full turn of the tide.

But instead she says: "It's no trouble to check the book out to your sister's card," and she writes the details into her ledger. She says: "Will you stay with Miss McKinnon long?"

He's balancing the book on one hand as if to guess its weight. "Long enough to read this and work out how it sprang from here."

"You don't like it here, Mr. McKinnon?" And she braces herself for a shrug. "My husband gave me this to read when we were traveling to the coast. I loved the idea that such a story could come from such a pretty seaside town. It felt incongruous or — I don't know — dangerous somehow." It's the first time she's mentioned Mac this casually since — since; she nearly falters — and she likes the ease of it, the sense that it gives him some currency. *Immortality:* she

risks thinking the word.

"You didn't grow up here?"

"No, no, miles inland, on the plains, dry as a biscuit. I didn't see the ocean until I was married, until I'd read *Kangaroo*. Were you and Iris children here? I mean" — she blushes, despite herself — "I remember you visiting a little, when we came, in '36, but I don't remember if your family . . ."

He puts the book down on the corner of her desk, the very corner, repositioning it until its edges match the edges of the wood precisely. The silence beyond her words grows and grows, and she's on the edge of repeating the question when he says: "We came for holidays when we were kids, for weekends when we were older. Later, then, our parents died, and Iris came to stay." And then immediately, "And I'll take another novel, to keep me going," so that she knows the other exchange is over. She watches as he moves along the shelves, tilting a spine towards him here and there, pulling out one or two volumes to skim through their pages, his nose pressed close, before he reshelves them — carefully, gently. Then, "I haven't read this for years," and he slides *Jane Eyre* across the desk.

"One of my favorites," she says. "But I expect a lot of people say that. That scene

where Rochester talks of sending Jane to Ireland — the cord he thinks connects them, from his heart to hers —" She stops, blushing. Mac had told her early in their friendship it was his favorite book: it was a large part of how she remembers falling in love. And here she is, on the edge of talking about this with a man she hardly knows, just for the sake of bringing Mac into the room.

"I only like reading it now I know how it ends," Roy McKinnon says as if she hasn't cut herself off, and she watches, appreciative, as he flicks to the last page, as if to check that its sentences still tell the right story. "The first time — all that suffering, all that separation; it's a terrible thing to confess but I think I skipped ahead just to make sure it turned out all right."

"My daughter does that sometimes," says Ani, recovering herself. "I like that it matters so much to her that a book's characters end up happy and well."

And he smiles again, tucking a book in each of his coat's pockets and turning for the door. Where he stops, scuffs one foot a little on the mat, and turns again. "It was nice to meet you, Mrs. Lachlan," he says carefully, his fingertips up towards the brim of his hat. "I was sorry to hear —"

"It was nice to meet you, too," she says quickly, across the condolence, and he blushes in turn. *He's shy,* thinks Ani. *I wouldn't have expected that.* Wouldn't it take a certain courage to write a poem? Didn't people talk about his bravery during the war? "And I'll see what I can do about the poetry. There are some new books due to come down next week."

He waves his thanks and goes, and she listens as his feet crunch across the gravel, disappearing under such a sudden rush of a train passing that she jumps.

She pulls a blank sheet of paper towards her, uncaps her pen. How would you start to write a poem? How would you put together a series of words for its first line — how would you know which words to choose? When you read a poem, every word seemed so perfect that it had to have been predestined — well, a good poem. Mac could do doggerel for Isabel, or funny limericks for birthday cards. But a real poem, a proper poem: Ani stares at the blank sheet. *How would you know what to do?*

She smoothes the page, writes the day's date at the top, writes the library's designation, and drafts the request for some poetry, if possible, in the next dispatch of books.

"For Mr. Roy McKinnon," she writes, "a published poet, who lives locally in these parts."

18

In the bar of the Ryans Hotel, Roy McKinnon and Frank Draper sit down for their first beer together after the war, the glasses cold against their fingers, the room dim and quiet around them. It's a Tuesday afternoon, a nothing time, when men should be working. But here they are, drinking.

"To making it home," says Roy, raising his glass. But Frank, rather than replying, simply drains his drink, and signals for another.

"Impossible, isn't it?" he says, etching a pattern into the glass's frost.

"I never let myself imagine it might happen," says Roy quietly. "Never let myself think about being back."

"What was the worst of it?" They are sitting close, each with his nose near his glass; each with his head slightly bowed. There is something supplicatory about it, as if they were receiving some sort of communion.

"The worst of it?" Roy asks. "The constant expectation of death — killing or being killed."

"Did you kill anyone?"

Roy's fingers tighten around his glass; then he picks it up and drinks it dry. "I can't tell you that; you can't ask me."

"All right." Frank signals across the bar for another drink for them both. "Then the best of it. Was there a best of it?"

And Roy laughs. "I met a bloke who gave his address, on his papers, his enlistment papers, as Thirroul Beach — not just Thirroul, not the village, not anywhere in the streets, but the beach itself, the very sand. 'That's where I belong,' he said, 'and that's where I'll go back to.' Dunno if he made it. Don't even know if I'd recognize him if I saw him."

"Not bad," says Frank. "I like that. My best was a garden of roses blooming a mile or so beyond one of the camps — so normal, so beautiful. They looked right, you know, and they smelled right. They smelled like they belonged in the real world, not those pits of death and misery. Everything else, even after the war ended, everything else was panic and rush — sending people home who could be sent home, the way they clamored and panicked for the trucks, as if

someone was going to snatch away their one chance of getting out of there. And just over the hill, this patch of roses was going through the normal course of a normal year. They were blooming as usual, and they smelled so good, I could have eaten them."

They sit awhile, sipping now and then. Roy McKinnon's fingers tap out a rhythm on the bar. Frank Draper rubs his hand through his hair every so often, and lets out a sigh that sounds like *anyway, anyway.*

"So what do we do now we're here?" Roy asks at last. "What happens now?"

"All falling into place, isn't it?" The doctor's voice is hollow. "You must be working on your first book of verse, my poet, and here I am ready to usher in life and death for this village's patients. Just as we always planned."

Roy shakes his head. "I don't know what to write about, now that I'm here. I don't even know how to write." His fingers circle the top of the glass, the friction between its wetness and his skin making the sailors' curse ring out. He stills himself. "I stand in this beautiful place, on glorious days, and the only images that come are from over there, back then. Not that some of those weren't beautiful or glorious. One night, there was a tiny island and no moon; you

know those nights you thank God that you're covered in pitch? We were buzzing ashore in some little boat, looking for the enemy in some new messy swamp, and the whole ocean was lit up with phosphorescence — the way it churned and turned behind the boat, it was like a carpet had been thrown over the sea. I sit and look at the ocean here, and I think of that, on a good day. Other days, I think of other oceans, of what it sounds like when the voices of drowning men finally stop." He takes a long drink. "I should write to someone about that bloke from Thirroul Beach — find out if he made it, find out who to tell about seeing him, if he didn't. That matters, doesn't it, Frank? Those messages must matter?"

He shifts his head, trying to find his friend's gaze, but Frank's eyes stay down, so low they might as well be closed. "I don't know, mate," he says at last. "I don't know. They're not going to bring anyone back to life, are they? Nothing can do that. And that's all anyone wants in the end, isn't it? To change that; to bring someone back. A message — well, I never did set much store by words, you know."

He means it as a joke, and tries to laugh, but no sound comes out of his mouth, and

they sit awhile longer, silent, their shoulders almost touching.

"Lawrence the poet, and Yeats's doctor," says Roy quietly. "Do you reckon we still have a chance of filling their shoes?" Their younger selves had set much store by any available precedents, leaning against village memories of renown, a writer from Notts and a doctor from Dublin: if two such men could find their way to this speck in an atlas and *do* something here — well, the young Roy, the young Frank had told each other their own opportunities in these fields might be limitless.

"Don't care whose shoes we fill, Royston, my friend," Frank says now. "It would just be a blessed relief not to be walking around in my own all the time." The doctor pushes back from the bar, shifts his hat on his head. "At least I can sleep," he says at last. "At least I don't tremble or stutter. I mean, my memory's gone, but I'd rather forget than remember — the war at least, and I can't remember when there was anything before that. Saw a bloke interviewed by doctors just last year — that's two years after this is all supposed to be over, and they still can't discharge him from the hospital. You know what he kept saying, over and over? 'I was a solid man before this; I was a solid man.'"

He shakes his head, wiping at his eyes. "And Iris? How's Iris?"

"You should see for yourself —" It's harder than Roy means it to sound, so he swallows the end of the sentence with his drink, fixes his own hat, and stands. "I mean, I think she's waiting — I think she's . . ." He shrugs. "You work it out, you two. It's been too many years."

"And you? What do you need to work out, now you're here?"

The two men stand on the curbside, looking along the main street towards the railway line, towards the ocean.

"I need to work out what kind of chump finds poetry in the middle of mud and blood, and can't string a sentence together about this mountain, this sunshine, this sky, and this place. Nothing to do beyond that."

The doctor grips his friend's shoulder, holding him in an embrace for just a moment. "Find yourself something new to think about. It'll work itself out after that."

"Fine advice from you." Roy McKinnon laughs. But it's good to laugh — and Frank, after all, is a doctor; his statements arrive with the authority of prescription. Roy grabs his friend's hand and shakes it, holds it, as a bus rattles southwards and an old horse and cart clatter north. "You were right to come

154

back here — it'll be all right, I reckon."

"Nothing will ever be all right, mate," says Draper, stepping away. "But if I'm going to come to terms with that, I may as well do it somewhere I've someone to drink with."

They walk along the main street together. Frank's face is hard and dark — catching sight of it in a window, Roy doesn't want to know what's happening inside his friend's imagination, or who is there with him. For himself, as he nears the railway station and glances along towards its buildings, he finds that he's thinking about a tall woman with light hair, standing silent among a landscape of books, and the ocean wild and vast beyond.

He waits for a sentence to form.

19

"This is how it was the first time I saw you."
When Mackenzie Lachlan butted up against the side of Australia, he was twenty-five years old with nowhere in particular to go and no one in particular to be. Walking up from his ship's anchorage on the too-bright, too-blue harbor, he turned at the sound of a Glaswegian accent — more angular than his northerly Scots, but still friendly for being familiar — and found himself talking to a rosy man called Ewan who'd been ashore a month and found a job on the railways. "It's way away, laddie," he'd said to Mac Lachlan, "out in the space where your family must be from," and he punched at his shoulder and laughed as Mac frowned. "A river called Lachlan, man; I'm taking engines out there, to the plains." And Mac Lachlan, who liked a good story, thought he'd like to see the river that ran along in his name.

At the yards the next day, with Ewan still punching and pummeling his shoulders, he was told there were no jobs for the minute, but — a nod, a wink — he might as well travel out with his mate. "Off we go, lad," Ewan boomed as he took a train — and Mac — out through the city's suburbs on their first run. "But y'picked a lousy place to come looking for work, or a lousy time." They left the coast the next day, the engine hauling them south and west through green space, blond space, dust-dry space, and white space that seemed to hold pure emptiness. "But you'll see your family's river," Ewan boomed again and again, and Mac laughed too, the vast landscape and its potential blossoming inside him. He'd dreamed of places this open, this flat, this inviting. This warm.

The ranges and the hills, the slightest inclines and hummocks, behind them, he could feel himself stretching out — wider, wider and wider — trying to see not just this intoxicating stretch of open land but the very curve of the earth he could make out at its edge. He saw birds high in the air; he saw animals bounding along beside the line. He saw mirages and shadows that loomed where there was nothing to throw them, and strange figures that seemed to

rise out of the tiny gap where the dirt met the sky, that ran with the train awhile, and then folded themselves back into that liminal rut. He saw different shapes picked out in stars, and different colors marking the phases of dawn, day, and dusk. And when he arrived, he rode out to see this river that was somehow his, its water khaki, its edges soft with the khaki leaves of gum trees. He even passed a tiny place that bore his grandmother's Christian name, Maude, to match the river that marked her surname, Lachlan. And he took all this to mean that this was the place, in all of Australia, that he was supposed to have found.

Back in town, he put out the word for any work and was told to meet up with one of the town's builders early the next morning for a job of roofing that was needed in a hurry.

He slept at the pub, his dreams spiked by tall, thin figures who darted, silhouettes, along the horizon. And when he woke in the morning it was still dark, a frost on the ground, and the sound of snoring all along the hall. He washed his face, shaved, wetted down the worst of his hair, ate porridge in the pub's kitchen, drank a huge mug of tea, and was out in the clear, cold air as the first birds began to call.

He liked the town, the way it pressed together instead of spreading wide in all the room it had, and he liked the sound his boots made on its roads. He followed the instructions the publican had given him, humming here and there, singing now and then — a couple of bars of *Speed, bonnie boat,* a premature snatch of *Morning has broken* — and still filled with the possibility of all the space around him. He was an ocean boy himself — the cuan, he loved it — mucking along beaches for whelks and crabs, swimming as far as the cold would let him, and heading out on the trawlers if he was able. But the span of the sky out here was a close match for the sea — as wide and as blue.

"My bonnie lies over the ocean," he sang softly as he rounded the last corner. He'd reached the edge of the town without realizing it and before him lay the shape of a house, low and spreading, and its roof, triangular and partial, open to the morning. The road dipped down a little towards it, the first brightness of sunrise beyond in reds, pinks, golds: he was walking directly east. "My bonnie lies over the sea."

"Good morning, Mr. Lachlan," a voice called from up in the air, and as he arched his neck to see where it had come from, he

made out two figures perched on the roof's narrow frame. "The kind gentleman in the public house said you'd be along early in the morning." It was an odd accent, soft, with the first syllable of each word leaned on a little, like a strangely rhythmic march. It was unlike any he'd heard before, and as his eyes adjusted to the changing light, he made out the man, tall, fair, with a tanned face and thick blond beard and mustache.

"Mr. Kalm," he called, "I hope I've not kept you," and as he raised his hand to wave, it shaded his eyes for a moment so that he saw her just as the ball of the sun came over the crest. Anikka Kalm, standing next to her father, watching the earth roll forward into a new day. Tall, like her father, and fair, like her father, her feet were set apart to balance on the beam — he thought, *She'd stand well on any ship;* he thought, *That's what lissome is, then* — and the bright rose-gold of the moment seemed to burnish her hair, her face, her skin, her shape with light.

"The first time I saw you," he would whisper to her afterwards when he told her the story, "it was just getting light. I took you for part of the sunrise."

But at that moment, in that morning, he simply stood and gazed up at her while she

stood above him and gazed out towards the sun.

Oskar Kalm swung down onto the ground, talked about frames and nails and slate and hours, and Mac agreed to anything, paying no attention to the conversation. He heard himself say, "I'm more an ocean man," heard Oskar say that one would have to be an ocean man to find oneself so far from home and in this part of the world. But then the memory of those words, too, disappeared under the sound of Anikka's voice.

"I've never seen the ocean," she said, her voice halfway between the roundness of her father's Nordic accent and the stretch of every Australian voice Mac had yet encountered. "It must be so wide, so blue, so . . ." She fumbled for a word, her fingers worrying at the air as if she might find it there. "So wet." And she blushed.

"My daughter," said Oscar Kalm, "was rudely landlocked by my ending up here." He swung a belt, a hammer, towards his new assistant, calling up to the girl that they needed to be getting on with the job they were there for. And Mac watched as she swung herself down — bending easily to grip the framework near her ankle, dropping down until her toes found the shape of a window below that, and then springing

back to arrive standing, next to him, as tall as him, on the grass.

"Mackenzie Lachlan," he said, holding out his hand.

"Anikka Kalm," she said, shaking it firmly.

"I could take you to see the ocean one day," he said, and blushed.

"I could come with you to see that," she said, laughing — although he wasn't sure if the laugh was for the suggestion of the ocean or the red flush on his cheeks. "It's nice to meet you, Mr. Lachlan. I'll bring some lunches out later in the day." And as she strode away, it seemed the sun kept pace with her movement across the ground.

Her blond hair so bright it looked lit from within.

20

Roy McKinnon returns *Jane Eyre* on the day it's due. Ani looks up from a box of books and he's standing in the doorway, scraping his shoes on the mat, taking a little too long to do as simple a thing as come into a room.

"I've brought this," he says simply. "I've been staring at it so long but I couldn't . . ."

"Mr. McKinnon," she says, "I'm so sorry if it wasn't what you wanted." As if she should have been able to guide him, to advise him on a happier book; as if she's failed in her job somehow.

But he shakes his head, seems to shake his hat right from it, and, bareheaded, finally steps inside.

"No, no, it was good; it was good, Mrs. Lachlan, and I've finished with it now. I wanted to hang on to it, that was all. I wanted to keep it close, but —" He smiles, holding it out towards her. "I wondered if I

could ask you to get me some particular poets, if that's possible — the British, from the Great War. I thought I might try them."

"Wilfred Owen? Rupert Brooke?" She's pulling names from the contents pages of the one anthology her own shelves hold at home, wanting to sound knowledgeable.

"No, no" — he cuts across her quickly — "not the ones who died; the ones who survived. Sassoon. Graves. The ones who kept living, kept writing."

There's an edge in his voice that she knows from somewhere, but it takes her a moment to place it. It's panic, the voice of mothers when their children can't be found for a moment; the voice of women against the news that their sons, their husbands, are not coming home; the voice of Anikka herself one day when Isabel inched too close to the edge of the station's platform — of Anikka herself, she suspects, in the hours, the days, beyond the accident.

"I made some tea, Mr. McKinnon, just a moment ago — could I get you a cup?" She's on his side of the desk now, pulling out a chair, clearing a space. "Was there something you were looking for in particular? Some poem? Some description?" The way he lowers himself onto the chair is as if he distrusts it, and she wonders whether

164

poets think differently about simple things like chairs and hats. Filling a cup, she wonders if it would be rude to ask.

As she turns towards him again, the tea carefully balanced, the afternoon's light hits that point before sunset where it softens and swells sometimes into a few minutes of rounder, warmer illumination. Through the window, the greens of the trees thicken slightly, the shadows lengthen, and the sky takes on a fuller shade of blue. The mountain, diminished at midday, surges again to its full height; the clouds flare a brighter white.

Inside, the last of the sun picks up the wood of the library's shelves, its floor, its desk, grazing the side of the poet's head and turning his dull grey-brown hair into something flecked by ginger and gold. For the shortest moment, Ani wants to reach out and touch it — to see if it's warm, to see if it's soft — and it's only the cup and saucer that stop her from making this movement.

"There," she says, blushing a little, "it's a magic time of the day when the sun goes over the mountain, don't you think? The way it makes everything glow."

He drinks his tea too fast — she knows how hot it is — gulping with each mouthful, until he reaches the layer of sugar at the

bottom. "Is it always like this?" he asks then, china rattling against china as he replaces the cup too forcefully in the scoop of its saucer.

"The light?" she says. "No — I think it needs particular clouds, or a wind. There's something more to it than just the end of the day, but I've never managed to work out what it is."

But he's shaking his head again; she's misunderstood the question. "No, no; I mean, how you say things — the light, the time — is it always like this? It makes you sound like a poet yourself."

The blush goes all the way up to her hair this time. "I don't know the first bit of poetry really," she says, a little desperate. "Although my husband used to read poems aloud to me sometimes — the Scottish ones; they rollicked along. I like to read, Mr. McKinnon. That's all." And she wishes for an instant that she hadn't given him the tea — even though it's already drunk and finished — or the chance of a conversation. It feels heady, or reckless, and she steps back until she feels the solid horizontal of the desk hard behind her.

"It's a lovely light," he says at last, but so quietly that she almost misses the words. "As if it's coming through stained glass —

even when you're outside. You know, I've never thought of it like that before." Unfolding an envelope from his pocket, he feels across the surface of her table, his eyes fixed on the middle distance between them. "May I — do you have a pen?" And she slides one towards him, spinning it around so it's ready for him to pick up and write.

"Is this . . . are you . . ." She wants to know if she's watching some act of creation, if something is coming into being in this library that didn't exist the moment before.

"Those terrible stories of the books burned in Germany before the war," he says then. "Do you remember? A city square on fire with great pyres of words — they burned Helen Keller, you know. They burned Jack London. 'Where they burn books, so too will they in the end burn people' — I read that somewhere years ago. And it will be years before we know how many people were truly lost through this war — before it started, when it was happening, and now, even now, when it's supposed to be over." His words come in a rush, tripping over themselves. "How many bodies burned in one city or another country or the whole rest of the world. And now your books, Mrs. Lachlan, are caught by the edge of fire, their spines red and orange, just there, just above

you. And it's beautiful." He pushes the pen away, puts the envelope, still blank, back into his pocket, carefully refolded.

"Are you writing now, Mr. McKinnon?" Her forthrightness flares the redness of her face again. "I mean, since you're home — these past years . . . I don't know if it's a question I should ask you or not, but it's always intrigued me how —"

"What intrigues me, Mrs. Lachlan" — there's a coldness in his voice and he's suddenly on his feet, adjusting his hat, and turning for the door — "is what sort of a man can find a poem in the middle of all that, and then come home to a place as pretty as this and find nothing, nothing . . ." He breathes in too long a breath, then tips the edge of his hat. "But I've become monotonous. If you could let me know when those books come in," he says, and is gone.

"I hope you're feeling . . ." she begins to say, into the emptiness. She wonders if he registers the tightness in his own voice.

Taking a deep breath herself, Ani pulls the ledger towards her again, begins to run through the books that will go back to Sydney the following day. *The Grapes of Wrath* has been popular, and Eleanor Dark's *Timeless Land,* while people wait for its sequel,

and Zane Grey, as ever. He's dead, but still publishing: what literary medium makes that happen, that writing from beyond the grave? Mac loved him, following his stories across every incarnation of the Wild West's frontier. And if Zane Grey is still writing books after his own death, maybe Mac Lachlan is still reading them. It feels a dangerously flippant thing to think.

She shakes her head to dislodge the idea, changing the angle from which she looks at her list. If she concentrated on which books were most popular in each batch, would she find the secrets of what this village thought and felt among the stories it borrowed to tell itself? It's a safer thing to think.

She pushes at her temples, unsettled, and sees Roy pulling the envelope from his pocket so that it shakes out to its full size, reaching forward — doesn't matter that it's her pen, her desk — for anything that might make a mark. With her eyes closed, she can make him Mac, the table their kitchen table. She sees her own hand push a pen towards him, sees him pick it up, begin to write.

She can almost see the words as her husband tries to make a poem.

And why not? *Why not?*

She blows a long breath into the empty room. There he is, there he is, Mackenzie

Lachlan, her man. He leans forward, finishes his first line with a flourish, looks up into nothingness — she's invisible — and then down again, the pen busy with another line and another. She watches for a minute, knowing she should leave him to do this on his own. No, if she'd had this moment, she'd have sat there, seeing it happen, soaking it in.

His hand slows, stops, and he's blowing onto the words, softly, as if to hurry them dry. What would he say next? Would he read it? Would he fold it up, slip it back into his pocket, promise to read it to her when it had sat for a while? Would he pretend that nothing had happened, that he'd been making a list of the things he needed to remember to do the coming weekend?

He's fading; the kitchen is fading. She's back in the library, staring somewhere between the titles of books she's spent the morning packaging up. Without looking, she pulls a sheet of paper from the stack on her desk, a pencil from the jar. So close, he was so clear. She can do this: she can pull a poem for him out of the air.

The light is heavy before sunset
The world encased in thick stained glass

— but that's stealing. That was the poet's line, and she's back in the room with a thud, Mac gone, the poem gone, the light gone, and the evening coming on fast.

The thunder of a train coming down from the north collides with the thunder of one coming up from the south and for an instant, out of nowhere, Anikka is certain they will collide, here, in her station, outside her window, in a great crash of metal and fire and weight.

She hates these thoughts, tries to shrug catastrophe away from her shoulders.

The light is heavy before sunset, she recites. "The light is heavy before sunset." She pulls another sheet towards her, writes out the poet's request for anything by Siegfried Sassoon, Robert Graves. She's read poems by them — she's sure of it, staring at the names until a line comes into her mind: *Everyone's voice was suddenly lifted; And beauty came like the setting sun.*

When Mac was hit, how long had it taken him to die? Did it happen immediately? Did it happen later in the afternoon? Did he go during daylight, in the darkness, or just as the sun set? Was there anyone she could ask? The inquest was coming, she knew, and she'd said again and again that she would not be attending, did not want to sit through

the details of injuries and blame. The time, and the light; she'd like to know about those. She could ask the railways man or the minister. She could ask Luddy; he might know. But there is something preserving in the idea that people could know parts of the story that she didn't, as if she didn't need to bear them all at once — she tells herself this and believes it is true.

She folds the request letter, licking so fiercely at the envelope that it slices her tongue.

"Damn it." She's never cursed anything before. "Damn it all." Closing the book before her tears fall onto its pages and make spots on all the lists she's taken such care to transcribe. "Damn and damn and damn."

"Mrs. Lachlan?" Iris McKinnon, the poet's sister, is standing in the doorway. "I'm sorry — my brother forgot to give you this one," sliding *Kangaroo* across the desk. "I hoped it might help him be here, but . . ." She fiddles with the clasp on her bag. "I don't think he got past the first chapters. And he asked me to apologize to you."

"For not reading the book?" Anikka hears a harshness in her own voice and doesn't care if Iris McKinnon hears it too.

"I don't know — he just said to apologize. It's hard, I think, for him . . ." Her voice

sounds tired of making her brother's excuses.

Anikka slides the book towards herself so it rests against her belly. "If he's staying with you for some time, Miss McKinnon, he should probably get his own card — so that you can keep borrowing as well." Changing the subject; filling the silence.

The other lady smiles. "Oh, I don't mind — I never need to read as much as he does, and it's nice to think I can do something for him, give him something that might help him . . ." She pauses, awkward. "Of course it's a great blessing that he came home and came home uninjured, and really that's all you can ask for."

Ani taps the spine of the book on the desk, as if its pages needed to be squared, and moves to reshelve it. "There are different kinds of loss, you know," she says quietly.

"Well, yes," says Miss McKinnon, her fingers fidgeting with a handkerchief as if she's thinking about dabbing her eyes or blowing her nose. "As you know yourself, Mrs. Lachlan, after all these years."

Anikka blinks at the thin woman's ferocity — it crosses her mind that she might damn her, and to her face, and this doesn't seem a bad idea, although Iris McKinnon is talking again.

"But as I always say, time heals all wounds — I remember telling you that a long time ago, Mrs. Lachlan, and I try to tell my poor brother every day now as well." Her back is rigidly straight, her face is set, and the weakness implicit in the handkerchief's brief flutter has been stuffed back into her handbag along with the white fabric.

The room darkens as the night properly begins. In the last moments of shadow before she reaches for the lights, Ani hears herself say: "No, Miss McKinnon, no. I do remember you saying that to me, and I've been meaning to say ever since that you were wrong. Time passes, and wounds close over, but the healing is a different thing altogether — and often, I think, you cannot expect that it will ever fully occur."

"Don't say that." The other woman's voice drops to a hiss. "Don't say that they won't all come back, the ones who lived. Don't condemn us all to widowhood, now that you have to make sense of it."

Ani blinks. Is that what she does? Is this who she is? She flicks the switch and the sudden brightness of the bulb above startles them both.

"I'll send a note when Mr. McKinnon's books arrive," she says at last. And the poet's sister turns and leaves without an-

other word.

Ani watches her go, and remembers, in an instant, a day in her own garden, Isabel fiddling with her first flowers, and Iris McKinnon naming each one as her daughter pried their petals apart. These losses, these slips: perhaps it took a larger one to notice all the other people you'd let get away. Perhaps it was only then that you wondered how they happened, if they mattered. *But perhaps I used to be a better friend.*

Ani works the book box closer to the door and kneels down in front of it, checking its contents against its list for the last time, and making sure the books are packed neatly and secure. She wonders if Miss McKinnon has read *Kangaroo* and realizes in an instant that any number of people she knows in this place might even have been here when it was written. They might have seen its writer. Ani would envy them that.

But we were closer, Iris and me, she thinks then. *I was the person who cut her brother's poem from the magazine for her — I was the person who gave it to her so she could read it. Years after Bella was born, I was still the person who would think to do that. I should know what happened with her.*

Perhaps the poem didn't matter to Iris McKinnon; *perhaps,* thinks Ani suddenly,

175

she wishes he hadn't written it. Perhaps she was embarrassed by it.

Closing the box and securing it at last, she resolves to be nicer to the poet. And when she walks home, later in the evening, she recites the first two lines of what she's already calling "Mac's poem" over and over in time to her footsteps, like a chant or a spell or a mantra.

"Look at this, love." Mac pushed the magazine across the kitchen table towards her, steering it around the mess she was making with some fruit. "Article about the northern lights, see. Did I ever tell you about the time I saw them, a little bairn out in the night with my gran, and all their colors snaking and swirling across the sky?"

"You did, Mac, you did — weren't you going to take me to see their show?" Her reflexive reply, co-opting his fantasy of return.

The house creaked a little, settling its shape in the evening's cool, and Ani waited to hear if this had disturbed their sleeping daughter.

"If we could get round the world, lass, see my gran, and the lights — and then a quick skate across the ocean to your da's country and his people . . ." He smiled. "And all that on a railwayman's wage." The smile

widening into a laugh.

She slid the segments of fruit into the saucepan, wiping their bright mess from the brighter red laminate of the table's top.

"Maybe I could get a job," she said after a moment. "Add a few more shillings to our savings."

But he shook his head, his attention back on the pages in the magazine. "What would you want to do, Ani? And what jobs would there be now everyone's back from the war?" He drew in a deep breath. "That smells grand, what you're making — what is it?"

"Just fruit — just some peaches: I thought I'd stew them up so you could have your favorite pie later on." She supposed it didn't matter about the money, and a job might be more trouble than it was worth. Iris Mc-Kinnon had been taken off the post round for some returning soldier and was raising hell about being replaced, the grocer said. *Still,* thought Ani, *secretly, she must prefer to have her time back to herself.* Throughout the war, watching Iris heave her heavy satchel along the village's streets, Ani had never thought she looked happy. *She never made it look like a thing you'd want to do.*

"Preserving for the winter." He laughed. "You do take care of me."

She stood alongside him as he sat at the table, pulled him in towards her, ruffled his hair. "Doing my best," she said softly. "Doing my best." The house shifted again, and Ani paused, listening for Isabel.

"She's a big girl now, love," said Mac, noticing her stillness. "Reckon she'd sleep through an earthquake most nights. Remember when she was born and that plane came down on the beach, all engines and kerfuffle, and she didn't even rouse?" He worked his arm around his wife, his other hand smoothing the page he was reading.

"The airplane on the beach? The mail plane in the storm?" Ani frowned. "That was 1936, Mac; that was just after we came, well before Bella was born. Don't you remember Luddy setting out that line of flares to make a kind of runway?"

"It was cars, wasn't it? A row of cars parked along the beach with their headlights on to show him how to come in — and I'm sure Bella was born; sure we brought Mrs. May in to sit with her while we ran down to help." Mac was rubbing at his own hair now, frowning and perplexed.

Ani pushed the pan of fruit to the back of the stove, watching as its bubbles settled into a low simmer. "I'll get my daybook," she said. "That'll fix your lousy memory,

Mackenzie Lachlan."

"Your daybook, your daybook," he called after her. "I'm sure it's just a little fallible now and then, Mrs. Mackenzie Lachlan — sure a bit of poetic license creeps in."

Coming back into the kitchen, leafing through the old diary, she raised her eyebrows in mock affront: "I don't know what you mean, sir. I am a mere scribe of events around me . . ." And she ducked as he threw a tea towel at her. "All right, once or twice I might have exaggerated. . . ."

"You had us sliding down the scarp in a tropical monsoon in your telling of our first bushwalk, Anikka Kalm, when it was the lightest shower of rain imaginable."

"Well, it felt heavier, and wetter, and it made for a better story with a bit of thunder and lightning — which I'm sure we *did* have. But I'd never change the year a plane landed on the beach, or whether our daughter was born or not when it did, or whether it was brought home by a line of flares lit by young Luddy or a line of parked cars."

Her fingers leafed through the book's pages, and she paused, reading random lines from its months.

"Here," she said. "One airplane coming down through thick fog and rain, March 1936, with a line of makeshift flares pushed

180

into the sand — we'd only been here a month or so, and it felt like the whole village came out to help. . . ." She paused. "Or were we all just prying?" She held the book out to Mac, tapping its date with her finger.

He hardly read the page, his eyes moving across it so quickly while he said, "All right then, all right," and then looked across at the page opposite, the day before. "See this, though, Ani love." Mac's finger traced the words. " 'And we talked about sailing north, sailing up to see Grannie Lachlan, and how we might find so much money for that.' "

She tilted her head, reading over his shoulder. "I always thought we talked about going later, when we had Isabel, so Grannie Lachlan could meet her. And you see, we could use some extra money — we even said so then."

Mac smiled, tapping at the page. "Yes we did, love: here it is. Written fast in ink." He squeezed her into a hug. "Stories are always changing, aren't they, although I could have sworn I remembered that line of cars — would've told you who'd driven them onto the sand, if you'd asked me. And what do you want with the bother of a job, Ani?" This talk of employment; if she wanted it, he supposed, she should do it, but he didn't want her turning into some hectoring har-

ridan like Iris McKinnon. His Ani, she'd be better than most men at anything she turned her hand to — he couldn't imagine she didn't know this herself.

Ani shook her head, stirring the softening peaches as the sound of a train braking hard cut through the night. "We'll never get north on a railwayman's wage," she said, but she was only teasing, and he knew it — although he felt it underlined by the train's noise.

"She's late tonight," he said. "And in a hurry to make it up too. Shall we get to bed then, Anikka Lachlan? Shall we read a little in the warm?"

And she lay beside him in the dim light of the lamp, listening as he read to her from the famous book about this place:

Then the train came out on the sea — lovely bays with sand and grass and trees, sloping up towards the sudden hills that were like a wall. There were bungalows dotted in most of the bays. Then suddenly more collieries, and quite a large settlement of bungalows. From the train they looked down on many pale-grey zinc roofs, sprinkled about like a great camp, close together, yet none touching, and getting thinner towards the sea. The chimneys

were faintly smoking, there was a haze of smoke and a sense of home, home in the wilds.

"The wilds," she murmured. "I never thought of it as the wilds. But home, yes, and the only home Bella has had, compared to our beginnings."

He watched as her eyes closed, as she burrowed her head into his side for the rest of the reading, as she slipped further away from the book in whose subsequent chapters, the ones unwritten beyond the narrative's end, she'd always suspected she was living.

22

They meet in the door of the co-op — Anikka coming out with sugar, tea, flour, and Roy McKinnon going in, his hands in his pockets. Her eyes fail in the sunlight after the dimness of the shop; his strain to see anything in the shadows after the brightness of the day; and for an instant neither can see the other.

They step awkwardly — she to her left, he to his right — so that the doorway remains impassable, and at the moment Ani laughs and Roy's eyes adjust to the gloom so that he can see her, and where he's going, and everything on the busy shelves of the shop, in more minute detail than usual. He's struck by the way she emerges, coming into focus, and by the patterns made by the different bits of produce tucked into their little bays and buckets on the wall behind the shop's counter. There's something to be said, he thinks, about what's available,

what's plentiful in this place, in this world, about the great extent of what might be found here. But as he thinks this, he looks at her again and sees that her laugh is distracted, uneasy, in this no-man's-land of space.

She used to love it, the gathering, the provisioning. Now she rushes through the shops she needs to enter, hating the whispers, the stares. Here comes Anikka Lachlan, her basket swinging and her eyes still down — the women pause in their talk as she moves past them, her shopping list tight in her hand. From the counter, they hear her ask for her butter ration and her tea. "She looks tired," says one. "Tired and pale — Mrs. May says her light's on late these days."

"And that job in the library," says another. "Good of the railways to offer it but it must be hard to keep the house going as well."

"They used to play cards with us, her and Mac, sometimes. I miss that. She was always so bright."

They pause as she counts the coins from her purse, pushes them over the counter. And they smile and murmur a greeting as she goes by again. Anikka Lachlan, still in the shadows, not yet found the light. She's cooked meals for most of the widows in this

town — now most times she comes home there's another dish, mostly anonymous, set waiting on her porch.

She's no appetite for any of it.

"Mrs. Lachlan." Roy takes another half step towards her and shakes her hand. "I wanted to thank you again — the Sassoon, 'Everyone Sang': just what I needed. That light, that hopefulness, that continuity."

A lady with a broad basket tries to squeeze past them clicking her tongue, perhaps over their obstacle, perhaps over the exuberance of the poet's words.

" 'The singing will never be done,' " says Roy McKinnon, still clutching Anikka's hand. " 'The singing will never be done.' "

And she smiles at last. "I'm glad you enjoyed it," she says. "We should . . ." Gesturing backwards towards the shop, forward towards the road, as another lady tries to squeeze past. They step as one into the full sunlight, Ani rearranging her parcels, Roy rearranging his hat.

"I was struggling," he says, dropping into such a long pause that she thinks perhaps that's all he wants to say, until, "with trying to write, I think I told you, even all this time after the war, and even somewhere as beautiful as this." His hand, sweeping up towards the escarpment, the sky, loops back

to include her in its gesture. "The Sassoon — I don't know, but it helped, and I'm sure I'm closer now to the beginning of something. A new poem." He bows a little with a stately gratitude that belongs in another time, another place.

"I'm glad the library could help," says Anikka, and her smile stretches wider than she can remember. "Poetry is — it's a sort of extremity, isn't it?" she says after a breath. "So whether the extremity comes from an extremely horrific place or an extremely beautiful one" — she retraces his arc across mountain, sky — "maybe both are possible."

A shiny black car purrs along the road, pushing Ani back into the memory of the night she heard about Mac, pushing Roy McKinnon into his own memory of official visits, important men.

"Are you following the trials, Mrs. Lachlan?" she hears Roy say at last, his voice quiet. "The Japanese ones, the German ones, the trailing detritus of this unending war?"

She had expected war to operate like a tap: on — as it happened; off — immediately it stopped, like life, or like breath, she realizes now. Now she seesaws between feeling that she can never know enough about

its aftermath and entrails, and wishing not only to know no more about it but to somehow forget so much of what it has already left lodged and jammed across the wide space of her memory and imagination.

And so the world still arrives folded into a newspaper in her front yard and is carried up her front stairs, and she sits every night after work, after Isabel is asleep, after the housework is done, obediently reading some part of it as if she might be examined. There's a new president in the United States, and Mr. Eliot has won the Nobel Prize in Literature — she knows this, if anyone asks. An American pilot is dropping chocolates and other sweets into West Berlin for its children, and seven Japanese men have been sentenced to death for their roles in the war. Yes, she's following the reports. She reads as much as she can in the evening; she cuts a strip from here, a story from there, to stick into her daybook. And then she sets the rest in the combustion stove, putting the world out of Isabel's way.

All this she says to Roy McKinnon — but the words are too much and come too fast, as if she hadn't spoken like this for a long time and is afraid she might have forgotten how. "It's to do with wanting to know what happens next," she says, "with feeling like

something could be rounded off, or made better, although I don't know how it can be. There was a man who danced through Martin Place when the war stopped — I saw him on a newsreel; he danced and danced for joy. But what were we celebrating? The awfulness of its finishing? All these articles about war that still leach out into the newspapers now, three years later: there wasn't a full stop, was there? The story just keeps unfolding."

"Perhaps it's something to do with seeing it all as a kind of continuity," says the poet. "There is no beautiful now, no terrible then, just these trails of things going on and on. Which perhaps means there are some things you can write about, and some you have to leave alone." He watches the slow progress of the local bus as it draws in, collects its passengers, and pulls out, heading south. "There's some comfort in seeing things go on; birds keep singing, buses keep running. But if you want those things to continue, perhaps you have to accept that the other kinds of things, unhappier, even horrific ones, will continue too. And that's harder."

His hand moves to wave as the bus passes and Anikka, turning, sees the face of Frank Draper, sees his hand wave in return. She looks away, shifting the weight of a small

bag of sugar against her arm, wanting to make no acknowledgment of his gesture.

"He was there, you know," says Roy, over the chug of the bus's motor. "He went into one of those German camps with the British. Did you know that?"

"Dr. Draper?" She shakes her head. "No. Mrs. Lacey said he'd stayed in service well beyond the war's end. She didn't mention anything else."

"He was one of the first men in — went into one of the worst of them, I think, if you could designate any better or worse. We hung round together, years ago: Frank, me, my sister, dances and the beach. Frank and me would have a beer and spin our dreams: he'd do his medicine; I'd start to write. And we'd end up here, somehow, when we were old and practiced." The bus hauls itself up the hill to cross the railway bridge, and disappears around the bend, taking its laboring engine with it. "Hardly recognized him when I first saw him. But then I wonder if he had the same trouble recognizing me."

"I remember seeing you, before the war, but I didn't recognize the doctor. And he's become quite . . . abrupt," says Ani, taking care with the word. "But no, I didn't know where he'd been." Dr. Draper would know what a body starved, a body shot, a body

hanged looked like. And probably a body mashed and squashed by something huge and powerful. She winces, and the poet sees the edge of it in her shoulders, her widened eyes.

"I've been puzzling at memory myself, Mrs. Lachlan," he says, trying for something that will bring her out of whatever dark place she has slipped into, "and how it is that I can remember your husband here before the war, but not you, never you. You'll forgive me," he says gently, "but you're someone who would have been memorable."

She brushes away the compliment as if it were a fly. "I didn't know you knew my husband," she says.

And it's Roy's turn to brush at the air, to clarify the words that hang there. "I wouldn't say I knew him, but I met him, certainly. And of course there was that wonderful story about him and his blackberries — the railwayman jumping down to pick a bucketful of fruit, and his mates unhitching the engine he's in charge of and leaving it, while they drive on with the rest of the train. He takes off after them, full pelt, and runs into the back of their train just around the corner, where they're laughing and playing cards on the side of the

track, just wanting to give your man a fright."

"My man?" She has no idea what the poet is talking about.

"That famous story about your husband," he says. "You know, when he jumped down for some fruit, and the rest of his train made off without him. He had us in fits telling us about it."

It's shocking to think that this poet knows some story about Mac that Ani herself has never heard. "Of course we've picked blackberries," she says slowly, "the three of us, up in the bush; we went every summer. But I don't know what you mean about . . ."

"It was well before the war," says Roy, "maybe even before your little girl was born." He turns away from her a little, as if he's trying to see far enough along Thirroul's main street to look into those days, those times. "Mr. Lachlan, as I remember, was working a bank engine to shunt trains up the hill and from one main line to another. He'd got a good long train up there, and then rather than going on with it, he hopped down to fill his bucket with berries instead. The blokes at the front of the train saw what he was doing, uncoupled his engine, and took themselves on — just having a joke, you know. But when Mac looked

up and saw his engine all on its own, he panicked, jumped in, and went after them hell for leather. Came round the corner expecting to be on the run after them and didn't have time to stop himself before he rammed into the back of their vans — derailed them, derailed his own engine's wheels. Got six weeks off the engines and back on the platform for that, he said, before someone interceded and said he could go back to his job. But I wonder if the berries were worth it, if you don't remember how he came by them."

Ani frowns, her basket heavy on her arm. "I just don't see how it could have been Mac, if it's a story that I don't know." It's hard enough accommodating death as the thing that interrupts a story you care about, let alone the shudder of realizing that there must have been more stories of life beyond the ones you'd actually heard.

The poet smiles. "There must always be things we don't know, mustn't there," he says, as if her thoughts are written across her face. "Impossible to know every moment of a person's life, every instant of their day. And would you want to, in the end, if it was stories about that bloody war — I beg your pardon, Mrs. Lachlan — rather than stories about berries that you had to take

on? They're the hard ones to put behind you," he says. "Perhaps you never do. My sister tells me Frank Draper's not even sure about being a doctor now, although that's what's brought him here. Well, at least they're talking. 'First, do no harm,' " he quotes from the famous medical oath, and his own wince mirrors Ani's. "Who knew how far a group of doctors could move from that idea in the name of some dreadful politics?" He shrugs his shoulders, the tops of his arms, as if to dislodge that abhorrent ideology and all that it spawned. "But what a thing to be saying to you, Mrs. Lachlan, on a day like this, when I really just wanted to thank you for the poetry."

"Come down to the library whenever you like," says Ani, trying to put the blackberries from her mind as she shakes his hand again. "I can send a request for anything you'd like." A train's brakes grate on the lines nearby, and she raises her voice, ignoring the interruption. "You know when we're open, don't you?"

She's never referred to herself as the library before — *you know when we're open* — and she likes the sound of it. Walking away, she finds herself reciting the Sassoon poem as she turns and heads up the hill:

Everyone suddenly burst out singing;
And I was filled with such delight
As prisoned birds must find in freedom,
Winging wildly across the white
Orchards and dark-green fields; on — on
   — and out of sight.

"And I was filled with such delight," she repeats, her steps slowing a little as she begins to climb. But her smile twists and stiffens. *No delight for Anikka Lachlan,* she thinks. Not now, not ever, not ever again.

In the brief instant of her eyes closing to blink, she sees an image like a black-and-white photograph of a body, dead, distended, horrible. And the worst of it is not knowing if she's imagining Mac, or remembering the poet's powerful wartime poem, or looking at some shard of the horror that the rude doctor had found, one of the first Allied liberators to walk into one of the worst places on earth.

But Mac did bring berries home from work sometimes, she thinks suddenly, turning the corner into her own street and marking her own house halfway along. *Buckets of berries picked beside the tracks.* She can even remember the first one, and how anxious she'd been when he told her about jumping down, running into the brambles, and rush-

ing back to catch the engine he was working on before it went too far. *If anything should happen,* she'd said, and he'd said, *But what could happen except berries for our teatime?*

How long ago would that have been? And was it something as stupid as fruit behind the last accident? Stopping again, she hates him for a moment, for whatever stupidity ever sent him off after blackberries when he should have been working, and whatever inconsequential stories he'd told to other people and never told her.

As she climbs the stairs to her front door, she sees a paper bag on the step and opens it gingerly, afraid of more tiny purple berries that might appear out of nowhere, delivered somehow from the past. But it's round blue plums, three of them, and a note from Mrs. May. *Because of your anniversary, and because they were always his favorite,* she reads. *These ones looked so fine.*

Plums? His favorite? All she knew about was peaches, his peaches. *Mac's* peaches. And their anniversary? Their *wedding* anniversary? How could she have forgotten the date?

It's some kind of assault. Struggling with the key in the lock, she's through the door and dropping everything — including the

196

plums — hard on the floor, where she sits and cries for everything forgotten, unknown, and undone.

Which is where Isabel finds her when she comes home, the pulpy plum flesh sharp and sticky, and Ani sitting with her fingers pressed into her eyes and her throat dry from crying.

"Does it bother you, Mrs. Lachlan, to ride in these murderous things?"

Spinning around at his words, Anikka doesn't know — never knows — what to expect from Dr. Draper. In the handful of times he's called at the library he's been charming and obnoxious in equal measure, complimenting her on a bowl of flowers one day, and berating her as an idiot another when the book she'd requested for him proved to be the wrong one. He came once with Iris McKinnon, too, and leaned against the shelves, scowling, as the two women transacted the business of the books. It was the first time in such a long time Ani had seen Iris smile — a bright contrast to the doctor's face — and she wanted to wish them well for it. But then Iris had made another grand claim for time's balm, and left Ani hating them both.

Now, she shakes her head and tries to

laugh, determined not to cloud another meeting. "I wouldn't have much of a life left, nor much of a world, if I let that happen, would I, Doctor?" She will not tell him how impossibly huge trains seem sometimes, or how she freezes, sometimes, in the middle of a journey, wondering if this engine, carrying her along so reliably, is the one that took Mac away from her. The one that killed him.

"You're of Miss McKinnon's school, then," the doctor continues, moving closer to Ani on the platform. "The old 'time heals all wounds.' "

Against the glimmer of a smile on his face, she steels herself and proceeds. "No, no — I hate that phrase, hate it. All the forgetting in it, all the ignoring, the papering over, the covering up, the pretending." Which is more than she means to say.

He glances at his watch and then down the track.

"Perhaps we're traveling up to Sydney together," he says, indicating the oncoming engine. "If you don't mind the company." The train slows, stops, and he steps forward, holding open the compartment door.

"Of course," says Ani, "of course," wondering if it might have been possible to say anything else. She'll have to concentrate on

him now, on whatever he wants to say. Out of nowhere, she wishes Roy McKinnon were traveling instead. *What would it be like, to travel with a poet?* But there's something treacherous in that thought, and she bats it away with her list of tasks for the city. Of course, she wishes no one were here. She wishes herself alone.

Settling into the forward-facing seat, registering the photographs opposite — the Blue Mountains, the Harbour Bridge, the famous roundhouse at Junee — Ani smiles at Frank Draper as if their meeting is the happiest coincidence of her day, and hopes he might nod off soon, as some men do in trains.

"Roy McKinnon speaks very highly of you," he says then, smiling back. "And your library," he adds, and she hears in his tone some implication that this second point, at least, is quaint. But he looks polite enough, with his dark suit, his hat, and she gives him just a little more latitude as he goes on: "I am sorry I've upset you on some visits to your library. McKinnon says I must have left most of my manners on the other side of the world when I came home — and I think sometimes he's right."

"He told me, Mr. McKinnon, about the work you did — about where you were, at

the end of the war, I mean." Navigating things she suspects are probably best left unsaid but wanting some sense of how far he might be pushed in return, she blinks at the glint of the roundhouse's glass as it passes her window. There are rainbows in its corners, small sparkles of treasure.

"He told you about hell, did he?" The doctor's voice is coated again in ice, and Ani pulls herself into her seat, the boundaries clear, and is thankful to be able to look out of the window and see the next station, and who might be on the platform, who else might be making this trip. "I'm sorry," says the doctor as the train begins to move. "I find myself unable to say anything useful about it, so I wonder sometimes how it is that other people can tell its story for me."

The landscape through the window begins to blur with the train's speed, the texture of the cutting changing from the roughness of individual rocks and layers to a rush of one uniform color. "You get used to people telling the version of your story that they want to hear," Ani says, quiet. "Well, you get more used to it than you might have thought you would."

"How long has it been now, Mrs. Lachlan? How long has it been for you?"

But it's still only months, the math of her

story, and his — she knows — is years. "It's like Miss McKinnon's recuperative sense of time," she says, trying to change tack. "It's not right, it doesn't heal, you don't forget, but you find some kind of accommodation. Don't you? Don't you?" She's making it worse, she can see, as he frowns and is silent. The train shapes itself around a curve, and she sees its engine away up ahead, dragging them on. She's never noticed this before — must never have looked out of her window at precisely the right moment to see it happening.

"I like that," he says suddenly, pointing towards the back of the train where the last carriages can now be seen curling around the track's wide arc. "That sense that we're all being safely carried along. It's all we want, most of us, isn't it?" The coldness has gone from his voice again, and Ani recoils from this latest change. These slams that skew from placatory to hostile: it's going to be a long journey.

"Sometimes it's nice to feel carried along," she concedes. "But mostly it's nice to know we can jump off, don't you think, if we want to, if we're going too fast, or too far?"

He snorts a little and stares at the ocean, until Ani wonders if she might get her book out of her bag without being rude. "Do you

want to know, Mrs. Lachlan," he says abruptly, "do you want to know what it was like when we went into that place? Do you want to know how far it was from here, from where you were, from your safe little village with its ordinary lives and deaths, its distant understanding of the scale, the mess of war?" And there's no ice, no coldness in his voice this time, just a great sense of tiredness.

"I think we know how far it was, how unlike here, anything here, anything that has ever been here, Doctor," says Ani carefully. "And now we hear more and more about it, and we understand less and less of how it could possibly have happened." She wonders how much he might tell her, and how much she might not want to hear. "I sat with women whose husbands had died, whose sons had died, whose brothers and fiancés had disappeared — none of them there; none of them where you were. But they seemed such individual deaths; there were still particular people attached to them. The way my husband is my particular story, the death people particularly associate with me." She smiles, quite a small, tight smile. "But where you were, what you saw, that was beyond — beyond anything, I think. Anything, perhaps, except those

bombs at the very end."

There's something about the accountancy of death, about how to look at more than one scale at the same time: hers now, for Mac; Mrs. May's, say, during the war, when her husband died making a railway in a jungle; the thousands in the bright blasts that ended the war; the thousands upon thousands in the long stretch of horror that predated it and has outlasted it. She doesn't know how to say this without making the war sound like a problem of mathematics.

"They sent me to the sick bay when we got there," says the doctor quietly. "I couldn't tell you how many people were there — it would be almost better to say there were none. There were remnants, shadows; there were bodies whose state, alive or dead, could hardly be distinguished. You have no idea, Mrs. Lachlan. I don't mean that to be anything other than a simple statement of fact: your world, your grief, what you understand of death. You have no idea. And there we were, the liberating army, to tell them it was over. To tell them they had survived, they had endured." He coughs. "Five hundred and fifty-five of those survivors died after we arrived. Five hundred and fifty-five people endured everything up until that point, and we could

not heal them, could not make them whole, could not lead them back into the world that they must have been promising themselves the whole time. I heard it was three thousand a day, in one place. Three thousand deaths, every day. I don't —" He puts his hand up quickly as she moves to say something. "I don't speak of this; I don't usually speak of this. And I'm very sorry for your loss, Mrs. Lachlan. I understand that everyone is, that it's a certain tragedy, and that it has a certain weight for them — and of course, of course, for you. But I carry those five hundred and fifty-five people; I carry their weight. The doctor who found them and failed them."

He fits the tips of his fingers together while his lips purse and twist. "And I sit in this place, seeing people with their colds and their burns and their boils, and I find it impossible to think of doing anything for them, when I failed the people who needed me so much more desperately."

He coughs again, a thick, heavy cough from somewhere deep in his chest, and she rummages for a small paper bag of cough drops — the smallest gesture, but she's glad to be doing something — and holds them towards him.

"Would you like —"

He shakes his head, clears his throat, straightens himself so that his shoulders are pulled back and square and his hands rest flat on his knees.

"We had this plan, me and Roy McKinnon," he says, "when we were kids down here for holidays. Me, off to be a doctor, and he had this mad idea to be a poet. I knew there'd been a medico on the coast who'd come from Ireland — knew Yeats, someone told me, and was a fine doctor, a good doctor, the kind of doctor who kept all the good people from this good little place alive through that terrible influenza in 1918. That's for me, I said. I'll be that man — and our boy Roy will be a poet.

"So we'd go off and make our way in the world, and we'd come back, older, respectable, with wives and children and yards of stories behind us. We'd come back here, and we'd talk about the world, where we'd been, what we'd done, and how it was to end up in a nice little place like this. We had it figured for a pretty good life too."

"Did you like his poem, Dr. Draper?" asks Ani, and frowns as the doctor shakes his head.

"I'm sorry — I don't mean I didn't like it," he says at once. "I mean, I didn't read it. I heard that it had been published, of

course, and I did drag myself out of which-ever mess I was in and write to him, saying that I was waiting to see it, to see what he'd done. He sent me a poem by Yeats instead: 'On Being Asked for a War Poem' — do you know it? I don't remember all the lines, but it starts, 'I think it better that in times like these, a poet's mouth be silent.' It took months for my letter to find him, his to find me. I never replied — never expected, I think, to see him again after that. I mean, I never expected to see anywhere like this again."

The yellow-grey stone of the escarpment flashes by on one side of the train; the different blues of ocean and sky flash by on the other. *Perhaps there are different kinds of death, or dying,* thinks Ani suddenly. Outside, there's not a cloud to be seen, and the sun's light picks out the different stripes and blocks of the world's colors at their most perfect pitch. Perhaps there are different kinds of resurrection too.

Tilting her head towards the window, she catches another glimpse of the engine surging forward, pulling them on.

"I was up in the city — years ago, before the war, before my daughter was born. And when I came onto the platform at St. James, the driver, a mate of Mac's — of my hus-

207

band's — asked if I wanted to ride in the engine. I don't know how many times I'd gone through those tunnels, peering out at the black walls, sometimes seeing the face of a workman staring out of an alcove, waiting for us to pass. But to ride up the front, to be looking into the tunnels head-on, rather than from the side, to see the way the train's lights pushed out against the darkness, illuminating the places I'd always seen as shadow — and then to see the day growing bigger and bigger once we'd passed through Museum Station and were on our way back out into the open. It was like I was on a train in another world. It looked so different, so exciting, from up there. I'd love to ride up the front around here one day — cutting through the trees, the tunnels, over the bridges."

From his side of the compartment, the doctor almost laughs, caught instead in another bout of such hacking and coughing that he has to lean forward and brace himself against it. "Perhaps Roy McKinnon is right about you," he says at last, taking one of her cough drops this time. "Has he started writing poems, do you know?"

Anikka shakes her head. "Really, Dr. Draper, I've only spoken to him a few times. There's an etiquette . . ." Her hands flail

and she blushes. "I don't know. But I know he's reading a lot of poetry, because it's all coming down in the trunks from Sydney — I've got another request list from him to drop in to them today." She doesn't tell him that she wonders about the mechanics of writing poetry, about the way a poet's hand might hold its pen. But she does say, finally, that she hopes he will write something soon; she does say that she hopes she'll be able to read it.

"Good old Roy," says Dr. Draper, leaning back and settling himself in the corner made by the seat and the window. "I guess it's something that we both made it back here. Whatever we might fail to do with ourselves after that."

As the train crosses the high viaduct near Stanwell Park, sunshine cuts stripes through the trees outside and Ani presses her fingers against her eyes so that sparks flare behind her lids. The train slows, stops, and she listens for doors opening and closing before the whistle sounds, and the engine begins to pull away. They'll be in the tunnel soon, cutting away from the coast, away from the ocean, and on the long run up to the city. In the seat opposite, the doctor closes his eyes, and is asleep.

She watches Frank in the light before the

train plunges into the mountain — he looks tired, she notices, but probably doctors are often up all night, with one thing or another. Keeping watch over someone — who said that, about the grace of watching someone sleep? Reaching out, she surprises herself by moving his hand a little before it drops from the armrest of his chair, and she's astonished by the weight of it, the solid, dead weight. She's astonished, too, by how much his hand feels like Mac's — *Although of course,* she thinks, *he's just a person, another person.* And she feels Mac diminish a little, this fraction of his being so easily replicated.

It's shocking. Ani pulls her hand away, tensing and flexing her fingers in a silent exclamation. But it's no more shocking than the next thought that comes: *What would Roy McKinnon look like as he slept?* she thinks, and more safely: *Or when he laughed or leaned back at the end of a good meal?*

They're still neither of them well fed nor well rested, these men, and in a flash of neighborliness, she thinks the village should be doing something about that. Taking care, keeping watch — that, she tells herself, is what her interest, her concern is all about.

24

Ani has been walking a good quarter of an hour before she realizes she has looked at nothing but her own feet, one stepping in front of the other in the stoutest shoes she could find — the muddy boots she uses for gardening, their familiar dark-soil mud now brightened by the orange clay of the track that winds up from Austinmer to the top of the escarpment, hundreds of feet above.

There's a group of them, a dozen or so from the church: the new minister — Reverend Robinson, young, enthusiastic, and known to own his own compass — has organized the outing, or "the hike," as he refers to it, and Ani has pretended to be merely acceding to Isabel's pleas in agreeing that they will go. It's a Saturday. It's gloriously warm. And it feels good to stride out, her legs stretching and climbing, and to know that she will lie down tonight properly exhausted.

"I wasn't sure you'd come, Mrs. Lachlan," the minister says, catching up to her as she climbs beyond tree ferns, sandstone boulders, a little marsh of reeds and bulrushes such as Isabel might hope holds fairies. "I mean, I wasn't sure," he corrects himself, "if the library kept you busy on the weekends."

Ani steps carefully over a fallen bough. "No, not all the weekends — they leave me something." She makes a show of indicating the view so she can catch her breath. "There's just more and more of it, the higher you go." She points out towards the sea, makes her breathing deep and slow.

"Have you ever traveled over the ocean, Mrs. Lachlan?" Reverend Robinson asks, following her gaze.

"No, no." She shakes her head. "My father came from Europe, and my husband of course. But I've always had the ground beneath me — apart from a little boat, here and there, a day's sail." She hears Isabel behind her, laughing with someone from school. It's lovely to hear that laugh. "Should we . . ." And she clambers over a scatter of rocks, pressing on.

The path tacks and weaves, straight up with ladders here, running along the cliff's face there, out in the sun on some stretches

and tucked into dankly fecund pockets of rain forest in others where the air is thick with the rich smell of the leaves, the vines, the growth all around. Below is Austinmer, the neat rectangles of its rock pools pushing out, constrained, into the ocean. Just south, Thirroul, with its busy space of rail yards, and the straight streets of houses running east to the coast, west to the base of this scarp. Farther south, beyond Wollongong, sit the steelworks, belching and sprawling — she had been so scared of their heat, their power, the ferocity of their furnaces and ovens when she first came to the coast. And then, during the war, her dreams had rearranged them to mirror its heat and ferocity. She was always grateful it was the trains, not the steelworks, that paid her husband — *even now,* she thinks, *I guess, even now.*

A plume of white steam pushes up from one of the stacks. One of the last stories Mac told her was about a group of Baltic steelworkers with a grievance against their German foreman — she didn't know if the grievance belonged to this part of the world or had traveled with them from somewhere else — who'd taken the opportunity of some construction work to push him down into a smooth tablet of wet cement. "They'll find him one day," Mac had said, and she'd

hated his casual unconcern. "There's always a war going on somewhere, I suppose."

She takes in the smell of the turpentines, the straight grandeur of one or two remaining cedar trees, and turns her back on the steel. *The war is always going on.*

"And good morning to you, Mrs. Lachlan." It's Dr. Draper, with Roy McKinnon at his side. "Beneficial to be out on *the hike.*" His voice mocks the label, a parody of doctorly advice. "Plenty of fresh air; plenty of exercise; you know what they say." His skin is still sallow, his frame malnourished, and the darkness under his eyes is darker than even the worst crescents Ani has seen smudging her own face.

"Dr. Draper." She smiles, set on friendliness after their train ride together a week or so before. "And Mr. McKinnon. You couldn't ask for a better day for a climb, could you, although I suppose Reverend Robinson has more power than the rest of us to guarantee the weather."

The poet smiles, adjusting his hat. "It's the sort of day you dream of, yes," he says. "But my sister's not one for heights — or hikes." He laughs. "I used to do this each year we came when I was a boy, racing up here, trying to make my time faster and faster. When you burst out at the top, and

you turn, and you see the whole coastline unfolded below you — that's something, don't you think, Mrs. Lachlan? That's a thing worth racing for."

Ani nods. "It's years since I was at the top — I remember feeling I could see all the way to South America. It seemed possible; there was so much world out there." She starts to walk, and the two men fall in step behind her. "Are there mountains along the coastline in Chile? I always meant to look that up, to find out what I was looking at, all that way away."

"Well, you've the perfect opportunity now, all those books at your disposal." Roy McKinnon leans forward to pull a low branch out of Ani's way, and Frank Draper steps through after her, changing the order of their line.

"And all that time," the doctor says quickly. "I often wonder who uses that library — it's almost always empty whenever I look in. I wonder how long the railways will keep it up, if there aren't enough readers for its books."

This talent he has, thinks Ani, *this talent for finding some brusque thing to say, some criticism.* "We've a good number of readers for a branch our size," she says, a little surprised by her defensiveness. "They're

talking of changing the hours and circulating the books more quickly between branches — and we're taking more requests now, which our readers like. Mr. McKinnon" — she smiles back to him — "has often availed himself of this, of course."

"She can get you anything, Frank," the poet calls. "Anything you like."

But the doctor doesn't smile. "I wonder if your daughter isn't too young to try a climb like this — you must be more fearful, more protective of her now." They round a corner and there is Isabel herself, half hidden behind a rock with two giggling friends, waiting to jump out at whichever parent passes first.

Ani laughs. "You can ask her, Dr. Draper, but she looks all right to me." She tickles her daughter as she goes by and, glancing back, sees the poet tickle the top of her head as well. Isabel giggles again and ducks.

"See you at the top, Mum," she calls.

Up ahead, the first knot of walkers disturbs a tree full of white cockatoos, and they rise up, protesting, their vast wings reaching across the sky.

"Did you see, when we were climbing, a whole tree of them, those cockatoos? We were up above it, looking down. It was like looking down into a Christmas tree, with

row after row of candles." Roy McKinnon has swapped places with the doctor again, and walks close to Ani. "I was looking for the angel to put on the top — an angel was all it was missing."

"And the fact that it's not yet December twenty-fifth," Frank Draper adds, louder again. "That does work a little against your metaphor, Royston, my friend — you always were premature with your celebrations."

"My father always cooks a Christmas meal for the pitchest night in winter," says Ani, "as dark and as cold as he can get, to remember the old country. Apple bread and herring and Christmas mustard — *joulusinappi* — although I could never work out what made it different from the mustard he ate at any other time of the year. Or where he found herring in the backblocks of Australia."

There's a bustle on the path behind them and a couple of women overtake, greeting the doctor as they glance at Ani and the poet, and asking Roy about his sister as they glance coquettishly at Frank.

"Say it again, the mustard word," Roy McKinnon says as they pass, and he stays her steps with a hand on her shoulder.

"Joulusinappi?"

"It changes, your whole voice changes

when you say that — a different sound, a different pitch." And he steps back, letting go. "As if a whole other person was speaking. I wonder who you would have been, Mrs. Lachlan, if you'd grown up speaking that language instead of this one."

"I'd have been someone even more enamored of this sunshine than I already am." It's good to feel the stretch and reach in her muscles, and there's a sort of warmth from the climbing too — or the talking. And although she thinks she can see the lip of the escarpment, the end of their climb, not too far in front of them, she wishes she could go on striding and climbing, ascending forever. "I don't know as much of the language as I should," she says, slowing down. "I meant to learn it before I came away from the plains, from living with my father — now he writes the odd word, here and there, in a letter. Like *käy pian . . .*" She smiles at the poet's blank face. "It's 'visit soon.' But I never seem to get away."

The path straightens and steadies and reaches the top. Ani pauses, staring at the pine tree that she usually sees from so far down below.

"Here we are then" — the doctor arrives, Isabel and her friends hard behind — "and the minister has made good on the promised

lunch." He strides over to the picnic rugs, already spread and waiting. "Satisfaction, at last. The repayment of repast. There you are, Roy, that's almost a rhyme for you."

"Your rhythm's all wrong." Roy laughs, sitting himself down beside his friend.

And it is good, Ani knows, to sit and eat and laugh — to look out across the view of the coast and not have every thought bound up with the last time she was here. It is good to see Isabel, smiling and playing. It is good to talk with the minister, with the poet — even with the doctor, although she wonders what entertainment he allows himself out of scaling an escarpment, as out of anything.

But she smiles herself, and she chatters. When the poet mentions his plan to see a movie with the doctor the following week, and asks if she'd like to join them, she smiles again and finds herself nodding — "Yes, I'd like to see that film; yes" — although she hasn't, until that moment, ever heard of it. And when another tree lights up with cockatoos and the matter of Christmas is raised again, and Roy McKinnon wonders aloud about celebrating it, Ani talks about inviting him and his sister to join in their meal. And thinks it a fine idea.

Reverend Robinson says grace, and they eat, quiet and busy with their sandwiches,

their pies, their fruit. To the south, the steelworks sends up another column of thick white smoke, and then another. Farther south again, Ani sees a band of grey clouds — a storm coming up; it seems so preposterous in the middle of such a rich, warm reservoir of sunshine that the picnickers ignore it, relishing their food.

But up it comes, so fast that they're only just packing the last of the plates when the first drops of rain fall, heavy and huge.

"If some of the ladies would like to drive back in the car that brought the picnic?" the minister calls, and there's a rush towards the parking lot. Mrs. Floyd giggles and touches her newly set hair; Mrs. Padman holds a tiny handkerchief over her head. The minister pauses, gesturing towards Ani, but she shakes her head.

"I'll walk back down — me and Isabel. We'll get a bit wet, but we'll be under the trees most of the way." She takes her daughter's hand and they make for the track's mouth, both of them laughing.

"Come on then, come on!" The doctor, of course, and the poet. And they set off, the track's sticky clay already a little more slippery, a little more malleable than it had been when they made their ascent.

Isabel darts ahead, Ani steadying herself

here and there on rocks and branches as she tries to keep up. She sees her daughter sit down and slide a little way, and as she catches up to her, she sits down as well, feels the wet ground pressing up through her scruffy trousers.

"This is great, Mum," Isabel shouts. "Isn't this great?" Thunder breaks out overhead and another nest of cockatoos rises up, protesting. "Your Christmas candles are back, Mr. McKinnon," Isabel says, stopping to let her mother pass. "I've always wondered what they do when it rains — isn't it bad for birds to get their feathers wet? Doesn't it make it hard for them to fly?"

"But what about seabirds, Bella?" Ani says. "What about cormorants and albatrosses and oystercatchers?" She takes the first rope ladder as fast as she dares, the uprights chafing at her skin as her palms rush over them. She can't hear the poet's answer, if he gives one, and for a moment she relishes the feeling of being completely alone and here, in the bush, in a storm, tucked in against the side of her mountain.

She pushes water out of her eyes and jumps down another stand of steps, and another — she hasn't felt this light, this nimble for the longest time. There's a crash in the undergrowth to the side of the track,

and she sees the back of a little swamp wallaby, with its delicate ears and tail, bounding away.

"Bell?" she calls. "A wallaby. Did you see
it? Did you see?" Her sweater, tied at her
waist, is heavy with water, and her shirt
clings and sticks to her like another skin. *A
sight we'll look, when we get to the bottom,*
she thinks, hearing her daughter whoop and
laugh. She springs down another drop, and
another, takes the next ladder almost at a
run, and slides away on the seat of her pants
again, wanting to whoop as well. What
would her father make of the poet, she
thinks out of nowhere. *What would my dad
make of a man like that?* A man like that,
running wet, in the rain, running home,
needing to be warmed, needing to be dried.
Needing.

She stops, hot and breathless, despite the
drenching.

"Bella? Isabel? Are you all right up there?
Are you coming?"

What is she thinking, out in the rain, her
daughter soaked to the skin and running
down a mountainside with two men she
hardly knows? What is she thinking, being
here at all? It's another minute before she
remembers the wet walk she took with Mac,
and the way they pushed themselves to-

gether afterwards. But it comes, this memory, and just as quickly goes: she's making a new story here, not reliving an old one.

The bath's water, clean and hot, is going to feel magnificent.

A call — a *coo-ee* — echoes around her; the doctor's voice, then the poet's, and then Isabel's. And they come around the corner, one close by the other, and catch up with her, pressing on together to the track's end, to the point where they began.

"Now that," says the doctor, shaking his hair like a drying dog, "that is what I call *a hike.*"

And for the first time, Ani sees him really smile.

25

Stretched out in the bath, on the night of Isabel's tenth birthday, Mac ducked his ears under the water again and again. "Just listening to the house," he said as Ani watched his head dip and rise, dip and rise. "There's such noise under the water; you can hear the pipes and the pressure and all manner of other sounds like some great machine pulsing away. When I get my deep-sea dive — no, now, Ani love" — as she shook her head against this mad desire — "when I get my deep-sea dive, I reckon I'll be able to hear the machinery behind the whole world. You're an embarrassment to us coast dwellers, you are, keeping your head above the water all the time." And he ducked away again, his eyes wide in mock ignorance of the words she was saying into the room's air.

"Come up, Mackenzie Lachlan: you come up and listen to me. I don't mind your

underwater thing — you can read about it and dream about it all you like. You can dive down from the highest board at the pool and you can duck your head under the biggest breakers that the surf pushes up. But under the sea, properly under the sea, so far down and so dark, so dark — I just don't know why you'd want to do something like that."

"You're still a landlubber after all these years, aren't you, pet?" he said, ducking fast under the bath's surface again as she threw a washcloth, a nail brush at him. And he stayed under this time, blowing a few bubbles, and then holding his breath until she leaned forward, her frown anxious, and scolded him again.

"I was going to offer to read to you while you're in there," she said then, "even from your silly new underwater book. But now . . ." She shook her head. "Your shenanigans." But she was smiling.

Mac pulled a towel from the side of the bath, rubbed the water from his hair, his ears. "You'd like the book, Ani. The creatures they see, and how beautiful it is down there. Even when I was little, I'd swim out into that cold grey Scottish water, peering down to try to see what was underneath — my gran had all these stories of the ashrays

and the selkies and the blue men of the Minch, and I was after a glimpse of them as much as any sort of fish or shells or proper sea life." He shivered, although the bath water, straight from the copper whose little fire Ani tended, was steaming hot. "I cannae tell you how cold it was, how cold, out there in that water. And I'd swim and swim with my fingers numb, then my hands, then my arms all the way up to the elbows — I probably wasn't in more than a few minutes each time." He closed his eyes and saw himself as a small boy, shivering across the shale on the other side of the world. "My gran always had the fire high and the soup on the stove when I gave up and came in. And she'd warm me up and fill me up — and tell me the next round of stories about the water lovers to get me ready to go again." He laughed, reaching for the soap. "But read me a bit, lass; there's a lovely bit about the color and the light — you'd like that part, I promise."

"This part?" she said, flicking through the pages. " 'At six hundred feet, the color appeared to be a dark luminous blue'?"

"That's it, Ani. That's it." He slid his shoulders beneath the warm water again and closed his eyes.

At 600 feet the color appeared to be a dark, luminous blue, and this contradiction of terms shows the difficulty of description. As in former dives, it seemed bright, but was so lacking in actual power that it was useless for reading and writing.

There are certain nodes of emotion in a descent such as this, the first of which is the initial flash. This came at 670 feet, and it seemed to close a door upon the upper world. Green, the worldwide color of plants, had long since disappeared from our new cosmos, just as the last plants of the sea themselves had been left behind far overhead.

At 700 feet the light beam from our bulb was still rather dim; the sun had not given up and was doing his best to assert his power . . .

She paused. "Do you want the next bit, about worms and things?"

"Just the color, Ani, just the color." His voice was low, his eyes closed, and his mouth smiling.

" 'At a thousand feet,' then, here," she continued.

At 1,000 feet . . . I tried to name the water; blackish-blue, dark grey-blue. It is strange

that as the blue goes, it is not replaced by violet — the end of the visible spectrum. That has apparently already been absorbed. The last hint of blue tapers into a nameless grey, and this finally into black, but from the present level down, the eye falters, and the mind refuses any articulate color distinction. The sun is defeated and color has gone forever, until a human at last penetrates and flashes a yellow electric ray into what has been jet black for two billion years.

In the quiet room, the space behind his eyelids replicated the shape of the bathroom light, the pale rectangle made by the bath itself.

"I think," said Ani, as Mac opened his eyes to look at her, "I think that I was afraid of the dark, when I was little. I remember, after my mother died, my father used to sit with me until I went to sleep, and sometimes I had a lantern in the room at night — I must have called out." She smiled, closing the book. "But I suppose your blue sounds lovely — your luminous blue. And I suppose I could trust you to a bathysphere for one ride down to see it, if you really had to go." This was Ani, he knew, doing her best to be generous.

"My birthday treat one year," said Mac. "I wonder if they'll ever have them available for rides? I could go down off the coast here, see all the coal ships lost off that old jetty, and the deep, dark drop where the continent falls away. That'd be something, to see what's down over that edge." But she was frowning again. "Too much? Too far?"

"No, no, if you like . . ." But he could tell she was humoring him. "I was just thinking of all the other ships trapped under the water now," she went on, "all the lives stopped down there. And would there be mines? Would there still be mines? How long would those mines go on floating in the ocean — and how would you know where they might end up?"

Mac eased himself out of the bath, dried off, found his pajamas, and kissed her, very slowly and gently. "Things needn't always come back to that war, Ani love. It's over now; it's over. You mustn't always be remembering it." And he kissed the top of her head, taking the book from her lap. "I'll make you some tea," he said quietly, and she nodded, brushing at her eyes.

Stoking the stove, he shook his head. She could just say something about wanting a dress made of luminous blue — which would be beautiful; a dress for dancing, if

ever there was one. Why must the war still feel so heavy for her, and so close? Three years now, he wanted to say — he almost wanted to shout it. *And we came through, we came through, love. Here we are. Together.* He hated the way she carried it with her, the way it surfaced so easily in her mind. It made him anxious; it made him fearful.

Tossing a handful of kindling into the firebox, he registered the spit of flame and the hiss of steam as a drop of water from the kettle's spout hit the plate.

"But could you not have a nice landlocked daydream as well?" she said, nestling in behind him with her arms hugging his flannelette waist. "A nice landlocked daydream that wouldn't make me worry about the dark and the depth?"

He was quiet awhile, measuring tea out of its caddy, setting the cups carefully on their saucers, thinking of different things he might say — how they might sound, what they might mean. The tea was drawing, the milk poured, before he spoke.

"If I do have a dream," he said, "it's that I might make a poem — just one, just one. I was thinking about it when we saw Roy McKinnon. Imagine that; making a set of words so perfect that had never been put

together that way before. I've never told anyone that, not even my gran. But it's something I'd like to do; I'd like to make a poem." It was magical, the way such a thing could make her smile — the way she'd smiled when he said he loved reading *Jane Eyre,* all those years ago. Such a little thing, he thought, it made no odds. And he knew it would mean the world to his wife.

The kitchen was still, ruffled only by the occasional crackle from the combustion stove, the occasional drip of water from the tap. Watching her across the smooth red table, Mac raised his cup and paused — the smallest toast — to drink. *That is marriage,* he thought, remaking yourself in someone else's image. And who knew where the truth of it began or would end?

"Thank you, Mackenzie Lachlan," Ani said. "Thank you for telling me that."

He watched the darkness of her eyes sparkle and change as she slipped into a daydream. Well, he would write her a poem, if he could — *or mebbe she is my poem,* he thought, *her and Bella.* Still beautiful. Still his. He didn't always believe that could be so in the bloody mess of the rest of the world. Which wasn't a thing to say aloud.

"You're lovely, Ani Lachlan," he said, reaching out to stroke her hair. "You're

lovely, my angel, my golden-sun lass."

She reached across the table, took his hand, and kissed it.

"There you are," she said. "Right there. I'd say that was the makings of a poem."

26

"Mum?"

"Mmmm?"

"Do you wonder sometimes, do you wonder where Dad is?"

The two of them, stretched like starfish in the backyard, their first Christmas morning without Mac, under the early blaze of a summer sun.

Anikka props herself on one elbow, looks at her daughter, looks at the length of her as she lies there — longer every day, if that's possible — at her stillness, at her calmness.

"I mean, I hear you some nights," Isabel goes on, "I hear you crying when you go to bed. And I wish . . . I wish you didn't. I wish you felt like he was somewhere good and quiet and peaceful."

Sitting up now, her back straight, Ani says: "Is that what you think? Is that where you think your father is?" Picking at bits of grass with her fingers, folding their stalks, and

233

flicking them towards the run where the hens peck and mutter.

Isabel sits up in turn, stretching higher and longer again. "I don't mean a Sunday school kind of place," she says, "just somewhere quiet. You know, somewhere that he'd want to be." She pauses, looking past her mother into some infinity. "You know that book he had, about diving and getting right down to the bottom of the sea? I think he's there. It'd be so quiet there, and all the fish and shells and things he could see, like he always said he wanted to."

Like he always said he wanted to.

Anikka remembers the book, remembers the day it came, wrapped carefully in brown paper, all the way from America. "My undersea explorer," Mac had said, smoothing its cover, flicking through its pages. "Remember the magazine story? The man in the bubble going half a mile down? This is him; this is his book." And Ani had smiled and nodded, scared, for the first time, that she might find her husband with weights tied to his feet, practicing holding his breath at the bottom of the big, tiled municipal pool. Scared, in an instant, for Mac and the sea.

And this is where Isabel imagines him. Ani leans over, brushing dried grass from

the back of her daughter's frock. "What does he do down there?" she asks at last, wondering at the steadiness of her voice. "How does he spend his time?"

"He draws the fish and the squid and the other strange creatures that go past. He writes down the things he sees to send in to the *National Geographic.* And he works out ways of keeping his light going — because you know, the men who dived, they were talking about how dark it was, and how long their light might last. I think Dad would have worked out a way by now to have the light on so that he could make days, and then turn it off when he wanted to sleep at night."

"I don't like to think of him being in quite so much darkness," says Ani. "And maybe not somewhere so far away, so on his own."

But Isabel shakes her head. "Oh no, I think there'd be lots of people down there — they'd have ways of talking to each other, one bubble to the other, maybe like those strings that connected the bubble to the surface. Maybe they talk through those, or maybe they talk to the stingrays and the squid and the stargazers."

"Stargazers?"

"There's a fish called a stargazer — its eyes are on the top of its head. Better for

counting at night, I guess."

Ani laughs. "Maybe I should read that book after all — I never . . . I never got round to it." If that's where her daughter thinks Mac has gone, maybe it's not for Ani to tell her she thinks it sounds dark and lonely. "When I think about where your father is, I think about a room at the very top of a house, with a wide view through a big window, and the most comfortable bed in the world. And he's curled up in the bed. He's comfy, and sleeping. Just sleeping.

"He might wake up sometimes; you know, when you wake up somewhere that's not your home, and it takes you a minute to recognize where you are. But he's never awake long enough to wonder about any of that, although he can look out of the window and see the stars, the moon, think about the tides. Then he snuggles down and goes back to sleep. Waiting for the morning." She's making it up, and she's sure Bella knows. Mostly, if she's honest, she doesn't yet quite trust that Mac is dead; mostly she avoids thinking of any of this at all.

Isabel leans back on the grass, recovers her starfish pose. "It's lonelier, yours than mine; mine's got electric light and conversation."

"Mine's got dreams," says Ani defensively.

"And there will be a morning — one day."
When I get to wherever he is, she thinks.
Even if I'm an old woman, breaking down the door. She stretches up herself, her fingers mimicking the starfish shape she and Isabel have cast on the grass. "We should start thinking about this Christmas lunch for Mrs. May and everyone — setting the table, checking the pork." And she stands, holding a hand out to Isabel, who springs up like a jack-in-the-box.

"What about all the men in the war, Mum?"

"All which men in the war?" Knowing perfectly well.

"All the men — all the people — who died? Do you think there's enough space for them all to have somewhere to go, or maybe even more than one place, like Dad, who's got a bubble under the sea, now, and a bedroom with a view?"

The woman whose son died when his plane tumbled into the sea, who imagined him floating on its wing, floating on the surface of the water, surfing a wave here or there, as if he were a young chap on vacation again. The woman whose husband died when the building he was in was bombed out of existence, who was sure he'd been blown all the way home by the blast, and

237

was somewhere out in the garden, checking on the last plants he'd put in before he left, and leaving her messages about watering here, pruning there.

"More than enough space, lovely," she says, keeping hold of Isabel's hand as they walk from the bright yard to the cool, shaded house. "It's probably like your kaleidoscope: you look at one piece of space, and every tiny twist or turn multiplies that into somewhere new — somewhere different. More than enough room for everyone to fit in somewhere, to be doing the different things we all think they ought to be doing."

She pulls her daughter into another hug, noticing her tallness again. The evening shifts she works in the library, the nights Mrs. May gives Isabel her tea, the nights Isabel's asleep when Ani gets home. Sometimes Ani feels she's lost her daughter as well as her husband. But then she pays her bills or buys the growing girl a new dress or sends a little money to her father.

She has to trust that this is the right thing.

Now, she hugs harder. "I miss you, Bell; I miss how things were." And then, quickly, against anything else that might be said, "But will you make the custard later, the way Mrs. May's been teaching you?"

And as she irons out the tablecloth, rubs up the silver, chops the potatoes, rinses the tomatoes, she sees Isabel back in the yard, her kaleidoscope to her eye and the lens up at the sky, turning it by the smallest of increments, remaking the big blue space.

Ani flicks the white linen across the table and the world disappears for a moment behind its movement. When she focuses again, she sees Mac's book, the diving book, perched on the edge of the sideboard, as if it might have been there since she read it to him in the bath on the night of Isabel's birthday. Perhaps Isabel's been reading it; perhaps that's what made her think about where Mac was. Ani pats its cover, but cautiously, as if some fanged fish might shoot out from between its pages, nipping and biting. Then she picks it up and it falls open, and she begins to read:

I sat crouched with mouth and nose wrapped in a handkerchief, and my forehead pressed close to the cold glass — that transparent bit of old earth which so sturdily held back nine tons of water from my face. There came to me at that instant a tremendous wave of emotion, a real appreciation of what was momentarily almost superhuman, cosmic, of the whole situa-

tion; our barge slowly rolling high overhead in the blazing sunlight, like the merest chip in the midst of ocean, the long cobweb of cable leading down through the spectrum to our lonely sphere, where, sealed tight, two conscious human beings sat and peered into the abyssal darkness as we dangled in mid-water, isolated as a lost planet in outermost space.

Ani slams the book shut. Cold and deep and dark and lonely, with that string, that fragile cobweb of string, the only connection.

It is as if I had a string somewhere under my left ribs — it's *Jane Eyre,* and it's Mac's voice, Mac's voice saying the words for her memory — *tightly and inextricably knotted to a similar string situated in the corresponding quarter of your little frame. And if that boisterous Channel, and two hundred miles or so of land come broad between us, I am afraid that cord of communion will be snapped.*

That cord of communion, that fragile cobweb, whatever it is that still connects her to Mackenzie Lachlan. *I am afraid that cord of communion will be snapped.* She bows her head, patting at the side of her body, feeling the exaggerated landscape of her rib cage. She has to remember to eat.

So long since she made a meal for anyone other than herself and Isabel — she's forgotten how nervous it can make her, and the dead space before the first guest arrives when she's sure the food will taste dreadful and no one will have anything to say, when she wishes, more than anything, that no one is coming, and is terrified, the next moment, that no one will. *And then what would I do with all this food?*

A saucepan of apples sizzles as some of its juice spits onto the hot surface of the stove. It's Christmas Day. There's a table to be set. People will come and eat and laugh and be together, speckling her white tablecloth with food and festivity. Mrs. May, of course, and Isabel, and Roy McKinnon and his sister. And Dr. Draper — scooped into the invitation at the end of the bushwalk. *Sit him next to Mrs. May,* she thinks as she sets out the cutlery. *She knows enough stories of undiagnosed illness to keep him busy for a week.* She places the glasses — wishes Mac could carve the pork, and then swallows hard against this automatic thought.

She'll put Isabel on the other side of the doctor; give him a dose of childhood and its optimism.

In the middle of the table, a small pile of gifts sits clustered around a bunch of

Christmas bush with its starbursts of dusty pink flowers. A special gift for Mrs. May, for all her help, and a little something for everyone else to open. A box of shortbread each for the men — the first time Ani's attempted Mac's proper Scots recipe — and a jar of homemade jelly for Iris. She's noticed them more and more, Iris and Frank, walking together, and Iris with that smile. *Some rapprochement,* she thinks; some recovery or some beginning — she's heard the edges of its story whispered in the post office and the shoe shop, and politely turned away. Of course she wishes them the world.

Isabel has wrapped the gifts, prettying them with ribbon and little sprays of the flowers. *So the table looks busy with treasure,* thinks Ani, *and everyone has something to take home.* In the dim room, she stands a moment, scanning the sideboard, the linen press — she pulls out a chair and is standing on it, leaping so quickly she might have flown.

"What are you doing up there, Mum?" The back door slams as Isabel steps forward, steadying the chair on which her mother is balanced. "What are you looking for?"

Ani blushes up to the roots of her hair, her tanned face hot and prickled. "I just

thought — I didn't know if we'd looked —"

"Your birthday present," says Isabel glumly.

Ani sighs. "I'm sorry, Bell; I shouldn't. And not on a day when I've had such nice surprises already." Her fingers brush the star-shaped coral brooch her daughter had given her that morning. "It's greedy of me — I don't know what I was thinking." And as she steps down, one of the chair's legs bows, its wood splintering. "And now look what I've done. . . ." She drags the chair onto the back veranda, worrying about who might mend it. Of course the table will look scrappy now, a kitchen chair pulled in to make up the numbers — although she'd spent half an hour setting and unsetting an extra place for Mac, and left it, in the end, set, but with no chair. Her table had been just big enough to seat the living.

Leave it alone, Ani Lachlan, she tells herself, packing up the extra place. *Leave what's lost alone.*

But the guests come and sit and eat and the pork is perfect and the pudding sweet and the conversation easy. Iris McKinnon tries to toast to absent friends, and Mrs. May distracts her with an anecdote about someone's son who arrived home unannounced after the war to be just in time for

Christmas lunch. "And you know, his mother had set a place for him every single meal he was away."

Thank you, thinks Ani, smiling at her neighbor. She doesn't want to cry.

They pass the afternoon with games — charades and codes and Chinese whispers. A film; four words; and the doctor is miming *Gone With the Wind,* blowing up a storm until his cheeks are red and his veins popping. A book; one word; and Ani's jumping around the room like a kangaroo. Towards evening, they cluster into the kitchen to sort out the washing-up, Frank Draper with his hands deep in hot water, and everyone else busy with tea towels and stacking and putting away.

Turning from the ice chest, Ani feels a surge of gratitude for this busyness, this festivity, for the very noise of its process. She stands a moment, watching her Christmas guests, red dress, blue dress, two suits, and Bella's bright golden hair; she sees flickers of their colors and shapes in the kitchen's windows, in the facets of the dresser's reeded glass doors. She stands a moment, still and pale, a light calico apron tied over her pretty white dress. She feels herself smile, and catches the edge of Roy McKinnon's smile in return as Mrs. May steadies

her heavy brown camera and clicks.

"A memento of our Christmas, then," Mrs. May says.

One last game of charades, one last cup of tea, and slices of pudding wrapped up to take home — Ani and Isabel stand on the front steps, waving their guests along Surfers Parade.

"Still no sign of my surfers." Ani laughs, one arm around her daughter's shoulders, her other arm looped through the crook of her neighbor's elbow.

"It was nice to have everyone," says Isabel, "and Dr. Draper was funny, wasn't he? He told me and Miss McKinnon the funniest jokes — I thought you said he wasn't very nice?"

"Well, he can be a bit odd," says Ani, squeezing her close. "But perhaps it was his Christmas cheer."

Later, as the night vibrates with the sound of the summer's cicadas, Ani lies back on her bed. *A good day, mostly,* she thinks, *and a happy one.* Which seems surprising; she's glad that it's over. Someone along the street is playing a recording of Christmas carols, fruity voices singing about stars and angels and joy. The needle stutters and jumps into the next song. Ani closes her eyes, and it's Isabel she sees, perched on top of a Christ-

mas tree, her arms out, like an angel.

A comfortable bed, a quiet room, a sky full of night stars, and, one day, a morning. *That's better,* she thinks as the light falls away. *That's better.*

By the time she passes Austinmer, heading north under the hot sun of a New Year's Sunday, the tide is running out, the dints and crevices reemerging in the rock pools below the Headlands guesthouse. It's silver this morning, and although the tide is ebbing, a thin sheet of the ocean lies across the rock shelf so that a fisherman walking out from the land with his line looks as if he's walking on the surface of the water itself. The sky is silver too, overcast but glowing bright with the hidden sun. Behind Ani, beyond the edge of the escarpment and to the north and south, wild bushfires are burning — the smoke is part of the air's silver thickness, and she can taste it every time she takes a breath. But down here, on the level of the sand, the silver-grey ocean curls down around the lip of the horizon. The world falling away.

The fisherman reaches the edge of the

platform, bends down to busy himself with something, and then casts his line out so that it leaves the smallest trace of a signature across the air. Mac was never a fisherman, never liked the flapping and thrashing that was the end of the fish's life; never liked the way the knife sliced so easily through the flesh for gutting — although he did it, when he had to, when they needed it for eating. Ani had always meant to offer to take on the task, imagining herself as someone more able to do it. But as she stands and watches the fisherman now, as she watches his line tighten and arc as he flicks it clear of the water with the slithering exclamation of a catch writhing on its end, she knows she'd have been just as bad as her husband. Or worse: she'd have thrown the fish back and settled for toast.

Beyond the rocks, a great wave builds and builds and finally breaks as Ani holds and releases her breath. It's the sense she has whenever she sits with her daybook, trying to retrieve another recollection of Mac. The store of memories had filled and grown for a while, just like this swell. And then, instead of breaking, it froze, suspended, not a drop more water to push into it, not a single extra moment or memory to be reclaimed. She cannot remember the last

words he said to her. She cannot remember how much breakfast he ate that last day. She is trying to make her peace with these gaps, these elisions — pushing away her journal and pulling towards herself any story by anyone else instead, as long as it has a man and a woman falling in love; as long as it has a happy ending. She disappears into the safety of these pages and reads herself towards sleep, where it's never Mac she sees now as the light goes down and she begins to dream.

Beyond the fisherman, farther north, smaller waves crash against the edge of the continent, flaring into anemones and chrysanthemums. And farther north again, there are surfers, three of them, slight shapes against the movement of the ocean, and then suddenly upright and balanced, riding improbably in towards the shore. If Mac wanted his bathysphere, wanted deep and down, he could have it. She'd take this any day, walking on water — or flying; maybe it was like flying.

She watches the pulse of the waves, trying to feel their rhythm and then predict it. Her breath catches a little when she senses that this one, *this one,* is going to rise up high and smooth, and sees two of the riders rise up with it, as if in confirmation. They're

suspended then against the silver sky, cresting and gliding on the silver water, and as she follows the line carved by their heavy boards, it intersects with the straight black dart of an oystercatcher, diving down, hunting and hopeful.

They'd taste of salt, the surfers, when they stepped out of the ocean. *In the nicks and folds of a surfer's body,* she thinks, *there'd always be the stickiness of salt, the way I could taste soot and smoke on Mac when he came home from work — here.* She raises her hand to her lips, her tongue touching the crease where her fingers join her palm. *Soot and smoke here.* Of course she hasn't forgotten him: he's here — his smell, his taste, his being.

It's the sun, hard and bright as it pierces the smoky clouds, that breaks her concentration, blinding her for a moment so that she calls out, shocked, when she blinks and sees the fisherman walking towards her and quite close now, emerged from the blazing radiance.

"I said if you wanted a fish . . ." he repeats, gesturing towards the bucket brimming with fins and scales and the cloudy dead end of so many dead eyes. "You're Mac Lachlan's wife, aren't you? Seen you walking along the sand sometimes. Think

my wife brought round a pot of food when we heard the news — but then I guess every woman around here was doing that. It's what you do, isn't it, food and so forth. Did you want one of these?"

Ani shakes her head, frightened of the fish, of the idea of carrying one home, and wondering if the man has seen her standing there, gazing out across the water, and licking at her own skin like an idiot.

"You're very kind," she says, and pretends to laugh, "but I'm not sure how I'd get it home."

The man shrugs. "I could fetch you some paper from up home, if you wanted." He gestures towards one of the low weatherboard houses set across the road and Ani, turning, is sure she can make out the shape of the casserole-cooking wife by a window, watching this conversation and trying to conjure its words. Once, when she and Mac weren't long married, she'd sat in a railway carriage, its windows jammed shut by too much paint, and watched the mime of Mac talking to a woman with gorgeous red hair; Ani had never seen her before, not in town or anywhere nearby. When Mac came into the carriage, he pointed back towards the platform. "Woman who came out on the same ship as me — cannae believe she'd

251

turn up out here, of all places." And Ani had smiled, and laughed too, and said something small about coincidence, intrigued by how frightening, how unsettling, it had been to watch her new husband have a conversation she couldn't hear with a woman she didn't know.

Now she makes a small wave up towards the house. "If you could thank your wife for the casserole — I was very bad with writing all the notes I should have written. But you take the fish; you take the fish. I'm not sure how long I'm going to stay here before I walk back." The water has retreated well beyond her feet now but she can feel the bottom of her dress pressed wet against her calves.

"Must be troublesome, not having a man about to do for you," the fisherman says as Ani watches him trace the line from her ankles, up around her wet hemline and the length of her legs, across her belly, her breasts, and up to her neck, where he stops, coughs, and turns to look out across the water.

"You've not much choice but to get on with it," she says, her hand at the V of her dress. "Ask any war widow." It's a harder thing than she means to say, but she gets a twitch of satisfaction from the man's blush.

"I'll get these home then," he says, pointing again to his house, the idea of his wife. But as he turns to go, he pauses, the bucket swinging from his hand. "There were a group of us used to take a drink in the wine saloon sometimes — your Mac was there once or twice; some of the boys home from the war had a hankering for the sherries they'd had overseas. And Mac said those thick drinks almost touched the edge of the whisky he remembered. He'd be on his way home, calling in — I'm not sure you knew." His eyes are fixed on his own feet now, his downturned head dampening his voice as much as the sound of the nearby water. "He sang us a Scots song once, his booming great voice and all the words about light and heather and the wide ocean. Brought a lot of us to tears. But I could never remember the tune when I set out to hum it, and I never had the moment to ask him if he'd sing it again." And he touches his forehead, the barest implication of a salute.

"There are days I can hardly remember the sound of his voice, the way his breath broke up sentences, the way his accent changed some words." Ani is staring into the nothingness, barely conscious of what she's saying. "If he was famous, someone would have made a recording of his voice

— singing, or saying something. A little bit of a movie, or a gramophone record you could play over and over. I can remember the way that man danced along Martin Place when the war was finally done with, but I can't remember the way my husband said his own address, where he paused, where he spelled things out." She shakes her head and peers into the bucket of fish. "I will take one of those, then," she says, "if you don't mind about the paper, and if you wouldn't mind gutting it too. You're right; there are things you miss having a man to do." And she clenches her teeth as his eyes sweep her body again before he goes.

Alone on the sand, she watches the oystercatcher coasting in the shallows, its head ducking under the water every so often. The surfers have gone, ridden in, she guesses, and now standing warm in the sun with their big planks of wood drying next to them. But she feels such a hum in the air that she wonders if she hasn't committed herself somehow to trying surfing, walking out across the water and gliding along with the rim of a wave, elegant and aloft and free.

And all this from a conversation about Mac and a dead fish.

She takes the parcel from the fisherman, nodding. "Thank you for this," she says,

placing it near her feet, "and for the story. Makes me feel a bit of a beachcomber, hunting more bits of someone I thought I knew everything about." She waves across the road to the house, to the implied wife, as well — an extra thank-you. Behind its tin roof, the mountain puts up its high, solid wall, the facets and faces of its rocks lit by morning's sun, and the smoke thick along the top. "Will it come down, do you think?" she asks, pointing to the traces of the inferno.

The fisherman spreads his hands like a question. "Must be due a burn through there," he says, "and it's been a blessed hot summer for it. But there are a lot of houses between us and it; a lot of people would try to fight it down before it reached the beach. If it does come over the top." He squints. "You never really know how worried you should be, do you? You never really know what's coming next."

And as she watches the fisherman go, an anyone in his rolled-up trousers, his smeary shirt, his felt hat, she squats down in the sand, next to the fish, her back to the sea, and one foot tucked beneath her so that it pushes hard against the hard bone, the soft space, between her legs. *His skin would taste of salt,* she thinks as he crosses the road and

scrambles up the bank to his house. *And he has a wife who might taste that.*

She licks at her own hand, and tastes tears.

28

Halfway through a lap of Thirroul's pool, Roy stops, letting himself float like a starfish. The sun is a bright disk — a nasty red — through the haze of the bushfire's smoke, and the air tastes sharp and bitter. This waiting for a fire to come, or not: he'd forgotten the powerlessness of such time, and how unbearably it stretched. Ducking under the water, he opens his eyes and kicks out towards the pool's edge, hooking his forearms up over the concrete and dangling, his back to the water, his eyes on the mountain. Through the previous night, he watched the red glow of the fire beyond its rim, wondering what he should do — or might do — if a runnel of flame suddenly leaped down over its edge. Wondering how glorious it might look if the whole face of the scarp was bright and ablaze.

Behind him, a kid comes hurtling down the slide and into the water, dowsing him

with spray. "Oy!" Roy hears his own voice, too loud and too angry. "Oughta watch where you're splashing."

"Oughta watch where you park," the boy calls, spluttering water and kicking away.

Kids on vacation — what kind of a bloke'd scold a boy for leaping? Roy leans forward on the concrete, its sharp edge pressing hard between his elbows and his wrists so that his forearms shake uncontrollably. He watches them spasm, mesmerized. *And what if that kid'd hit me? What if he'd knocked me under and held me there? Or pushed me down so my head slammed the concrete? What if I was down there now, down under the water, the life shaking out of me, some kid pushing me under, and all this, all this life and light almost over?*

"You all right, mister?" The slippery-dip kid pulls himself onto the wall, alongside Roy, pointing to his quivering arms. "You having a fit or something? My grandpa has fits. You want me to get someone?"

Roy shifts his weight, pulling himself out of the water and holding up his recovered arms like trophies. "I'm all right," he says. "See how far out you make it on your next go." Sending him back to the ladder, the leaping, the joy.

There was something beautiful in the

boy's smile, Roy thinks as he jogs across the grass to his sister's — it's the first time he's had a nice thought about a kid, he realizes, since the war expelled him from his classrooms. But it's replaced in an instant by the more beautiful idea of being held under the water, his limbs still. He kicks at a stone and wants to shout and cheer as it lands directly between two of Iris's potted plants.

"Is that you, Roy?" she calls as he scuffles at the door.

Who else? he thinks, calling, "Yes — I'll just hang out my towel." She's in the bathroom, the air thick with the competitive smells of eucalyptus oil, vinegar, and methylated spirit.

"You don't want a wash, do you? I'm halfway through doing the bath — didn't expect you until the end of the day." Kneeling on the lino, she's hunched forward over the tub and scrubbing so hard he can see her muscles working through the fabric of her dress.

"It's a hot day for cleaning, Iris," he says. "Can I get you something cool to drink?"

"Well, there's nothing else that wants doing today, so I thought I'd get on and do this. Didn't expect you home until nightfall," she says again, and he nods in acknowledgment this time, giving her half a smile.

259

"All the smoke out, it's no weather for walking. And the pool's full of kids on their vacations. Almost brained by one of them, little bugger." He watches her arm drag the scrubbing brush back and forward, over and over. What would she say if he told her about the tranquillity of drowning? What would she say if he told her the boy's smile was beautiful? Then, "Any of that Christmas shortbread left? I could get you a piece, with a drink, if you like."

"There's lemonade there." Iris leans back on her haunches. "A jug of it. But I'll finish this first, you go on." They watch each other a moment, a strange staring contest while Roy tries to pick what his sister will say next. Something about lunch, or a job; safe bets both.

But, "Frank Draper dropped a book in for you." Her hand wipes across her eyes and fusses with the edges of her hair. "*Kangaroo* — I told him you'd had it already from the library and hadn't made much headway. But he said you needed it until he could get you some Yeats."

Roy grimaces. "Bloody Frank." Every second time they saw each other, Frank was loaded up with mementoes of their dreams, their plans, as if an accretion of these might cajole Roy back into his vocation. Every

other time, Frank's mood hovered somewhere dark and bleak, his conversation snapped and icy, his observations weighed down with despair.

Roy saw his friend on the same seesaw with Iris: there were days when Frank walked out with her and smiled at the smiles of the town, and days when he snapped at the very mention of her, and Roy knew he'd snap at her in person too. *Just kiss her,* he wanted to say. *Just walk down here now and get this over.* The man of action, the man of motion: that's how it used to be with Frank. If anyone was hesitant, or reticent, Roy knows it's himself.

"Look, how hard can it be to start?" Frank had blustered at the pub one afternoon. "One sentence, right now, top of your head, worst thing you saw: get it out — don't think about it."

And I said, the way a man looked nothing like a man when he'd met a machine gun; the way no woman would meet your eyes when you were carrying one.

"Okay, good — that's a start; that's a start." Frank had drained his beer in a gulp, signaling immediately for another. "Now the best thing — best or most beautiful. Top of your head. Come on."

The way the ocean glowed green some

nights; the way the little boats used the light of the Milky Way, used its pathway, to navigate.

"There you are — write that down. I reckon you're on to something here, Roy. I reckon you're cooking."

Even now, Roy knows, the scrap of paper on which he obediently wrote these ideas is folded neatly in the top drawer of his bedside table. He unfolds it every morning and rereads it, waiting to see what will happen next.

Now, in Iris's kitchen, he opens the box of shortbread and breaks the last piece into two, reaching for a glass with his other hand. "I'm taking this around the side," he calls. "Want to keep an eye on the fire." He drops the shortbread into one pocket, Frank's copy of *Kangaroo* into the other, and settles himself against the wall beneath his bedroom window, where he can see the mountain to the west and the wide reach of the beach to the east.

There are more flames now, licking at the scarp's edge; you could never say aloud that it was exhilarating, thinks Roy, *but it is, it is.* He reaches in his pocket for a pen — there might be something in this; the anticipation, the terror, the threat of conflagration — and finds the paperback instead, watch-

ing as it falls open at a dog-eared page:

Cripes, there's *nothing* bucks you up sometimes like killing a man — *nothing.* You feel a perfect *angel* after it. . . . When it comes over you, you know, there's nothing else like it. *I* never knew, till the war. And I wouldn't believe it then, not for many a while. But it's *there.* Cripes, it's there right enough. Having a woman's something, isn't it? But it's a flea-bite, nothing, compared to killing your man when your blood comes up.

What is *this?* Roy rakes at his hair, at the air, at the mushy mess of the shortbread he spat onto the grass when he began to read these words — to feel them, to taste them. *You feel a perfect angel:* what the devil thing is that to say? Where's Frank's fancy-sounding psychoneurosis taking him now?

Roy stares at the page until the words blur into grey lines against the yellowing paper. *You do bloody not feel like an angel, mate, and the last thing you think you can ever do again is trust yourself with anything as gentle as a woman.* Something moves across the road, and Roy sees the boy from the pool padding along, a bucket swinging from his hand like the arc of a pendulum. All the

nights Roy's tried to swing himself to sleep with his watch; all the nights he's watched the back and forth of its face. And they awoke the next day *refreshed and able to carry on.* That's what the paper said.

Bunkum.

Turning his head from side to side, Roy lets his gaze pan from the fire to the water and back across the landscape in between. *How long before I find my deep and refreshing sleep?* he wonders, his head jerking still as he sees her step out of the brightness to come along the beachfront: Ani Lachlan, her pale dress wet around the bottom and a lumpy newspaper parcel held awkwardly across her body.

That's why he hadn't read *Kangaroo* when he borrowed it from her — all those lurking traps of violence and brutality when all he wanted was the scenery of it, this place. As for killing a man . . . Roy snorts. Frank Draper could hold those five hundred souls on the knife edge of his conscience for as long as he liked, but it was nothing compared to seeing a man, and lining him up, and pulling a trigger, and watching him fall.

From the top of the mountain, a single line of flame picks its way down through the trees, slower than Roy had expected, as if it is considering its every move. Yet even

down here, the smoke is thicker for its incursion, stiffening the air and sharpening it somehow.

You do not use a word like "angel" in a sentence like that. He tears at the offending page of the novel, ripping it out of its binding and screwing it into a ball to throw away. The word "angel" — he looks out through the infernal day, beyond the limitless sea — the word "angel," the very idea of such a being: that belongs to someone like *her*. And Roy raises his arm to hail Ani — "Hullo" — the word swallowed by the width of the road, the sound of the sea, the purposefulness of her stride. The look of her on Christmas afternoon, soft and gentle in her light, white dress, and smiling as if she'd just realized there was life in some place she'd thought otherwise desolate.

And there it is, the beginning of his poem:

Let this be her.
A folding of the light
And she stepped through, candescent
    messenger

"Candescent messenger." He uncaps his pen and scrawls the phrase across the endpaper of Draper's wretched offering.

"Mrs. Lachlan," he calls again, but her

head is down and she doesn't turn.

She looks, he thinks, *like an angel in a lost world.* Is that who she is — his muse? But he closes his eyes and sees her as she was on Christmas Day, and he knows there's something more to it than inspiration.

"Desirable," he whispers, "lost, and lonely, and desirable." It would be something, he thinks, to make her smile, and he lets himself imagine her, her hands out to receive a gift from him — a sheet of paper thick with words that she's inspired. There'd be such light and joy in her face.

If he's going to be a poet, he'll give her this one thing a poet can give; he will write a poem for her. No, better: he will make her a book full of beautiful verses and set these words — his words for her — as their climax, their culmination.

He smoothes the paperback's rough page, folding his first new sentences over and over in his mind until they are certain and secure, embedded in his imagination.

"Let this be her, a folding of the light," he says again, and loudly, his gaze moving between the surreal red trickle of the bush-fire and the last glimpse of a woman going home.

29

He wakes early, before dawn, but with no intention of going to the service. Anzac Day; the dreadful glory of that war that was going to end all wars. Not even for his sister will he pin on his medals and walk about in the smell of rosemary. No, Roy McKinnon is not for that sort of remembrance. He turns in his covers, feeling them twist tight around his legs, his body, until he almost panics.

What's wrong with you, man; what's wrong with you? Shaking himself free, he stands to stretch by the window.

In the next room, Iris is awake and dressing — she will go to the service. She will say, *Someone should; it's our duty.*

Let her go, then, thinks Roy. *She can do her own remembering.* He watches through the window until the front door clicks, and she is hurrying away along the street. *And let Frank be there,* thinks Roy, *waiting for my sister.*

He pulls on a sweater and trousers and goes into the kitchen to make himself some toast. So rarely hungry, he must have dreamed good dreams to wake up and want to eat.

And perhaps she was in them, he lets himself think, turning the bread as it browns on one side. *Perhaps she was there.* He glances up the hill, towards the street that runs along its crest. From Iris's back door, he can glimpse the front of Ani Lachlan's house. *She will go to the service,* he thinks. *Ani Lachlan would care about those things.* Not letting himself touch the idea that she might go for the chance of seeing him.

The way he's carried her, these three, four months since he found the first lines for that poem; the way he's crafted her and shaped her, forming a suite of stanzas so right, so perfect, it almost takes his breath away. The poem's final draft on a sheet in front of him, he lets his fingers rest gently against the lines of which he's most proud:

. . . her white dress,
So light she might float clear,
Were she not tethered by the limitless
Surprise of being here.

The limitless surprise: he sighs. It's as if he's

been in the deepest and most intimate conversation with her — and it astonishes him, every time he sees her, to remember that she has no knowledge of it. Yet.

On the table in his room, the thing he's been making is finally finished — transcriptions of great and stirring poems by great and stirring writers, and his own new poem, right at the end. He's typed them out on thick, creamy paper, reveling in the fake sound of industry coming from his Remington Rand. *Not my words,* he thinks he should say when his sister remarks on the busy clatter, but there's something reassuring in being thought productive at last.

The poems complete, he found some fine red silk thread in one of Iris's sewing boxes — the remnant of long-abandoned embroidery — and stitched his pages together, binding them hard with two pieces of card covered in red. At school, he remembered, he always loved the presentation of his projects as much as composing the words that filled them, and as he sat cross-legged on the end of this narrow bed in his sister's house, with his meticulous needlework, he was a kid again, all happiness and potential. *So maybe this morning,* he thinks, steeling himself. *I could sneak it in while she's away.* The thought of her face, the thought of her

smile — these daydreams have collapsed into the possible embarrassment of shame, or her displeasure, or of having offered something unwanted. He's not reassured enough to face that, he thinks, flat.

"And then what?" he asks himself aloud. "What happens then?" The unknowable thing. But he makes himself leave the house before he can change his mind again, is up the hill, through Ani's gate, and around to the back door before the sun has cleared the horizon.

Ani's house is empty; he knows that immediately. She and Isabel are certainly not here. Very slowly, Roy eases the door open and steps inside. His heart is pounding, his hands damp against the rough, red linen of his gift.

Into the lounge room, over to the mantelpiece; he is ready to shove it in anywhere and leave, when he stops, pauses, and takes in the volumes the shelf already holds. She spoke of this, the books she and Mac shared — she told him the story of unpacking them like a dowry and putting them here. *You're a rude bugger to want to muscle in on that sort of memory,* nodding at the authors, the titles. *All the places she's been through these pages, all the people she's met.* Where else would she have ended up but in a library?

Stepping back, he looks around the rest of the room. There's an engraving of Edinburgh Castle over the fireplace, and another of a three-master on a high sea over the chiffonier. A pair of slippers, some pencils, and a drawing sit abandoned on the floor — he reaches for the paper, admiring the likeness of the house he's standing in to the one in the picture that Isabel has made. *She's a bright one, that one,* he thinks, setting it back on the ground, and for the first time in almost a decade, he misses the bright girls he used to teach in tiny schools. He misses teaching them how to dream.

He moves towards the hallway, noticing the way the light comes in through the stained-glass panels in the door — when Ani is here, it's always propped open for the breeze. On the sideboard, a small white bowl holds four blown-glass Christmas ornaments — two red and two blue — so delicate, the lightest touch might shatter them. Beyond these, two photographs. The first is Mac, in a smart suit and tie — Roy is almost tempted to turn it facedown. *At what point is it appropriate to court a widow?* he thinks, clinical. *And who's the appropriate person to do that courting? Not some sneak who breaks into her house, not some twit terrified of his own shadow, not some fellow who*

wants to swim out to the horizon and keep going, mate.

He stares at the picture, remembering Mac's size, his momentum, the way he strode along a street or ran along the football field. *You, one of those men of motion; bet you never thought it would come to this. Bet you never thought I'd be the one alive, and standing here —* as if Mac would have thought of him at all. Which seems a pity, somehow. He'd have liked Mac Lachlan as a friend.

Because he did like the man, he thinks suddenly, and remembers all at once standing shivering in a cold predawn, talking with Mac about the mess of the world. Before the war — was it '37, '38? And what had Mac said? That he wouldn't go, if it came to fighting; that it was *nowt to do with him,* and he'd stay here with Ani. *And wouldn't you, wouldn't you,* thinks Roy as he turns to the second photograph, Ani and Isabel, taken by a street photographer in Sydney.

That's Martin Place, he thinks, smiling at the silly sunglasses, the silly smiles both are wearing. Must have been during the war: Isabel four years old or so.

"Nice way to spend an afternoon while we were out saving the world," he says aloud, as shocked by the slam of his mood

and the iciness that freezes around his voice as he is by the words' presence in the still, quiet house. *Makes me sound like Draper.*

Turning again, he sees the doorway to Ani's bedroom, and stops. *What the blazes are you doing here? What if she comes home? Take the book and get out of here — give it to her yourself when you see her, you great fool* — all this, as he mistakes a sound for footfall on the porch stairs and hurls himself back through the house, towards the back door.

And stops, hearing only silence.

All right, Roy, all right. Back at the mantelpiece, he slides the thin red book in between two paperbacks, and then turns and runs, tripping on the mat, leaving it disheveled, half looking for her reflection in the corrugated surface of the kitchen cabinets as he skirts past — their plates and glasses rattling a little as he goes — and on, through the back door and through the gate before he has time to draw breath.

The inverse of burglary, he thinks. *And now, now what?*

He can't hear for the sound of his heartbeat in his skull. He can't stand still for shivering against the autumn's chill. But he's pleased with it, this thing he has made — the best of the world's best poems, as he

sees them, and the finest new thing of his own. Then, clear and complete, he remembers that autumn night, twelve years before, when he and Frank Draper huddled over a radio for news of a bombing in Spain. *More than a thousand dead, they said — and how few that number sounds now.* It was shocking, the way his head had pounded then with his own useless vitality. *Women and children, going to market.* And they'd stood and talked of it with Mac. He stops, breathes deeply, tries not to retch.

From across the village, he hears the sound of a train, and then, high above, the purr of a plane's engine — it's all he can do not to dive under a hedge for cover.

It doesn't get any better, he thinks, making himself keep walking. *It doesn't get any easier, the being here, or the being.*

Twelve years since that bombing and the mood Frank had been in when they'd heard the news and walked home through the night. So dark, so bleak, so pessimistic.

So right.

How many women and children since? How many market days? Back at the bottom of the hill, he takes a deep breath at his sister's front door, his pulse quiet, his sweat dry. Across the road, someone is surfing on the wide sheen of the ocean, riding the smooth

waves up and in, closer and closer, only to drop down out of sight at the last moment, before the break, and paddle out to do it again.

There's something futile in it, and something quite beautiful.

One day, thinks Roy, *one day I will try that. I'll take a board out past the breakers and see what the sea makes of me.*

A car honks as it passes, and he spins round as if he'd been caught in some terrible act — bloody Frank, with his new wheels, and probably off to deliver some baby. *Ah well, Iris will be disappointed.* On it goes. But there is consolation, even optimism, Roy tells himself, in the fact that he presumes it's birth, and not death, that has his friend on the road so early.

He closes his eyes, the image of the surfer overlaid now with an image of Ani Lachlan, rising and falling on a sunlit sea. *You're gone, mate, completely gone.* He's done all he can, he tells himself — written the poem and delivered it to her bookshelf. He breathes out, as if his breath has been held tight for years and years on end. The surfer stands, rides the glassy wave, drops down, and paddles out again.

Going in, Roy keeps him in his sights as long as he can, almost shocked when the

closing door finally shuts off his view of the water, the light, and the surfer's body, miraculously aloft.

30

She doesn't know how many times she's looked at the mantelpiece, how many times her eyes have scanned its books, taken one out, or another, and read it, and replaced it. But she's never noticed this before, a thin red paperback like one of Isabel's schoolbooks, its silk-stitched spine unblemished.

Her heart lurches as if she'd stepped forward and found no floor to stand on. And as she looks around, quickly, she catches an unexpected movement — but it's only the curtain blowing against the window.

All right, she thinks. *All right.* But she cannot quite reach out to take up the book.

She's tired, that's all — it's Anzac Day. She woke at dawn to watch the sun rise, the men march, the women weep or cheer. Standing so still as the parade passed by, Isabel's hand held so tight, that she wondered if she was turning into something like

the rock from which the cenotaph had been carved. *Important to remember; it's important to remember.*

"Good morning to you, Mrs. Lachlan." As the last of the marchers rounded the corner, Ani had turned to see Iris McKinnon standing quietly alone. "I wasn't sure you'd be here — it must be tempting to sleep in when you don't need to get down for the library. And you were always keen to avoid being part of the war."

"Miss McKinnon." Ani had held out her hand, ignoring the largeness of this small woman's words. "Iris, good morning to you. It's a large turnout, isn't it? The library, yes, it's busy, and then there's Bella . . ." She ruffles her daughter's hair. "I don't know where the weeks go." She looked around for the doctor, expecting to see them here together.

"He's not here," said Iris McKinnon, riffling through her bag for a handkerchief and blowing her nose. But as Ani murmured something about the unpredictability of medical demands, Iris cut across her and said, "Not Frank, I mean my brother. My brother will have been sorry not to come." Then she blew again, and Ani jumped at the sheer force of the noise. "I think it means a lot to him, having someone like

you here — I never was much for reading, you know. I never know how to talk to Roy about these things, or trying to write." She sniffed, and Ani wondered if she was crying, but she turned her head away. "Still, he seems better for being here now, and being busier with your books and things. It's all you can ask for, isn't it, that these men find their way back home."

Ani blushed. "I'm pleased to be able to find him the books he's after — it's what we're here for, after all." She gestured beyond the stone statue of the soldier to the railway and its library beyond.

"I'm not sure I mean the library," Iris McKinnon said slowly. "I think it's more than that. He thinks the world of you, you know — I'm not sure I should tell you that, but there's something wrong with a world where such things aren't said."

And it was Ani's turn to fumble for her handkerchief, to bring it up to her face, to look away. "Well, I've had a bit of luck in getting books down from Sydney," she said. "I'm sure that's all it is."

They stood a little longer, neither saying a thing, before Iris McKinnon took half a step forward, reaching out. "Whatever it is, it helps," she said softly, taking Ani's hand

and holding it a moment before she walked away.

Isabel circled, grabbing onto the hand that the poet's sister had just held. "What's 'thinks the world,' Mum?" she asked her mother as Iris McKinnon walked towards the war memorial. "What does that mean? How can someone 'think the world'?"

Somewhere behind her, Ani could hear a group of women talking — something about a wedding, and a bride being married *by* the man she loved, instead of married *to* him. "Years of silence," someone said, "or willful misunderstanding."

And then there was talk of the poor speeches, a desultory dance, and a short honeymoon in a flash hotel in Sydney. "And he doesn't know, the groom, the poor fellow. He just thinks she's a nice quiet girl, and he's lucky in his choice."

"*His* choice?" another crowed. "He had no choice about it, and never will." They laughed, although Ani, unable to identify whoever the story was about, could not quite see the joke. *It's too hard,* she thought blankly, *trying to keep track of all these different situations.*

"I like it, 'thinks the world,' " she heard her daughter say. "It's like some funny riddle. 'What would you think about to

think the world?' The answer'd be twenty-four thousand, nine hundred miles, maybe, which is the world's circumference at the equator, or maybe fifty-seven and a half million square miles, for how much land there is."

"No one likes a braggart, Bella," said Ani quietly. "Let's go home. It's just a thing people say." And she'd spent the rest of the morning planting out rosemary bushes, Mrs. May passing seedlings from the basket, until the garden pulsed with that pungent, particular smell.

Now, as the sun clips the top of the scarp and slides through the west-facing windows of Isabel's room, the street is quiet. In the shadow of the living room, Ani steadies herself against the mantelpiece. She had planned on going to the pictures that night, on seeing the latest news from Europe. Sometimes she meets Roy McKinnon there; sometimes she meets Frank Draper with him, who, once or twice if it's a comedy or a musical, has had Iris on his arm. And sometimes they walk home together, talking — the two men sometimes stammering, sometimes inappropriate, sometimes caught, one or the other, in a long, silent hiatus — about the movie, the news, the night.

"We are all too old for this," the doctor had said once, and Ani had seen, for a second, their middle-aged parody of four young folk out for a night on the town.

He thinks the world of you: she isn't sure she wants to know what that means, or what she'd like it to.

And now, the day feels overwhelming. *I'll stay in, take a long bath, forget the news of the world.* So tired, she thinks, that she can't even reach out and work this unfamiliar little book free from its place on a shelf.

This thing she's been looking for, and she's found it on this day of remembrance. But her hesitation has nothing to do with tiredness, she knows. *You're afraid, Anikka Lachlan. You're afraid of what you've found.*

The house is too still, too silent. For a moment, she thinks there's someone standing behind her, but when she turns to look, it's only the curtain again in the late-afternoon breeze, and Isabel's slippers, forgotten by the sofa with the picture she was drawing the night before. She spins slowly, scanning the room, and sees the photograph of Mac facing her from the sideboard, as if he was peering around into the sitting room, waiting to see her react.

A deep breath, and another. Ani lays her hand along the other books, walks her

fingers across their creases and ridges until she reaches this new red thing. She feels its stiff cloth cover, slightly longer, slightly wider, than the papers it holds. She opens it, feeling the texture of paper that's thick like velvet, and rough-cut. Luxurious.

Here it is, here it is at last. This untitled volume: what else but the present Mac meant for her? She pulls it out quickly and sinks onto the floor, cross-legged, patting at its bright shape.

There's no title, no author, no words of any kind — she opens to the endpapers, the frontispiece: all blank. A journal? she wonders. Or was it the beginning of something he never had time to finish?

But as she balances its spine in the lectern of her two hands, the covers fall open and there is text inside, typed, the letters pressed hard into the first page. She tilts it towards the light. Where had Mac ever found a typewriter? How had she never heard its keys?

But still, here he is. Here he is.

Holding her breath, she opens the front of the book again and finds a one-line inscription — *For Anikka Lachlan,* written neat and careful — before she turns to read its first poems: Shakespeare's lover like a summer's day; Byron's walking in beauty like the

night. She skates across lines she doesn't know, and lines she does, and on through stanzas and verses to Elizabeth Barrett Browning counting the ways of her love. *And, if God choose, I shall but love thee better after death.* Line after line of love, and of longing, and of other places and times. Title at the beginning, author at the end, all carefully transcribed for her.

She turns the page, almost at the end of the book, and finds the last poem, "Lost World." Such a lull in the room. The curtains hang still and outside there's not a breath of air, not a single bird. She leans back to look through the front door: not a single leaf is moving, nothing.

She's holding her breath.

Let this be her.
A folding of the light
And she stepped through, candescent
    messenger
Announcing to my sight

Another sense,
In this lost world whose color
And form flared round her, ever more
    intense,
And as she passed grew duller.

I took this place
For some cartoon of hell,
Among whose mud and mayhem I would
    pace,
The ill-drawn sentinel.

Instead I found
The water and the light,
Light on the water, light in which the
    crowned
Escarpment trees ignite.

I looked for loss
And found what pledges are:
Pale hair, brown cheeks and stone-grey
    eyes, across
Her breast a coral star

As silver-pink
As dawn. Life's vortex spins
Around her. Come, she offers. Eat and
    drink.
Each door and window twins

Her moving presence,
Alive with promises;
She speaks, she laughs, among the
    iridescence
Of all her likenesses.

And her white dress,
So light she might float clear,
Were she not tethered by the limitless
Surprise of being here.

Still. She may throw
A shadow, but bears more.
I saw her too, too quiet, to and fro,
A figure on the shore,

Or in the snare
Of some wild dance, head back
And flailing, frenzied, almost unaware,
Almost demoniac,

Or heavy with
A sorrow not to quell,
The painting of a deity from myth
Lost on the lip of hell.

Which is not here,
No matter where I gaze.
With her the reckoning might well be near,
The tally of our days.

From where she stands
A single line's drawn out,
Weightless meridian that from her hands
Will loop the globe about.

All this in her,
All things, all places furled
And folded in her, the bright messenger
Who comes for a lost world.

And then she's glancing ahead, to the next page, and the next. But there's nothing more, and no author at the bottom.

Squaring her shoulders, she reads it again from start to finish, only letting out her breath when she's done.

Mac's poem, she thinks. *Mac wrote me a poem.*

A folding of the light, and she stepped through. And *her moving presence, alive with promises.* And *the limitless surprise of being here.*

The limitless surprise.

Small noises fill the room, fluttering as if they've traveled a long way. It's only when she leans forward that she realizes they're coming from her own mouth, like *oh, oh,* and *oh.*

The miracle of it — not just the present found after so much looking, but that it's this, *this,* as if she has somehow been allowed one more conversation with her husband, one whole new exchange. She presses her fingers lightly against the words and is certain, absolutely certain, that she

can feel the pressure of his fingers pressing back as they set these letters onto this page — only now, right now.

And what more could you ever want, she thinks, *than the chance of just one more conversation?*

"Sweetheart." The word rattles around the empty room. *There you are. There you are.*

She touches her fingers to the poem, word by word, and then reads it in a kind of rush, taking whole lines in a gulp, before she sits, quietly, her fingers stroking the fine red cover. Opening the cover again, she finds her own name — *the writing,* she thinks, *I thought Mac's A was more triangular, where this one loops around.* But it's a careful and considerate script — *and he would have concentrated; he would have wanted to make the penmanship perfect.* Who knew that he could make such a thing? Who knew he had it in him? she wonders, wincing then at how discourteous, how impolite it is to imply that a poem was beyond him. A poem, any poem, *let alone this beautiful thing.* And where had he found a typewriter?

Before a quarter hour has passed, she has it by heart. She wants to run into the street and shout to everyone about her discovery. She wants to hold it close to herself and

share it with no one, not even Isabel. *That's right,* she thinks. *That's better.*

Her fingers pick out the letters that form her name from random words in the poem, the way Isabel used to find the letters of her own name in any words on any page when she was first learning to read. *Would he have read it to me? Was that part of the gift?* And she can hear it in his voice, so clearly, the thickening of "lost," the softness of the *g* in "messenger." No trouble remembering those sounds today; it's as if their echo is rising up from the book.

After this, she thinks, *everything changes. After this,* she thinks, *nothing can change.* This strange feeling, as she reads the lines again, that she's somehow been confirmed with him, connected to him — that all the aching, all the grieving can be put aside to make room for him, him himself, returned somehow, and revitalized.

It matters that he had the chance to do this. It matters that he had the chance to make this thing. He's alive in it — she can almost feel his breathing — and when she presses the page against her chest, she can almost feel the shape of him again.

She stays there, sitting on the floor, and when she hears Isabel coming up the stairs an hour or so later, she pushes herself up,

all stiff and awkward. Slips the book back into its place on the shelf as the screen door opens, and has her arms ready for a hug.

"What a day, Bella, what a glorious day. I was just thinking about a quick swim before dinner — I know it's late, but what do you think? Will you come?" And she swings her daughter into a kind of dance in the middle of the room, like she used to when Isabel was small enough to be swung entirely off the ground, laughing when Isabel starts to laugh. "And a baked custard for supper, I thought. A baked custard — the way you like it."

"Like a special treat?"

"Like a very special occasion." Ani squeezes Isabel close, rests her chin on the top of her daughter's head, wonders how much longer she'll fit in that way. *You have these things for as long as you have them,* she thinks, *and then you get something entirely new.*

But as they make their way down the narrow steps cut into the cliff, the sea roils and swells, enormous, from the shore below.

"I don't care," Ani calls above the pounding surge. "I'm going in."

But, "Mum," Isabel calls, high and excited, "your green — look, your shiny green." The water is picked out with swirls

and spreads of shimmering light.

Luminous, thinks Ani. *Glorious.* On top of the poem, it's almost too much. She stows her shoes, her dress at the bottom of the stairs and skips towards the water like a girl of Isabel's age.

The water is colder than she expects, but she ducks her head under and laughs at the way the shining color runs down her body, her wet hair as she surfaces.

"Come on, come in, it's beautiful," she calls, dipping down again as Isabel walks tentatively towards her. "We won't stay long; we won't go far." And she watches her daughter's head duck down and come up. *What a crazy thing to do.* The two of them diving, again and again.

They stand then, as still as they can among the movement of the choppy ocean, watching the lustrous carpet ebb and flow along the shore, Isabel tucked in against her mother, held warm and close.

"So there's your phosphorescence, Mum," she says, cupping her hands to carry the exquisite water ashore. "Maybe it was here lots of nights and we just never looked at the right time."

Ani smiles, wrapping herself in her towel, her clothes, and feeding her sticky feet back into her shoes for the climb up the cliff.

From somewhere deep comes the idea of asking Roy McKinnon his professional opinion of her husband's first poem, but something in the thought makes her throat grab. *Because it's mine,* she thinks, possessive: *I want no one else to see it, to be able to breathe its words.* Maybe one day, years from now. Maybe then. *There's always time.*

31

On the first anniversary of the war's end, Mac worked an early shift and walked the long way home, looping down to the library via a quick drink in the billiards hall and a haircut next door. *To celebrate,* he told himself. *Lest we forget. Et cetera.* He slid his books across to Miss Fadden, taking care not to knock her half-worked game of Patience. *Not a bad life,* he thought, *to sit in a room full of books and have time for a card game now and then.* He could think of worse ways to pass the time.

"If you'd like something new for Bella," said Miss Fadden, shuffling her cards away in an approximation of busyness, "there's a lovely book came down today about a little French girl called Madeline — made me think of Isabel; I think she might like it." She set it in the middle of the desk with Mac's card on the top, waiting.

"You're good to keep an eye out for her,

Miss Fadden," said Mac, running his finger along the shelves. "But what about for me? Any nice books about French girls for me?"

He liked to make Miss Fadden laugh. "Here, for you," she said, when she'd had her giggle. "A new Hornblower — and I do believe he sails up the Seine, so you can keep an eye out for your own Madeline while you're reading it. And tell Mrs. Lachlan I still can't get her *Brideshead Revisited* — I think everyone must be wanting to read it at the same time."

Mac smiled, pulled two more books from the shelf, and pushed his pile across the table, complete. "And what are you reading, then, Miss Fadden? If you've any time to read at all among the busyness of the library?" He wasn't sure he could remember a time when there was another borrower in the room beside himself.

"There's a lovely new Georgette Heyer romance I'm waiting for, Mr. Lachlan, and I always like to read the children's books, to make sure I know what I'm recommending. Lovely things, when they're well written — but you'd know that, from reading with Isabel. How is she, little pet?"

"It's just an excuse for me to read them, of course." Mac laughed, tucking the books into his satchel. "And she's grand, she's

grand. I'll let Ani know about her book and tell her to keep her fingers crossed for next time." He waved as he went, whistling across the yard and calling to Luddy as he passed the stationmaster's office, "Will there be fireworks down here tonight, mate? The anniversary? The victory day?" He gestured over towards the empty football field where effigies had been burned and bonfires lit.

Luddy shook his head, coming out onto the platform. "Doesn't feel like anyone's making that much of it," he said. "To be honest, I think most people want to forget it ever happened."

Mac sighed. "I didn't even fight in the thing and I reckon we should do better than that." He glanced up at the mountain, at the afternoon sun. "What do you reckon, Luddy? How many years of eternal peace will this one get us?"

But Luddy waved him away. "You go home and make your own memorial. It'll be years before they sort out the statues and the sandstone."

Coming across the football field, Mac broke into a slow jog — years since he'd played a game, but he could still hear the calls of his team and the sliver of a crowd that turned up to watch. *You're an old man now, with your rickety knees and your daugh-*

ter outrunning you. He slowed, crouched down, and sprang out across the final yards of the field. There it was, the rush, the surge of acceleration he used to love, flying down the wing, heading for the line.

Mebbe I'm not so old after all.

He climbed the hill and turned into his own street — *Surfers Parade, and Ani wondering when there'd be a parade of surfers coming along with their great, long boards.* It sounded like a dream, or an apparition, but he'd like to have seen it himself. They could run along the road and dive out from its end — maybe they'd clear the rock shelf if they sprinted fast enough, flying with their boards out over the open water, away behind the waves.

Like Isabel, when the war ended and the barbed wire along the beach came down; she stood for hours watching surfers hover on the lips of unbroken swells. "They're standing on the water, Dadda; they're riding it. They're riding it. How do they do that? Is it magic?"

And he'd wanted to tell her it was, wanted her to think that there was magic in the world.

32

On a winter's morning in June 1949, Ani wakes suddenly in the darkness, wanting to be anywhere but in her bed, in her room, in her house. She used to joke about it with Mac, that latent Scandinavian sense of long, cold days; the uneasiness she felt in even this most temperate place. Now, she pulls on any clothes, any shoes, and one of his sweaters — the only one she's kept — before she turns to see Isabel standing in the doorway.

"The beach?" Ani asks, and her daughter, already dressed, nods.

Two apples in a bag, the end of a loaf of bread, a piece of cheese, and a jar of water: "I hate waking up this way," Ani whispers as she pulls the door behind her. "Let's get down to the sea." And they run along the street, hand in hand, around the corner, and down the stairs to the sand, almost tumbling with haste.

A smooth ocean to the east; a sliver of moon hanging over the dark escarpment to the west. Isabel flies along the shore, her hair shaking free from its plaits as she runs, and Ani stretches her legs out so that her steps match the footprints left by her running daughter. Isabel turns a cartwheel, another, and another, and Ani laughs. *That's better,* she thinks. *Much better.* She wishes she were brave enough to try one herself, but she's never quite understood how to push on her arms so her legs will spin up and around her body. She's forgotten how light she herself used to be, springing all over the unfinished houses her father worked on — up to their highest point, and down again in just a step or two.

"Just try, Mum, just try." Isabel is running towards her, spinning again, and springing into a somersault.

Slowly, deliberately, Ani puts down their bag of breakfast, pushes up the baggy sleeves of Mac's sweater. The summer Mac had taught their daughter how to cartwheel, Ani had absented herself from the training; someone had to be ready with bandages and ice wrapped in tea towels. *The two of them,* she thinks now, *they always made it look so easy.*

"All right," she calls. And then, quietly,

"All right." And before she can think about it, she reaches her arms high up to the sky, leans over to plant her right hand on the ground, kicks her legs out hard, and finds herself standing again, standing and laughing, brushing the sand from her hands.

"You didn't look much like a wheel, Mum," Isabel says with a laugh. "But it was a good try." Then, "Try again," she shouts, making another cartwheel. But Ani shakes her head.

"Maybe tomorrow," she calls. "I'll need to work up to it." And she makes a great show of gathering the bag, settling its contents, looking up and down the beach for any unexpected spectators.

She sees him then, ahead on the sand, and probably looking straight along at her, at her mad jumping — she can't tell, with the glare of the sun. She points: "And anyway, there's Mr. McKinnon." She nods towards him and waves. "He doesn't need to see that sort of thing at this time of the morning."

"I don't think he'd mind your cartwheeling, Mum." Isabel is balanced on her hands now, her feet pointing up towards the blue. "We never laughed at him about him perching up the pole, did we? Remember when we saw him? On my birthday? With Dad?"

Ani shakes her head. "We didn't, no. But

still, I don't think he needs to see such an amateur display before breakfast." *If he wasn't here,* she thinks, *if the beach were empty, I'd do it over and over.* There's something embarrassing about his having seen; but there's a tiny part of her that's exhilarated by the idea of it too.

As for the cartwheel, the great loop itself — that had almost felt like flying.

"Anyway, where are we walking? Along to the jetty or . . ." She trails off. Beyond the southern headland, beyond the next beach, sits the cemetery where the small box of Mac's ashes has been placed. Maybe today, maybe this morning, maybe after a cartwheel and a bread-and-cheese breakfast, she can manage to go there at last.

Isabel nods, following her mother's gaze. "We should go, shouldn't we? He'll be wondering why we haven't visited."

And Ani flinches at the pragmatism of it, at the implied neglect.

"Have some food, love: let's sit here and have some food, and then we can walk along and find . . ." She can't say *and find him.* She can't say *and find what's left of him.* She can't say *and find his tombstone,* because there isn't one yet — she's not sure she wants there to be.

She spreads their towel on the sand, slices

the bread, the cheese, the fruit, and watches as her daughter eats. *One of the greatest happinesses,* she thinks, *feeding a child — no one ever tells you that.* And only as Isabel finishes her second helping does Ani begin herself.

At the cemetery, they jump over the low fence, heading for its coastal edge. "This is Catholics," calls Isabel, matter-of-fact. "And there's Anglicans down here, and Baptists," walking farther east again. "Kids' names at school," she says to answer her mother's unasked question. "Look: Rafferties and Larkins and that old lady who lived behind Mrs. May. Here are the Presbyterians."

Ani glances at the stones on either side of her, at the shorthand of their names, dates, relationships. *In memory of my darling wife. My beloved mother. My son, Tommy, aged nine, killed on his way home from school —* "Oh Lord." She clutches her hands together. The date is more than a decade ago; the stone still as polished and shiny as if it had been set only yesterday. *Our mother, and our father,* she reads: Is that her future, then, dug in here beside her long-dead husband? She feels Isabel pulling at her hand.

"Here, Mum, I think. Here." After all this time, there's a pile of wizened brown petals

heaped up in a rotting mound, a small white cross with his name written in black.

Don't think about it. She almost says it aloud: *Don't think about it.*

Crouching on the grass, she presses her fingers into the rich, dark soil. Two rows over, Isabel's bright hair bobs up and down among the stone angels, the granite blocks, the urns and the pillars and the open marble books. *Life,* thinks Ani. Her fingers fiddle with a loose pile of earth. *And what comes after.* She shakes her head. She cannot imagine that there is anything to do with Mac in this place. She cannot imagine any remnant of him being here.

Still, taking a deep breath of the salty air, she brushes some loose dirt from the little cross and murmurs, under her breath, the lines of his poem — "Life's vortex spins around her. Come, she offers. Eat and drink" — while Isabel paces and prowls between the headstones and monuments, giving her father a wide berth. A few rows away, a spark of rosellas lights up a tree like tiny fireworks, their feathers brilliant reds and blues. Mac never tired of their brilliance or their beauty: "There's nae a lass as bright as you in all of Scotland," he'd call to them, scattering seed across the grass in the backyard at Surfers Parade.

"Nice that you're here," Ani whispers to them now. "Nice that you're near him." She closes her eyes against their movement and her mind flares with the colors of their plumage. *How long does a bird live?* she wonders. *Did any of you see my husband in his prime?*

"Bella?" She sees her daughter pause and turn towards her name. "I think I want to get home, love. What do you think? Can we make tracks?" And she's sure she's taken care not to pass again the grave of that small boy killed on his way home from school, so shockingly accidental, until she glances sideways as she walks and reads, this time, its full inscription.

He left for school as any day
No thought of death was near
There was no time to say good-bye
To those he held so dear

The morning sun dries the tears on her cheeks as her running feet clear the cemetery's boundary and reach the sand again. "Maybe there'll be dolphins on the way home," says Isabel, catching up to her, and Ani kisses the top of her head, catching her breath, wiping her eyes.

"Now that would be something, Bell," she

303

says. The pod of dolphins they watched on the day Isabel turned ten, at the beginning of the last week of Mac's life. How impossible not to have known that's what that week would be; how impossible not to have seen that coming. How impossible, now, that Bella was heading towards eleven.

Cresting Sandon Point and heading north, Ani remembers the great marble map on the library floor in Sydney, the beauty of its waves, its ships, its angels and dragons, the straight line that stood in for this coast she's walking now. *Walking along a coastline that didn't exist.* The size of the oceans, the size of those old ships: what were the odds of anywhere being discovered?

About the same odds as a man called Lachlan crossing a country he'd just arrived in to see a river that had borrowed his name.

"What chance your dolphins?" Ani calls to Isabel. "What are the odds we'll see them?"

Isabel shakes her head. "I don't really understand how to do odds and chances yet — although Dad tried to tell me using this long story about billiard balls."

"Billiard balls?"

Isabel nods. "He said whenever he went to play billiards he worked on the theory that he had a one-in-four chance of winning

304

every game and about the same chance of sinking the balls. There was something about the eight ball and who else was playing and . . ."

But Ani has stopped in the middle of the sand. "Billiards?" she says. "Your father never played billiards in his life."

Isabel looks at her feet, twisting a little so they disappear below the sand.

"He said he never played at the hall on the western side of the railway, but sometimes he'd pop in to the one near the shoe shop, on our side, if he finished early. It was a secret." Her voice drops to a whisper. "I wasn't meant to say. But I saw him coming out one day. That's the only reason I knew."

Ani closes her eyes, sees a wide green table, a triangle of bright balls in the middle. Someone leans in and breaks the balls' triangular pattern with a single swipe of a cue. She hates the crack the wood makes as it strikes the hard, shiny Bakelite. The balls fly away, running in all directions, a muddle of color and motion. She opens her eyes.

A cloud passes across the face of the sun and she shivers instinctively. Out in the water, a single dolphin leaps and dives. The beach is empty; there's not so much as a seagull along its length.

"I wonder what other secrets your daddy

had," Ani says then, as lightly as she can manage. That word, "daddy"; they never used it. It sounds spiteful now, and mean. But it still throws her to realize she'll learn nothing more directly from her husband, only second-hand anecdotes about him. And such things can never be hers to claim.

Isabel paces out the beach, kicking an empty bottle that she's found in some seaweed to make a strange, syncopated beat. Behind her, Ani makes hard work of her footsteps, deliberately laboring in the soft sand. *What does it matter — a game of billiards? What does it matter, now and then?*

"I don't mind the game," she calls at last, aloud, to her daughter's running back, "or even the secret of it. I just wish I'd had him longer, to have learned these things from him."

"I never knew husbands were for learning from," says Isabel, slowing down to fall in step with her mother and taking her hand. "Does that mean it's easier if you marry a teacher? At least you get someone who knows what they're doing. Maybe that's an idea, when you marry again. Try for someone who knows about teaching."

Ani shakes her hand free, pushing her daughter away. "Damn it, Isabel, you say some ridiculous —" And she sees the girl

shrink into herself, her shoulders hunched, her head dropped down. Ani drops the bag and kicks it, relishing the pain as her toes strike the thick glass jar. She can feel her teeth grinding against each other, and she wants to run and run and run. *The second time I've yelled at her,* she thinks, desperate at the thought. *The second time I've yelled at my gorgeous little girl.* "Bell? Bella?" She holds out her hand, but Isabel shies away.

"It's all right," she says, her voice very small against the beach's great space. "I know you're sad; I know Dad's dead; I know it was a horrible thing to see the tiny space for his ashes; I know it was a stupid thing to say." And she sets her pace just ahead of her mother's, staying out of reach until they're almost through their own gate, when she works herself under her mother's arm and lets herself be held.

At home, in the bathroom, Ani runs the cold water until her hands stiffen. If only she could curl herself into the white curve of the basin and numb her entire being. *I yelled at Bella; I yelled at Isabel.* She stares at her eyes in the mirror, shocked that they look the same — grey, wide — instead of the flashing glare of some terrible monster.

On the afternoon Mac died, before she headed for the station, Ani had stood

awhile, surveying herself in this very glass: her suntanned skin; her spots of freckles; her cheekbones — "Your mother's," her father always said, "she was known for them"; and new lines, deepening, around her eyes and the edges of her smile. Isabel had turned ten, and Ani had scanned herself, candid, for any evidence of that particular decade.

Now, nine months later, her skin is paler — less time spent out of doors — and the lines are deeper. The whites around her fine grey irises are specked with red, messier than she remembers, and thick smudges of tiredness reach down towards those famous, inherited cheekbones.

She's never felt time so etched across her skin, and she rubs at it hard, pushing it up and around, trying to see the old face, the other face, the person Ani Lachlan used to be.

33

It comes from nowhere, the sense of being watched, and when she looks up she sees him through the library's window — Roy McKinnon, looking in, but looking through her, beyond her, so that she's not surprised when she raises her hand and smiles to no response. How long has he been there? Or is Ani herself no longer there, disappeared somehow? She pats at her cheeks, her collarbones, to check her own existence.

A train pulls into the platform opposite, and Roy draws in a deep breath, pulls back his shoulders, and turns away. Behind him, in the gap between two carriages, Ani sees passengers moving towards the southbound train. *He must have been almost against the wall to have been looking through the window in the first place,* she thinks. *And staring at what?* She pats at her hair, brushes down her skirt, self-conscious, almost smiling.

Roy McKinnon, she thinks. She likes it

somehow, the idea of knowing where he is, of talking with him about his books and the world. But then, people do say the silliest things, turning simple friendships into galloping gossip and noisy surmise, *in which I am now cast as librarian and relict.*

The other week, running into him at the pictures with his sister and the doctor, she'd sat beside him in the darkness and watched the way the light from the movie refracted and lit up his hands, his lap, the cracked leather on the arms of his chair. The way a film's images jumped around — a shot from one camera, the reverse angle from another. It would be nice, Ani thought, to be able to shift so smoothly to another person's point of view — to see what her hands looked like, perhaps, if you were a poet, or what this dark room of picture watchers looked like from up there on the screen.

"Are you all right, Mrs. Lachlan?" His voice had been low and quiet, near her ear.

"Yes, yes," said Ani, in the too-loud response of any word spoken in darkness. "I just . . ." She gestured towards the screen. "My mind was wandering — sorry to disturb you." And as she watched, he raised his hand, and she half expected him to take hers, to grip her fingers, comforting. She had to work against a sense of disappoint-

ment when he didn't, brushing at something in front of his eyes instead.

At the picture's end, they stood apart from Frank and Iris in the foyer, unraveling the movie's plot and trying to remember other films in which they'd seen its stars. Then, "I wondered what you made of that bit-part engine driver," Roy McKinnon had said. "He seemed a brutal man, and I would never have thought it a brutal profession." It seemed an oversized observation for a small and inconsequential character.

Ani had frowned. "I didn't really think about it as if it was anything real," she said — she'd hardly noticed this character at all, or anything much of the film. They never drew her in the way books did, as if her imagination functioned better when it had to make up its own pictures, its own movements, rather than having them all laid out in front of her. But she liked the pause they gave her, the opportunity to sit still in the dark awhile and not have to think much at all.

"What I envy the railwaymen," said Roy McKinnon, "is all that motion, all that movement — the sense of spending your day traveling from one place to another and back again. I found the classroom bad enough, pacing around its four walls, but at

least I had the children in there with me. Now it's me, and a desk, a blank page, and nothing else. Perhaps I should write for the pictures — perhaps I'm attempting the wrong form. What do you think, Mrs. Lachlan? A picture show set here, with all the trains and the coal and a writer at work on the edge of a cliff."

Ani laughed. "I think I know what you have in mind," she said. "But I'd come and see it. I'd love to see this place all big and silver on the screen. I wonder if I'd see myself anywhere." And she'd smiled to see him blush, almost say something, and then hurry forward to help Frank with their ice creams.

"The first time Bella saw one of these," Ani said, taking a chocolate-covered ice-cream heart from him and holding it with care, "it was after the war — Mac had told her about them, all her life, when of course you couldn't buy them. And she couldn't believe such a treasure would really exist. 'Chocolate and ice cream,' she kept saying. You'd've thought he was handing her the stars."

And they'd talked then of things that had seemed wonderful to them when they were children — the delectable softness of pussy willow catkins, said Ani; the perfect sweet

thickness of a custard's skin, said Roy — and of the strangeness of realizing that somewhere, sometime, for no reason either of them could remember, these things must have stopped feeling remarkable or special.

"I miss that," he'd said, gazing out from the theater's front steps as if he was trying to pinpoint the source of something wonderful now.

Their ice creams eaten, the other two dispatched, they'd walked the long way home, with Ani telling the story about the night at the end of the war when she and Mac had danced along the sand behind the loops and curls of barbed wire. "I can't remember how long it was before they took it down," she said, "but I remember being shocked that it didn't happen immediately."

"Did you trust that it was over, when they said it was, when you saw the man dancing along Martin Place? Did you really think a thing as vast and awful as all that could just stop?" There was a tightness in Roy's voice, and a sharpness.

"Of course," said Ani quickly. "It was what we'd been waiting for for months." She looked across at him; he'd ducked his head down so his eyes must only have been seeing the forward steps of his own feet and the strips of road on either side. "Look, look

there, I think I just saw a shooting star." A half-truth — she hardly knew what she'd seen; it might have been a gull in the light — but it made him look up and smile.

He stopped then, gesturing towards his sister's house. "Here I am," he said superfluously. "I won't offer to walk you home; I know the way people would talk."

And Ani had smiled — "of course, of course" — and said something about hating town gossip. "I'm used to it now, hearing the same story about myself, told over and over. I suppose it's a way of getting used to what's happened, when you realize you're hearing about your own husband's death, or even talking about it yourself, and you hardly even register the conversation." But walking up her own stairs, five minutes or so later, she wished she hadn't finished with a story about herself, about Mac. She wished she'd taken her leave with the story about wonder.

The air shakes as the northbound train arrives, and through the window Ani sees Roy McKinnon straighten his coat sleeves, his hat, and step into one of its compartments. Does he look better now than when he first came? she wonders. Is his face a little tanned, a little rounder? Or is it that she knows what he looks like now, and is no

longer surprised by his lightness, how whittled down he looks, how insubstantial?

The train whistles as it prepares to pull away. Ani raises her hand again in acknowledgment, and when Roy McKinnon — through her window, through his — tips his hat, she's not sure if it's a response or a coincidence.

Settling himself on the train, Roy tips his hat to the empty platform, to the edge of the library and his reflection in its window, to the beauty of the mountain rising up behind it. He has something at last, something to show, and he's heading up to the city to meet a man at a magazine and pass on his poems. His first new poems in more than four years — written arduously, daily, in the weeks since Anzac Day. All that, for four or five he's happy with. Four or five, that is, apart from Ani's poem; he's kept that back. That's his; that's hers. But four or five new poems nonetheless.

The thought of it almost makes him laugh.

The compartment's framed pictures offer him the Hawkesbury River, the Blue Mountains, and the view up the coast, from Stanwell Tops, where box kites were launched. *Three options, where would you take her?* He usually avoids thinking so directly about An-

ikka Lachlan — it's too much, mostly, to look head-on at so bright a muse or messenger — but it's as if, this morning, a new recklessness, a new confidence is seeping from the lines he's written into the center of himself. *This is what Iris would call "feeling better,"* he decides. And perhaps there's something to be said for plain language. Stanwell Tops is too close to Ani's world. And she came from the plains, he knows that. Maybe Katoomba, or the Hawkesbury — the mountains or a river. It would be something to take her somewhere new, to show her that other places exist.

The most direct, the most proprietorial thing he's ever thought about her. He wants to call out with the daring of it. But instead, he pulls his poems out of his pocket and skims their lines again. They're a start, a good start, neither as sharp nor as fluid as the ones he managed during the war — and perhaps neither as lucid nor as elegant as the one he wrote for Ani. But they're feeling their way on towards those things, he's sure of it. All they need is to step clear of the last of the mud and the bodies.

Which is what the editor says, looking over them quickly a couple of hours later while their lunches sit, untouched, in the middle of a rather grand hotel dining room. "You've

got to get past the war now, McKinnon. You've got to find other stories to tell." And he slides the pages back across the table, pinning them with Roy's fish knife as if a strong wind might rush through and blow them away.

Roy stares at them there, a white rectangle under a silver bar. It seems disrespectful to take up this paperweight and start eating his fish, but he's not sure what else to do. He shifts the pages to his bread and butter plate, flattened by the man's easy dismissal but enjoying the fact that his unworthy words have almost disappeared.

"I thought it might be too soon to show you," he says, awkward and blushing, "but I just wanted to feel as if I was . . ."

"Absolutely, of course." The editor has almost finished his fish, is most of the way through his vegetables — three or four chews per mouthful and a swallow that makes his whole face shudder. "You wanted to feel you were back on track, back in your world. And you are, sir, you are on your way." He sits, a forkful of potato poised midway to his mouth. "You're just not there yet." He chews. "But there must be something new you want to write about in this place you're living down the coast?" And he tells Roy the story of an envelope he'd

received from another returned poet that had spilled the hard, parched landscape of some remote place across his desk that very morning, enough trauma and pain in it to sense what the man had seen and survived, but nothing explicitly, overtly military. "I accepted the poems immediately."

Roy nods slowly. *Enough of this now, that's what they all say. Enough of this.* "It's a beautiful place, where my sister is." He closes his eyes to see it. "This lovely escarpment folding into the Tasman Sea, the water and the light, and the trees. And there are people there, good people." He smiles, his eyes open again but seeing Ani's brightness. "I've started writing about them already."

"Well," says the editor, wiping his plate with the corner of a slice of bread, "I'll wait to see those. And if Lawrence could manage it, I daresay you will." It's a generous comparison, a generous endorsement, but Roy can see it on the man's face: *It's the least a chap can do, throw another chap a chance.*

The editor raises his glass. "There are fine poems to come from you yet, Mr. McKinnon. If the war unearthed their source in you, the peace will make it flourish." He's used this line on more than a dozen young men in this very dining room.

318

Roy makes his way through his fish, his vegetables, as quickly as he can, aware of the other man's empty plate. The editor is rattling through gossip from the publishing world — authors Roy knows only from spines and title pages, although the editor talks about them as if Roy is surely at all the parties and gatherings he himself attends. He invites him to one or two, and presses him to say he'll accept when Roy demurs: the length of the train trip he'd have to make, the difficulty of getting up from the coast.

In the hotel's lobby, the editor stands on one big black tile while Roy shakes his hand from the middle of a big white one: they look like pieces stranded on a chess board. *Remember this*, thinks Roy, feeling for his pen as soon as he's on his own in the street, and he scrawls the image on the back of the rejected poems and makes his way towards the station.

Everywhere, the city is busy with lunchtime, and he stands a minute in the shade of the post office's colonnade, watching as surges of people come and go. This is where she said it came from, the image of the man dancing at the end of the war. This is where someone had caught happiness for Anikka Lachlan to watch on a newsreel.

And his happiness? He closes his eyes: Anikka Lachlan turning a cartwheel on the beach — a gift of a moment, beyond acknowledgment, beyond words.

He opens his eyes and the city bustles on, a few shouts and sharp calls, the occasional horn, and not so much as a smile on most faces. *That happiness, that big thing ending,* thinks Roy: *you'd think that joy as big as that would have hung around in this place always.* But had he danced and spun when the news of the war's end found him? No. He'd crouched on a beach and cried awhile, for the waste of it, the time and the death and the waste.

Stepping into the crowd, he sees a tall woman with blond hair striding out in front of him, takes three fast steps to catch her in case it's Ani, fumbling awkwardly with his hat, his lapel, when he draws level with her and sees that it isn't. *Of course.*

That's his poem, he knows. Or rather, she is. And it's the only one that's any good, the only one that's real. He'll send it to the editor tomorrow; he'll show him he has found something beyond the war.

It's nearly two months since he secreted it in Ani's house — two months' torturing himself that she hasn't found it, or that she has and can't speak of it to him. He hates

himself each time he takes his leave from her without asking about it. *A poem's nothing without its readers,* he thinks, recklessly. *And she can't ignore it if it's in the world.* It's a simpler thing to stamp an envelope than say "I wonder if you've found . . ." or "I made you this thing."

Settling into the train's first carriage as it pulls away from Central, Roy unfolds his newspaper and distracts himself with its stories — strikes and blackouts, foreign ministers arguing in Europe, new missiles being built. *June 14, 1949, and it's as if the war never stopped.* He turns the page: a denazification court has commuted a sentence for a top German banker — *Denazification: that's a mouthful of a word. Should have hung them all.* And a father has confessed to throwing his two-year-old son onto a concrete path in a temper.

Roy closes his eyes. *This world, this bloody world.* What chance could you have of happiness or joy? He pulls his papers from his pocket, crumples them one by one into misshapen balls, and throws them through the open window as hard as he can to clear the tracks and the wind the train drags in its wake.

But then the train shudders, the wheels

screeching against the rails as Roy scans the racing results with their grainy photographs of tiny horses. *Such names,* he thinks: *So Happy. Jovial Lass. Full o Fun. Amused.* He closes his eyes and sees Ani's clumsy cartwheel against the morning sun, startled as the carriage lurches suddenly to a stop. *All we want to be — So Happy. Full o Fun.* There's an eerie silence; the noise of his newspaper hitting the floor is too big, too amplified to seem real.

Have they stopped the train to pick up my rubbish? he wonders half seriously as he looks back along the track for his jettisoned papers.

A shout; a whistle; and then another cry. Roy opens the window as far as it will go, leans out as far as he can to look ahead.

"Someone's been hit," the driver calls from the engine. "At the crossing here; someone's down."

"Is there anything we can do?" He's swinging down onto the tracks before he's finished asking the question, his feet uncertain on the uneven ballast.

As he draws up to the engine, the driver leans down. "You a doctor?"

And Roy feels himself nod. *Why not? I've seen enough bodies.*

"He came from nowhere" — the driver

gestures towards the fender. A mangled bicycle, a mess that had been somebody, shoes flung away, and a pair of glasses glinting on the other side of the tracks.

"I see," says Roy. "I see." He leans forward, unsure if he should touch the man, trying to imagine what Frank would do or say.

"Is he going to be all right?" the driver calls, pale in his high-up cabin.

Roy tilts his head, noncommittal, taking off his coat and covering as much of the accident as he can. He's not sure if he can see the man's chest rising and falling, or if this is just terrible, wishful thinking. *Either way,* he thinks, and says, "It would have been very quick." And, "Are you all right up there?" He likes the command he can hear in his voice.

And the driver nods.

Crouching down, Roy picks up the cyclist's glasses and wraps them in his handkerchief. There must be a wallet in one of his pockets, something to give up the man's name, his identity — but Roy draws back from touching him, certain now that he can see a tremor, a shudder, rattling through the body like alarm. Someone with real authority can take it from here; somebody with real authority can feel for a wallet. Still,

he reaches for the man's shoes, unsure where to place them.

A couple of currawongs land beside the tracks and watch him; a car's horn blares nearby. He touches his fingers to the smooth, warm metal of the railroad tracks, and thinks of Frank Draper's stories. At the end of the war, at the end of a railway line, a camp full of leftover pieces of people, mostly dead, the rest close to dying, among mountainous great piles of the everyday things they would never have thought twice about before — sturdy shoes, good traveling bags, and useful pairs of spectacles.

Along the line of carriages now, windows and doors open, and passengers crane to look, pulling away as they realize what's happened. *Nothing to do with them,* thinks Roy, *just a delay on their way to or from somewhere else.* He closes his eyes, sees Frank's mess from the other side of the world, so far from here, from the sun, and the air, and the pleasant day passing. He can't imagine that those camps would have felt any more real on this side of the world, even when that war was under way and being fought.

Now there's this train, this engine, this driver, and how could anyone not know that this is happening? Yet even in the next street,

people would be living their day without the slightest idea of this hiccup, this accident. *The world is so many individual bits and pieces,* thinks Roy. Millions, he supposes. Millions and millions.

Bits and pieces: his eyes focus on a splat of blood, then another, and another. Who cleans up these things? Would the railways dispatch people with buckets and mops, or someone with a hose and a broom? Years ago, when he was younger, he saw a team of scrubbers on the pylons of the Sydney Harbour Bridge — it must have been just before it opened — washing away the blood of a worker who'd fallen to his death. Roy was sure he could still see the mark on the silvery granite when they'd finished and gone home. He'd never felt safe crossing the bridge, seeing that, as if that stain might have tarnished or weakened it somehow.

If he thought of his own war, he thought of bodies on beaches, facedown along the shoreline where the ocean leached the marks and stains away. He has little sense that there was blood, but he knows this can't be true. Perhaps he's hosed it into some dark part of his memory where, if he's lucky, it will never breach its levee.

He wills himself to stare directly at the cyclist; he wills himself to see a glimmer of

life. And can't. How quickly it can stop, then, just like that. *So you have to take your chance, Roy; you have to chance your arm.* Make sure Ani Lachlan knows her poem. Send it to his editor for the rest of the world to read. Anything to shatter this inertia.

Damn it but he is sick of the waiting, and it's exhausting, he sees suddenly, to be unaware of something it would be so simple to find out. Maybe she hated the poem. Maybe she was embarrassed by it. Or maybe she simply hasn't seen that there is something new sitting among her other books. *Wake up, mac,* he thinks, startling himself with the inapt appellation. *Do something, once and for all.*

And so he moves the dead man's shoes, placing them next to each other and aligning their toes: it seems an appropriate gesture to make. *What was he doing here today?* Roy wonders. Where was he going — and what was he thinking that he didn't see the train, or hear it? Did he think he could beat it? Did he try to stop and fail?

Or did he see the train and just keep riding? Did he push and pump his pedals even faster? Roy shakes his head, rubs his eyes. *We've one way of coming into the world,* he thinks, *and so many ways of going out of it.* Above him, the driver slumps down to sit

against the wall of his cabin, cradling his head in his hands.

"What'll I tell the wife?" the man asks. "What do I say when she asks about my day?"

Who drove the train that killed Mac Lachlan? Roy thinks suddenly. *Who was the driver — did Ani ever ask?*

Maybe she didn't, and maybe she'd been right not to. Maybe it was better not to know.

He looks down at the mess at his feet, the blood, the skin, the shredded clothes. *Is this how he looked, the minute he died? Is this how Mac Lachlan went out of the world?* He balks at the way his pulse quickens, but there's a perverse intimacy in seeing this body, in imagining it belongs to Ani's husband. This thing she would probably die rather than see. *But I can take this on — I can see this for her.*

As if this is anything to do with her at all.

The currawongs call, and Roy turns in the instant they rise off the ground — a motorcycle is coming around the corner, its noise and movement startling them to flight. He brushes his hands together, straightens himself to attention as a young policeman gets off the bike.

"Take it from here, sir," the younger man

says, touching his forehead in half a salute. "What was your name?"

"Draper, Dr. Frank Draper," says Roy in that borrowed, stentorian voice. "He was dead straightaway, I should think." And he stands a moment, watching as the younger man lifts the corner of the coat up and away from the body. Then he turns and strides away from the train, towards the main road of this unknown suburb, glad to be back on the move.

He should have said something over the man, he thinks, something soothing or benedictory — in case he did have any sense of where he was, of what had just happened, or what was coming next. In case he had known it was the end and hadn't wanted to be alone.

What else is there, after all?

But the only words Roy can think of, in this belated instant of concern, are from the Yeats poem he'd sent to Frank all those years before:

I think it better that in times like these
A poet's mouth be silent . . .

Death has its own rituals, funerals and burials and prayers said and memorials written. Frank has told him of a German

328

woman who killed all her children just before the war's end — *to spare them their denazified future,* he thinks now, paraphrasing the newspaper — and then sat playing Patience, working the cards again and again, trying to get them into four neat piles of suits. Ani Lachlan has told him of a widow for whom she'd made food, arriving with a saucepan of soup and half a cake. As she reached the doorstep, she said, she was pulled up by a low and guttural howl that sounded like it belonged to some wild and cornered animal. She'd frozen, she said, hardly daring to breathe, and the sound had dropped away.

"And then it began," she said, "a low, slow song like a lullaby, over and over. The woman was singing her husband out of being, singing her husband into the longest sleep he would have."

Ani had left the food and gone quietly away. And at the end of the day, she said, watching Isabel sleep, she had stood with her hand on her daughter's blankets, singing the same lullaby and hoping that this newly dead man would hear it somehow, no matter where he was, and no matter who was singing.

Roy wonders, now, if the story was about Ani herself — that terrible sound he had

heard the night Mac died, as he raced along her street. And he wonders what song he should sing for this cyclist.

He closes his eyes, sees the body on the tracks, the body of the little boy who'd been dashed down against concrete, the bodies of the first 555 people Frank saw die in a world where war had ended. And as he takes the next step, he stumbles down the edge of a culvert — the shock of putting your foot out and finding nothing there.

Shuffling cards, dealing cards, sorting cards, aces at the top. *And your children dead in the next room.* He brushes his eyes. *This bloody world.*

His hands fumble in his pockets for his handkerchief and find instead the dead man's glasses. He takes them out, looks at them a moment, wondering if he should return them to the body — or the policeman. Then he rubs one lens clean, and the other, and holds them in front of his own eyes.

The world blurs.

If they could show what they had seen — if they could show you the last day of this man's life, show what happened to him, and why. He squeezes the glasses, their wire frames cutting into his palm. If he's honest, there was something glorious in the shock of the

accident; he squeezes the glasses harder, hoping the pain of their wire against his flesh will transform his reaction to proper abhorrence.

Then he wraps them again and puts them back in his pocket, aware of their shape and their weight, like a talisman, or a warning.

34

Pulling the heavy book box towards her across the library's smooth floor, Ani is back in their first night in Surfers Parade, unpacking Mac's box of books. She'd pulled *Jane Eyre* out of the box — he must have packed it last, because it sat on the top by itself, pristine and secure in a nest of recent news. It was 1936: people on the move — the Germans in Rhineland; the Italians in Abyssinia; the beginning of the war in Spain; and the British king abdicating for his love. She'd fallen in love with Mac himself, she suspected, when he told her *Jane Eyre* was his favorite book.

Digging deeper into the box, she'd found Agatha Christie and Dashiell Hammett, adventures and westerns, and Arthur Conan Doyle's *The Lost World.* And she'd laughed. Some were books she'd read; some she'd always wanted to read. And below that, a handful of magazines — *Smith's Weekly,*

some exotic *National Geographics,* and a few *Harper's.* She'd flicked to their contents pages, hungry for the stories inside, and laughed again.

He'd come in at the sound, his face quizzical.

"I didn't know the extent of your dowry," she said.

"It's where my money goes," he said, as if he were confessing to horses or the dogs. He'd smiled then, and she felt entirely happy. What more did you need to share a life with someone but a stock of new stories to tell?

"Samanlaiset linnut lentävät yhdessä," her father had written in her daybook on the morning of her wedding. "The same kind of birds fly together."

Now, as Ani takes the last consignment of books from its trunk, a gust of wind catches the door, making it slam. And in the silence after its surprising noise, Ani realizes she's hearing a greater silence, a greater quiet, and has been hearing it for ten minutes, fifteen, half an hour, maybe more.

There has been no train.

She stands slowly, smoothing her skirt as she crosses to the window. There are passengers waiting on the two platforms — waiting. Waiting. She sees Luddy talking to

333

this one, to another.

"Sounds like there's a problem with the trains coming through." That's what he'd said to her. "An accident along the line and they're not letting anything pass." She could still hear the exact pitch of his voice, the easiness of it. Just passing the information on, and offering to let Mac know that they were held up, and they'd decided not to wait, that they'd see him at home at the end of the day.

And we went to the beach and found a shell that shimmered like an evening gown. And we went home. And I started dinner. And Bella sat and waited. And then they came.

There was life before; there'll be life after — sometimes, now, she thinks she can almost see what it might look like. That moment, that news — the dinner cooking, and the men, and the story of Mac's death — that's the dividing line. That's all.

She crosses the gravel, waving to the stationmaster.

"An accident, a bicycle, they said." He grimaces. "Nasty." Grimacing again. "They say the track'll be right again soon."

Ani looks along the empty line, thinking about Roy heading north earlier in the day. It can be nothing to do with him, she thinks, safe in the size of the carriages. But still;

but still.

"It rings, the silence, doesn't it?" she says. And, "I still can't hear the ocean — how is it such a big sound can disappear when it comes from something so close by?"

Luddy shakes his head. "You'd notice the waves if they stopped too, I reckon."

To the north, the roundhouse windows glisten and sparkle. Ani blinks at their semaphore. "Did you know, that afternoon when Bella and I were waiting, and the trains were stopped? Did you know it was something to do with Mac even then? I know you said you didn't, but . . ."

He stares at her, his mouth open and his eyes blinking fast. "Of course not; of course not. Oh, Mrs. Lachlan, of course not."

She brushes his words away. "I'm sorry, Luddy, I don't even know why I asked you. I've never thought such a thing before." Maybe she'll ask one day to read the coroner's report; maybe she'll fill in the excruciating details of a story she's recast as a random disappearance.

Luddy shakes his head, and the movement breaks her reverie as a bus rattles by. "I'll just tell these people they're better off with a bus," he says, waving towards the other platform.

Ani nods, waving her own hand towards

the library. "Could you come and tell me when they're starting again? I think I'd like some warning of the noise — today."

And he nods, smiling again. "You don't want them sneaking up on you." He blushes, but she's laughing as she walks across the gravel.

"Exactly," she calls. "Unless you can do me a big D57. Those things are magic."

Early one morning, just after the war, she'd walked to the station through a dawn thick with sea mist. It had softened hard lines, made edges disappear, and transformed the streetscapes Ani knew so well into surreal shadows, dubious connections, hovering impossibilities. The wall of one house blurred towards its neighbor; a bathtub of water for horses hovered above the ground; a jacaranda tree transmogrified into something from the northern fairy tales of her childhood.

Something had happened to sound as well, magnifying it. The scrape of a kettle on a stove; the slam of a screen door; someone singing in a round baritone; someone else suggesting jam or marmalade for breakfast.

Climbing the main road towards the railway bridge, Ani felt she was walking through one of her father's memories of

winter. That's what she'd ask for for her birthday, she thought suddenly. She'd ask to be taken to see snow. She laughed. *Let Mackenzie Lachlan solve that on the east coast of Australia in 1945.*

It was only when she stepped onto the platform that she realized it was there — a great steam engine, a D57 class locomotive, puffing and blowing, its front end sawn off with a stubby funnel above. She couldn't imagine how she hadn't heard it, but there it sat, its steam indistinguishable from the morning's fog, and its big wheels waiting to spring forward, on and up the coast.

It was like walking around a corner and finding a dragon.

She looked for the driver but the cabin was empty, so she walked on, running her hand along the strong, smooth metal. "Two-fifty tons she weighs, with sixty-five square feet of fire grate, and two hundred pounds per square inch of boiler pressure." Mac could recite these figures like poetry — he loved these engines, their brawn, their sheer heft. "Get them going straight enough and I reckon they might fly," he said.

She reached its nose, patted as close to the big round headlight as she could, and turned back along the platform.

"Morning, Mrs. Lachlan." The driver, a

mate of Mac's, swung himself into his compartment. "Early for you this morning — give us five minutes or so and we'll have you under way."

And she'd smiled, following the engine's line past its truckload of coal to the passenger compartments beyond. This great, powerful thoroughbred, just sitting there, breathing, and waiting for her.

It was magnificent, and there wasn't another soul in that morning to see it.

Now, inside the library, the sun touches the cedar shelves, the polished floor, finding oranges, golds, like harbingers for spring. Pressing her hands to the warm wood, Ani wonders whose wife, whose mother, will open her door this afternoon to the insupportable news of a train, a collision. She's still there, she knows, standing spotlit in her own hallway, hearing the news again and again. She'll always be standing there, listening. And as she thinks this, she feels it, a sharp splinter wedged hard into her skin. How many times has she stroked this shelf, and why, just this time, did it harm her?

If you cannot sit in a quiet room of words and pages and unravel the idea of random or accidental harm, or the illogical and unpredictable ways of protection, how much harder to walk through war asking why that

bullet found that person, why that mine was there, and why do I keep walking clear?

"I want to know," she says at last, surprised by the strength of her voice. "I want to know how to understand."

But all she can hear is the sound of her own pulse pounding in her ears.

35

They catch her unawares this year, these profusions of color — purple first, when the jacarandas begin to bloom, and then the deep red of Illawarra flame trees, *Brachychiton acerifolius,* Isabel's favorite proper name for a plant, because she thinks it sounds like a dinosaur.

They follow each other into being, bursting out along the coast and up the escarpment. The jacaranda comes with the spring; the flame, a little later, lasting a little longer. They mark Ani's months; they mark her year. And now they mark Mac's anniversary.

"Did you want to do something, Ani, to remember him, these twelve months?" Mrs. May delivers the question directly, having arrived at the front door with an invalid's food of soft butter cake and some soup.

"I'll ask Isabel," Ani says, not wanting to have to answer. "I'll see if there's anything she wants to do." And she reaches out to

hug her neighbor's arm. "You take such good care of us."

This long and slow year. Wars have ended in Israel, in China, in India, and in Greece, although there are bound to be new ones before long. There are planes that can fly around the world without stopping, and Russia has made a great bomb like those that were dropped on Japan; Ani still cannot think about these without shaking — paralyzed by the idea of such noise, such heat, such silence.

Now, as she waves to her neighbor, she sees the first purple blossoms: a jacaranda can cover itself with color in a week, and then the red of the flame trees will come.

Scooping potatoes, carrots onto her daughter's plate that night, she says: "Mrs. May was wondering if there was anything you'd like to do, you know, for the anniversary of Dad's . . ." To say "death" still feels impolite, or somehow embarrassing.

Isabel looks up from the schoolbook she's packing away. "Are we supposed to?" she asks.

Ani shakes her head. "No, no, love, I don't think that's what Mrs. May meant — I think some people . . . you know, they like to mark the moment. We could walk round to the cemetery again or ask them to do a special

reading in church. We could have a special meal, ask Mrs. May to come in. I don't know." She smiles, her hand resting on her daughter's shoulder. "I told her I'd ask you if there was anything you particularly wanted to do."

Frowning a little, Isabel pulls her plate towards her. "Should we do something? Like it was a birthday? Is that what you mean, Mum, what you want . . ."

Ani watches as Isabel pushes the rounds of carrots into a line, the largest disks on the left-hand side, and ranging down, perfectly graded, to the smallest on the right. It's been happening most mealtimes they've eaten together, she realizes, and she's not sure for how long. "Isabel," she asks now, "what are you doing with your dinner?" She wonders why she's let it pass before.

"I'm not really hungry," says her daughter, shrugging as she molds the dollop of potato into a perfectly right-angled triangle.

Anikka sits opposite with her own dinner; she's not that hungry either, if she thinks about it — can't remember the last time she was, the last time she actually tasted something she ate. "Maybe I should have warmed up a bowl of Mrs. May's soup — that's never let us down when we've needed

342

nourishing."

Her daughter's smile flares, and Ani smiles wider: there she is, her bonny little girl, as Mac would have said.

"Maybe we could take Mrs. May for a picnic — down to the beach." Isabel spikes one carrot from the middle of the row with her fork, makes a great show of putting it into her mouth, chewing it twenty times. "Or we could go just the two of us; I wouldn't mind that either. But you decide, Mum; I don't mind."

Another single round of carrot disappears. When Ani looks down at her own plate, she sees she's started to make the same orange line of vegetables through its middle. She mixes the mashed potato across it, destroying the symmetry.

"Let's think about it tomorrow," she says peaceably, "and concentrate on dinner now." Pushing the problem away.

It was never a struggle to make conversation when there were three of them. It was never a struggle to eat. Ani scoops up the mashed potato: she's never thought such a thing before about dinnertime, about any time with her daughter.

And what did Mac's voice sound like?

Washing the dishes later while Isabel dries, Ani stares through their reflection in the

kitchen window and into the darkness beyond. "Do you still hear him?" she asks as her daughter stacks the plates. "Do you still hear your dad say things sometimes?"

Isabel aligns the stack carefully. "Sometimes I think I do," she says after a long pause. "But there are lots of things I know I don't remember now, so I don't know if the things I think I can still remember are real or not. I think I remember him wishing me happy birthday that last time. But maybe I just remember the day and maybe it's someone else's voice. I think he sounds like my teacher at school, and I never thought that before. If people's fathers have to die, someone should make a camera for their voices."

Her hands warm in the soapy water, Ani laughs. "Something like that. I thought your kaleidoscope might have caught a piece of him for us — I haven't checked for a while, but I know he wasn't there back at the beginning."

"I guess that's because he was down under the water, and it's hard to look all the way down to a bathysphere."

"You still think he's there?"

Isabel nods. "It's better than thinking about ashes," she says — too pragmatic, Ani thinks, for someone who's not yet eleven.

She squeezes the dishcloth and hangs it on the front of the stove, as she's done every night she's lived in this house. She likes the predictability of it, that she can trust that the wet things will dry, always, and in a certain amount of time; that she can trust that process, that progression.

"Anyway," she says, drying her hands, "there's your birthday for us to celebrate first of all — I'm looking forward to our bushwalk and our picnic lunch with pasties." She stokes the fire, smiling at its flames. "I'm still anxious about keeping the meat end separate from the jam, but Mrs. May assures me it's all in the pastry."

Her homework spread out again on the red laminate table, Isabel props her chin on her hand, her pencil poised. "Where do you want to go for *your* birthday, Mum? You haven't said anything yet, about your excursion, or your dinner, or your heart's desire."

The house creaks a little as the wind rattles its gutters and eaves. Ani reaches for the tea canister, the pot, wondering how to answer.

"For my excursion," she says at last, "I'd like to take the train into Wollongong and look at the shopwindows and have a milkshake, like we used to." The ritual never again attempted after that last aborted at-

tempt. "For my dinner, I'd like you to cook me blancmange, with the peach leaf, like they taught you at school. That was beautiful, Bella, the night I came home and found that little dish waiting for me." She takes another long, slow breath. "And for my present," she says quietly, "my present . . ." Her fingers turn the coral brooch her daughter gave her at Christmas; she wears it almost every day. "I don't think there's anything I need, my love."

Isabel contemplates her mother awhile, sucking at the end of her pencil. "I think I found the thing Dad was making you last year," she says at last. "The thing he'd always wanted to make — I think I found it, under the house. I didn't know what to do about it, how to tell you." And she's out of her seat now and through the back door before Ani can say a word.

The house creaks and settles again, the wind puffing a little smoke back down the chimney and out through the stove. Ani swirls the tea, wondering what her daughter is about to bring into the room.

A scrape across the doorstep and Isabel appears, walking backwards and dragging something across the newly washed linoleum. Ani frowns — at the shape, rather than the mark its movement might be mak-

ing — and tilts her head, as if the adjustment might transform the shape and being of the thing itself. But there's no question: it's the frame of a box, with brackets, shelves fitted to some of them, and it's fixed on a round base, like a plinth, so that it can spin and turn.

"It was under the house, behind a trunk full of clothes — I found it when I was putting away those shoes of Dad's you wanted to keep." Isabel rocks it from one side to the other. "I've never seen it before, and there are tools down there as well. I thought it must be . . . whatever it was he was making."

"A bookcase, it's a revolving bookcase — a spinner, they call them, although my dad used to call them *bibliothèques,*" says Ani, stroking the smooth, dense-colored wood. There's a delicate calligraphy of whorls and patterns in its markings. *Perhaps it's silky oak,* she thinks, tracing its complexity. Her father would approve of the choice. *That's a fine grain, Mackenzie,* he'd have said, admiring his son-in-law's efforts and checking that the mechanism that turned the shelves didn't jar — just as Ani is checking now.

"I didn't know your dad was such a handyman. It took him two years to put up a shelf in the kitchen when we came here."

347

She presses her finger onto the wood's lines: it's like a fingerprint itself, or a piece of marbled paper. "Maybe the book was meant to go on the bookshelf," she says then. "A set, maybe, to start a new library." She laughs. "Which is funny, isn't it, because a new library is exactly what I got for my last birthday, in a roundabout way."

"What book?" Isabel parks the cabinet by the end of the kitchen table. "Did you find another present?"

Fetching the book from beside her bed, Ani passes it to her daughter without a word, watching carefully as Isabel takes it and lets its spine rest on her hand. The book opens automatically to the last poem, "Lost World."

"He said he wanted to write a poem, your dad," she says as her daughter begins to read. "I didn't find the book until months after he'd died. But I've been reading it at the end of every day. And it seemed" — she hesitates — "it seemed a private kind of thing." She laughs at Isabel's anxious blush, at her hurried closing of the page. "Nothing like that, Bella. Read it, it's lovely. I'm not sure why I didn't tell you. I found it on the mantelpiece on Anzac Day — remember, the night we went for a swim with the phosphorescence? Like you said, like you

348

said about the green, it must have been there all the time." She smiles. "Perhaps he slipped it in while he was working on this." And she lifts the spinning shelves up onto the kitchen table, closer to the light that makes their wood glow.

"Lucky we didn't give you the spinner, though," says Isabel, concentrating on the poem again. "The piece of wrapping paper I'd painted would never have been big enough." Her fingers follow the lines down the page, tapping the rhythm of the final words:

All this in her,
All things, all places furled
And folded in her, the bright messenger
Who comes for a lost world.

From the other side of the table, Ani scans the poem upside down — not that she needs to look at it; she knows it by heart, reading it twice, three times a night, every night, before she turns out the light. Some nights, it conjures an angel for her, someone soft and light who watches as she sleeps. Some nights, it's herself she sees, dressed in white and her hair pale in some spotlit glow. But never Mac, no matter what she does or thinks or hopes. Whether he's asleep in that

high room she imagines for him, or down fathoms with the stargazers of Isabel's imagination, his poem is all there is of him now at the end of her day.

"Oh, Mum," says Isabel, caressing the book. "It's like a proper poem, like they make us read at school. I knew he wanted to make you something special but I never knew he could make anything like this." She moves her hands to pin the book open on the table, her reading so concentrated that Ani half expects to see the words sucked right off the page. "And it *feels* so nice, doesn't it?" Isabel goes on. "The way the rhymes work, the way the lines lilt. Dad really knew what he was doing."

My daughter the critic, thinks Ani, coming around the table to read Mac's words again herself. Below her, Isabel's shoulders pull back and her little-girl chest puffs out. *And she's proud of him,* thinks Ani, proud.

Pulling one of her schoolbooks across the table, Isabel opens a clean page and begins to transcribe her father's "Lost World" — from above, Ani watches, mesmerized by the reenactment of these sentences coming into being. It's like ventriloquism, through her daughter's hand. She watches as Isabel's pencil loops high on the capital letters and low, with a flourish, on the *g*'s, the *y* of

"mayhem." Her pencil slows as she comes up to the need for an *s,* and on the fourth or fifth time, Ani sees why: she's pausing to replicate the precise way Mac would have written that letter.

"I've never noticed before that you write like your dad," says Ani, tracing her daughter's script with her own finger.

"I've been concentrating," says Isabel, following her mother's finger with her own. "I can always remember what his writing looks like even if I lose his voice sometimes. And I try to make my letters as close to his as I can." She holds up her schoolbook for her mother's approval. "I think the *f*'s are pretty good, and the *g*'s. But I can never get that kink in the top of the *s*'s, and you need the letter *S* for lots of words, you know." She blushes. "Like 'Isabel,' and 'authoress.' "

Ani smiles. She can see the size of the revelation her daughter has made, the courage it takes to say this aloud, and she appreciates its distraction. "An authoress." She strokes her daughter's hair. "That's a lovely word, Bell, and a lovely idea." And she watches a raspberry blush flush Isabel's face.

"I mean," says Isabel, "it's just a daydream, just an idea. I wouldn't really know what to do. But if Dad could do this" —

she taps the velvety page, her fingers settling below the poem's last full stop — "well, maybe, as Mrs. May would say, it's in the blood."

Laughing at Isabel's impersonation of their neighbor's turn of phrase, Ani pushes a blank sheet of paper towards her, uncaps a Biro for her too. "I think the way you start is that you simply start," she says, straightening the rectangle of whiteness as she hears herself go on, unplanned and unexpected. "Or you could ask Mr. McKinnon. I don't know the difference between writing poems and writing stories, but they must all begin somehow. And I'm sure he'd be happy to know that someone else wanted to make new sets of words around here." The image of the two of them, sitting with their pencils, the air around them thick with sentences never before thought of — she likes it, and that thought makes her own face bright.

Turning sharply, she knocks the teapot, gasping as the hot liquid scalds her hand and floods onto her daughter's books. "Oh, Bella, Bella, the mess I've made —" which touches the thought of her daughter and the poet as much as the sudden puddle of staining tea.

"It's all right, Mum." Isabel has the books tilted high in the air, tipping the liquid down

into her saucer. "It doesn't matter; I can fix it."

"I'm sorry, love; I got distracted" — she tries for a joke — "thinking of the day I'd have your books to shelve in my library." And Isabel blushes again.

"Don't even talk about it," she says softly. "Don't even pretend it might be real."

She was never a very childish child, thinks Ani, *and whatever else Mac's death has done, it's pushed the last of that out of her. Or perhaps that was me, the way I was — the way I am.* She digs her fingernails into the soft skin of her arms. *I should have done better with this; it's all I should have done.*

But she wipes at the spillage with her dishcloth, patting the table dry before she lets Isabel rearrange her books. And then she sits, very still, and very quiet, and watches her daughter's busyness, watches her hand fly across the pages, filling their lines, watches her stop and pause, thinking of a word, working at a sum, before the writing starts again.

If she thinks of Mac writing, he's signing the register on the day they were married; she can still see the way his hand moved to shape his own name on the page. It was a looping, gentle gesture, like a caress. She'd never seen anyone write anything that way

before. But it's there in Isabel's writing; it's there in the way she does even this ordinary set of homework.

As her mind settles into her wedding day, Ani looks at her daughter without seeing her, a fond, middle-distance stare as she reaches out and tucks a strand of Isabel's hair behind her ear. Her fingers touch something unusual and she leans forward, back in the room, back with her little girl, worrying at whatever it is as she focuses, frowning. She frees the thing and holds it carefully between two fingers — a bit of a dandelion's puffball; the kind you might blow on to wish.

Ani smiles, opens the kitchen window, and blows it gently into the night. Beyond, in the shadows, she has the sense of something good, something still and calm, nearby, and getting closer.

"There," she says softly, tucking Isabel's hair back again. "There. That's better."

36

It's the children's voices that wake him, laughter and shouting and the kind of singsong banter he remembers from so many playgrounds. Roy stretches, yawns, and looks at his watch — almost four, and he's slept since lunchtime. It's long enough to feel miraculous.

Out in the kitchen, Iris is clattering saucepans and their lids. Inching out of sleep, Roy can find no other explanation for the cacophony of sound, and he rubs his eyes and pulls on a sweater, intending on going out to help her.

The kitchen, though, is empty, except for Iris's three chickens, inside somehow and making their way around the shelves and the cupboards. A baking dish tumbles, another in its wake, and the chickens step on, unimpressed or unaffected by the racket.

"Out, out." Roy runs at them, his arms flailing as he herds them towards the open

door. "Iris? Are you here? Your chooks have broken in." But there's no answer — he can't imagine she'd have left them pecking in the garden, or left the door open, for that matter. "Off you *go!*" Shouting the last word, as if the hens might move if he matches them noise for noise.

They regard him with their sideways eyes, and set their heads down to peck at the pattern on the lino. One of them drops a wet brown poo, and Roy yells again, imagining his fastidious sister's horror.

Amazingly, the chickens respond, bobbing their way across to the back door and on out into the garden. He closes them into their coop and looks around for Iris's ever-present mop. "Our little secret," he whispers darkly at the birds. "But do it again, and I'll have you in one of those pans." He's never killed a chicken, and suspects he wouldn't be able to. He wonders if the birds know this — they pay no attention to his words.

Splashing eucalyptus oil liberally into the bucket of water he's boiled, he takes a deep breath of its aroma and sways with the movement of the mop. If this is cleaning, he thinks, he can see why Iris likes it — there's a rhythm and a grace to it, and something seductive about seeing the difference you've made. *Perhaps I've found my calling at last,*

he thinks, twirling the mop as if he were Fred Astaire. But he stows it again as soon as the single soiling is dealt with, rinsing it carelessly and knowing his sister will find fault with its treatment.

Hat in hand, then, he makes for the beach, pausing on the esplanade to mark the snake of children heading north along the sand, the snake of children heading south. *The beach at the end of your each day at school,* he thinks. *It must not get better than that.*

In the shadow of the pump house, a knot of girls has gathered, their bags piled haphazardly in the soft grass that fringes the sand, and their voices high in the afternoon's air. Roy heads towards them, aiming for the jetty beyond, but slows as he hears the words they're calling — "Nut!" "Jerk!" — and sees them trying to start a fire with a small pile of books. Enclosed in the mess is Isabel Lachlan, so still and quiet that it takes Roy a moment to realize she's the butt, the center, of whatever's going on.

"Hullo!" he calls, watching the gang's immediate reaction. "You should take care with those books on the beach — sand in the binding; it ruins the glue." Ignoring the insults, ignoring the matches.

The girls step back, wary, watching for what he'll do next. They've probably been

warned about him, he thinks, the crazy man who walks around all day and night, calling out words to himself.

"Are they your books?" He turns now to Isabel, stepping towards her and smiling. "Would you like some help getting them home?"

Her smile beams as the other girls scuff their way through the sand, trying to look casual as they pick up their bags and disperse.

"Thank you," she says. "Thank you, Mr. McKinnon. It's the reading they hate, and I know big words too. Like 'floccinaucinihilipilification' — I just learned that one; or 'honorificabilitudinitatibus' — that's in Shakespeare, you know. They think I'm saying I'm smarter than them."

"You probably are — smarter, I mean, not saying so." He squares the books into a single pile and slides them into her bag. "What were you doing down here?"

Isabel takes the satchel from him, fastening its clips and placing it carefully onto the grass. "I come down after school sometimes — I've been practicing tunneling, and cartwheels. Mum's at the library, you know, and Mrs. May doesn't have tea on till later. So I like to come down here and play. They usually leave me alone when we're not at

school."

"I suppose the daughter of a librarian couldn't help but be a big reader," says Roy, squatting down in the sand beside her and looking out across the water. "Your mum must be very proud."

"I think she still misses Dad," says Isabel, and Roy blinks. He's forgotten the leaps a child's mind might make, and of course, for Ani, and perhaps her daughter too, everything must still come back to Mac.

"She used to read all sorts of things," Isabel goes on, "and now it's all romance and happy endings." She screws up her pretty face. "I suppose that's okay, but it's not what I'd want to write —" And she blushes across the size of saying this, and to this man, of all people, who must know about these things.

"Not another one." He feigns horror. "I don't know if this village has room for the both of us — so you're lucky I don't do much writing these days. The stage is clear for you, Isabel Lachlan. You should give it a try."

Her blush deepens. "It feels dangerous to make jokes about it," she says quietly. "Did you make jokes about it? When you were little?"

"Constantly," says Roy. "I still do." He's

forgotten the fake bonhomie of distracting a child — he loves it; he's missed it; he could sit here for days. "Now these tunnels," he says, switching her attention again. "What's their purpose? What are we making? Is it transportation you're thinking, or defense?" And before he knows it, he's bent down and is following her instructions for an intricate series of ramparts around her latest sand city, shoveling sand through his legs with the stance of a busy cartoon puppy.

"I told Mum I was thinking about writing," says Isabel after a while, "but I didn't know quite how to start. She said I might ask you about it. Would that be okay, if I did?"

Roy straightens up, pulling his shoulders back and pushing his stomach forward. "I'm probably the worst person to ask," he says, serious. "I was almost five years between poems, can you believe it, and you know what got me started again in the end?" She shakes her head and he pushes himself forward on the serendipity of the meeting, the bravery of seeing off her foes. "Your mother, Isabel, it was your mother. The first poem I wrote after the war, I wrote about her." His voice is quiet now, as if he's forgotten he's talking to anyone but himself.

"Did you publish it?"

"The pragmatic questions of youth." Roy smiles. "Not yet, but I'm going to, I hope. I did leave a copy for her — but she mustn't have found it. She never mentioned it, did she? A small present? A tribute from a poetic admirer?" You can say anything to children — he's forgotten that too — and they'll sift out the gold from the dross.

Isabel shakes her head. "She found a poem my dad wrote — he must've written it before he died. It's so beautiful — maybe she'd let you read it. I guess all her attention for poetry has been taken up with that at the moment. That's how it is," she says, stretching her shoulders, her stomach, in imitation of him, "with things to do with Dad."

The exquisite torture of infatuation: standing tall next to this young girl, Roy registers how foolish he must look with his shoulders back and his gut out, how foolish, when he's no reason to be proud or sure. There's a burning taste at the back of his throat and his stomach knots around unknowns — if Ani has mistaken his poem for one by Mac, and the gall of thinking a railwayman might make such a thing. *It wants elegance, and talent, and craft to make a thing like that,* he wants to shout, like a man discovering he's been double-crossed.

And beneath the bile and the spasms, there's something else, the memory of Mac charging down a football field, powerful, broad, and alive. Roy can see him as clearly as if he were bearing along the sand right now — *she's mine, McKinnon, mine to dream of, mine to know.* He steps aside as if to dodge the apparition, surprised by the real, wet feel of the ocean's water against his feet.

He would run me down in a heartbeat, Roy thinks as the outer edges of Isabel's metropolis is saturated by the sea, and weakens, and falls. *Why not throw down a poem from the other side of death?*

But I'm alive, he wants to shout at Anikka Lachlan, or perhaps even at her daughter. *I'm alive, I'm here, look at me.*

And then I could stamp, the way a ten-year-old girl might stamp. He laughs at himself, shaking his head. *They taught me well, those kids I used to teach.*

The next wave surges across the sand, washing out one section of Roy's ramparts, and he leaps to repair it as if it were the most pressing problem in his world. Well, either Mac did write a poem and Ani's not found his, or she's found it and taken it as a gift from someone else. Either way, she'll know who made it soon enough. He'd balked only twice before handing it over at

the post office and seeing it off on the next mail train, bounding home with a palpable sense of relief as its vans disappeared from view. *It's beyond me now,* and his editor would read it soon enough, Roy was sure, and print it after that; he was sure of that too. He knew its worth.

The magazine would come; Ani would read its words. And then — well, and then.

He scoops the sand and packs it hard, drizzling wetness like mortar along the top to hold it firm. "This is how you can re-inforce buildings," he says. "But I'm sure you know this already, a practiced sand architect like yourself."

Because her citadel has reached the base of the pump house, she pokes the triumphant banner of a Norfolk pine's needle into its last edifice before turning three cartwheels to get back to Roy.

"Did you teach your mum to cartwheel, or did she teach you?" he asks, applauding.

"Cartwheel? My mum can't cartwheel."

Roy smiles, tries a cartwheel himself, and lands in a heap on the sand. "I saw her — I saw you both one morning. I have to say, you made it look quite easy." He tries again, and fails, laughing.

"I think that's the only time she tried — it was a rare sighting, Mr. McKinnon, of a

rare species: the cartwheeling Anikka Lachlan." Her hands curled like the twin tubes of binoculars, she's scouting the landscape for this beast when another wave comes, washing at her feet and demolishing another section of her city wall. She lets out the wail of a much younger child.

"Come on," says Roy, "we can triumph over this. We just have to make it bigger and stronger," ignoring the logistics of an incoming tide.

He watches her from the corner of his eye, the way she scoops the sand up so quickly, marking out ramparts and skyscrapers while he beavers away at small things — reinforcements, buttresses — and makes much less progress. She's set on the task, he can see that, while his own attention wanders now and then, registering the yellow flowers that have bloomed among the grasses that fold down towards the sand, and the satisfying crunch this undergrowth makes under the pressure of his feet as he climbs in among the greenery, picks some of the pretty blossoms, and carries them back to fashion a garden along the inside of one of the citadel's smooth, sandy walls.

Down at the waterline, he retrieves tiny shells and tendrils of seaweed, planting them here and there across Isabel's expand-

ing complex. He picks at the edge of the cliff face itself, astonished at how easily the fine pink sandstone becomes its original grains. Up above him, towards the top of the headland, he can see narrow bands of siltstone, and coal above that, striping the cliff like a licorice allsort. He's never noticed the delicacy of all these colors and their transitions before, and he wonders how he might thank Isabel for making him pause here this afternoon and look more closely at this place.

"Look how much you've built up," he calls then, astonished at how far her work stretches north along the beach. "What happens at the end of the day? Do you leave it for the tide or jump it down yourself?" He'd do that, he thinks, with the satisfaction of destroying something you'd labored so hard to make.

She's working in the fold where the beach meets the rest of the continent as he speaks, and Roy watches as she turns towards his voice, glancing west towards the setting sun and out, hasty, towards the encroaching tide. *Her hair,* he thinks, *lights up just like her mother's.*

"What was it about, your dad's poem?" he says, not wanting to let go of the girl or this sweetly cross-purposed conversation. "Did

you read it, did you say?"

"It said Mum was like an angel," says Isabel softly, "and it was lovely, really lovely." She sits back, digging her hands in her pockets. "What about yours? What did yours say?"

"Well, it's funny, you know," says Roy as the sun dips down behind the edge of the scarp, "but I think mine was about that too." Watching her closely, as if he might see Ani's own reaction through her child's.

"Wowee," says Isabel, softer still. "I wonder if someone'll write me a poem like that one day."

"If you're a writer, you can write your own," says Roy, matter-of-fact. "Takes all the bother out of having to rely on another person."

She considers this, considers him, considers the rim of light where the sun has disappeared behind the mountain — and suddenly looks at her watch.

"I have to go, Mr. McKinnon," she says, twisting the face of her watch towards him — although whether she means for him to admire it or read its time, he's not sure. "My teatime in ten minutes. Oh, do you like this watch? It was my dad's, you know. But I can wear it now, to be in charge of wherever I have to be."

He catches her wrist and does good work admiring the timepiece. "Your dad would be proud you're in charge," he says, brushing the sand from the watch's webbed band. "It was nice to see you, Isabel Lachlan, and don't worry about those girls. They'll grow out of their jealousy and you'll leave them far behind." He hopes she can wait that long.

"Thanks for the help with my sand work," she says, shouldering her bag and turning to go.

"And listen," Roy calls after her, casual and diminishing. "Can you ask your mother if she did find my poem? It's no trouble if she didn't — it's bound to be published pretty soon. She can see what she thinks of it then." Buoyed by the unexpected afternoon.

Isabel nods, settles her satchel, and heads up the hill. But halfway home, she sees a small brown rabbit ambling along the verge, stopping and nibbling, its ears and paws as winning as a picture-book drawing. She crouches for a while — the time, the message, the dinner all forgotten — picking nasturtium leaves and bright-green grass stems, and holding them out to it as snacks.

When she finally reaches Mrs. May's table, the rabbit is all she talks about,

wondering where it came from and whether it needs a home. And by the time she sees her mother, later that night and home late from the library, Isabel is almost asleep and even the rabbit is almost lost.

"Mum? Do you think we could get a bunny?" Her words slur towards each other, their consonants blurring. "There was one near the beach, and Mr. McKinnon . . ."

"Shhh now, Bella, we can talk about it in the morning."

"But Mr. McKinnon said, he said . . ."

"I didn't know Mr. McKinnon was anything to do with rabbits," says Ani gently, smoothing her daughter's hair, soothing her into sleep, and wiping the thought of the poet from anything that might be remembered in the next, new tomorrow.

While Roy, heading home, finds Iris sitting on her own front doorstep, her cheeks flushed and her smile wide.

"Hullo, dear. Did you leave your key? I was just over at the beach — you could have found me. . . ."

"I've just proposed to Dr. Frank Draper," she says, leaning back on her hands and looking triumphant. "I was so sick of it, I just asked him. The silly bugger, of course he said yes."

Rounding the street, Mac looked up and saw the tail of a shooting star — extraordinary — and stopped. If Ani were with him, she'd make him make a wish. He slung his bag over his shoulder and breathed in the crisp night air. He loved these nocturnal starts, loved walking through the village as everyone else lay inside, warm and sleeping — it was like being able to walk through their dreams. Occasionally he'd hear a dog bark or a baby cry; occasionally a light would come on as he passed by a house, and he'd wonder if it was his footfall its inhabitant had heard.

Tread softly, he thinks now as he passes along a street of darkened windows, *because you tread on my dreams. That's Yeats, that is* — Ani had read it to him in the evening — *and you couldn't get better than that.* His steps lengthened, crunching the gravel as he ran through Yeats's words:

Had I the heavens' embroidered cloths,
Enwrought with golden and silver light,
The blue and the dim and the dark cloths
Of night and light and half-light,
I would spread the cloths under your feet:
But I, being poor, have only my dreams;
I have spread my dreams beneath your
     feet;
Tread softly because you tread on my
     dreams. . . .

Then came another crunch, and another, out of time, and Mac peered into the darkness to see the young doctor — Draper — and Iris McKinnon's brother, Roy.

"Good evening, to you, gentlemen — or is it good morning? I'm never quite sure at this time." He enjoyed their start; Roy McKinnon almost jumped. "And where might you be bound at such an hour?" As if he had the perfect right to interrogate anyone he encountered on his way.

"Good morning to you." It was the doctor who spoke. "A fine morning for a walk. A fine morning to feel the air around you." His voice was tight, his face flushed — Mac wondered if the two of them had been up somewhere drinking.

Roy McKinnon patted his friend's arm, and then held out his hand to shake Mac's.

"Don't mind Frank," he said. "We've just been listening to the latest news from Spain — some terrible bombing raid — they're saying there might be thousands dead, and thousands of children orphaned too." He shook his head. "It's no news to greet a man with on a fine night like this; I'm sorry."

"A marketplace, man, they bombed a marketplace. Are they safe in their beds" — the doctor grabbed at Mac's arm, clutching it tight — "the people you love? Do you have a wife? Or children?"

Mac stepped away from the man's fingers, let his own hand rest on the doctor's shoulder. The flush, the tight breathing: he was just like Ani when she tried to take in too much of the world's news. "I've been following the stories, Doctor. It doesn't bode well for the world, not at all." And he watched how the doctor's hands shook as he took a cigarette from the packet in his pocket, how the flame of the match quivered in the darkness.

Silence then, and then a long breath made of smoke. The doctor held the packet out to Mac, to Roy McKinnon, shaking his own head as each of them refused. "And what can you do, then, what can you do?"

Mac tipped his head back, looking up at the stars and the wisps of cloud that ob-

371

scured slices of the constellations here and there. There was the Southern Cross; there was the Milky Way running up from the south towards the high dark line the mountain made to the west. "My wife is at home, asleep, yes, and we're not yet lucky enough to have a child." He shrugged. "That world is a long way away, and I hope if it comes close, I can keep my wife safe from it — and any children too."

"As every father in Europe has thought before you."

The tip of the doctor's cigarette flared bright as he inhaled; Mac stared as its color flickered. There was something hypnotic about these wee licks of fire people carried around with them, but then, he was like that with any flame, always drifting a little closer than he should. It scared the life out of Ani when he had to work a spell near the engines' fireboxes, he knew, as if she feared he'd be sucked in and immolated in one random rush.

"Every father everywhere, I suppose." Frank Draper threw the cigarette down on the ground, stamping at it impatiently. "I want a train that goes far enough and fast enough to take me away from stories like this — and I know that there'll only be more and more of them to come. A pessimist, my

friend here calls me a pessimist. But I'm a doctor, a man of rationality and investigation. And I say this is what we men do best — we fight, we kill, and we use our best imagination to find newer ways of doing it."

"Come away, Frank," said Roy McKinnon. "We're keeping this man from his business — come away."

But they stood there, the three of them, like the fixed points of some perpetual triangle. An owl called, and another answered, and in the next lull Mac heard the turn of the waves, sneaking along streets in which they usually kept their silence. "The oceans and the skies," he said, "and the sun coming up each new day. That's all there is, I think. That's what it matters to think on, not the news and the wars and the dying and the loss. It's not a bad sort of insurance."

The doctor laughed, and clapped Mac's shoulder hard. "And I thought Roy here was the poet — didn't know this place had managed to infect two of you." He pulled his coat around him, fastening another of its buttons. "All right then, let's get on. I could use a drink to settle me down — a dram of whisky." He tried to mimic Mac's accent, and laughed again. "You'd go, wouldn't you, if there was some mad call to fight?"

And Mac, without thinking, found he was shaking his head. "No," he said slowly. "I've never thought of it before, but no. It's not my war, not my world. I'd stay here, you're right. I'd stay here and keep my wife safe, and my children." He could feel his shoulders straightening with resolve.

"White feathers this time? I wonder if people will do that again." But Dr. Draper smiled. "I'm with you. It's not to do with us and ours, you're right. But I've a sense we'll all be pulled into it, with some nasty inexorability." He fumbled in his coat pocket, drew out his cigarettes, and then put them away again with a sigh. "So when you do go, sir, as we all will, you make sure you leave someone here to take care of your people. That's a better insurance than your waves and your stars."

Hitching his bag higher onto his shoulder, Mac tipped his hat. "Perhaps I'll see you gents for that whisky sometime — I shoot billiards now and then, if a run gets in early. We can unravel the ways of the world some more. You can tell me your plans for this war you say is coming."

Roy McKinnon coughed, rubbing his hands for warmth. "I suppose we'll all end up in it, no matter what we think. Frank here will stop doctoring. I'll stop teaching

— and dreaming my silly poetical dreams. And maybe someone else will see your trains through the stops of their timetables." He pointed at the guard's lamp that swung from Mac's bag. "Hang on to your happiness if you can. We should none of us let them make us change what we do in the world."

Mac watched Roy's mouth as it spoke its words. This man was the one who dreamed of becoming a poet: what a weightless thing to do. No momentum, no material, just a blind gaze out in the direction of the future. "So you're the one who wants poetry," he said. "My wife's a reader — read me Yeats this very night." His chest expanded a little with the story: *Bet you'd not expected that.*

But from farther along the road, he heard the sounds of an engine coming up to steam — he could hear clanking and grating and puffed exhalations, and he knew how every particular sound was being made. That was his world; he was a railwayman. The engine bellowed again, and Mac stepped back a little more.

"An odd pleasure, to find you on my way to work — an odd pleasure to talk of this much in so short a time, and just here on the road I happened to be walking along. All the best to you both." But he nodded to

the doctor. "You should meet my wife, Doctor. I think you and she could terrify each other with the ways you take on the world." He tilted his hat again and headed towards the shunting yards, leaving Roy McKinnon and Frank Draper to head on to their whisky and their beds.

And as he walked in and out of the puddles of streetlight, he thought about Ani, perhaps still awake, and waiting to hear his train. If she could see him now, as she waited to sleep again, she would see him walking fast, and free, and strangely exhilarated. If she could see him now, as the night crept towards sunrise, she would see him fly on to the yards and up into the guards' van, his light bright with its beacons of red and green.

Maybe a bairn next year, he thought, swinging himself into his carriage. *Or mebbe a war.* Who, apart from those old Scots' women with second sight, who could ever know what would happen next in a story?

A nice couple of chaps; he was glad to have met them — not that there'd been any proper introduction; he wished suddenly that he'd told them his name. But then it was such an odd meeting, he almost wondered if he'd dreamed it, if they'd both walk right past him if they met again somewhere

in the village streets in the brightness of a day.

Who knew which characters ended up in which story. *Another question for that second sight,* thought Mac. And as he jumped down to wait for the signal from his driver, another engine came surging along the tracks beside him, leaving Mac to leap clear, and fast, out of its path.

His heart beating, he climbed into his box again, and sat, his breathing rapid. *You're all right, you're all right.* He pressed his finger against his pulse, could feel his blood racing through his wrist. *You always check, mate, you always check.*

He closed his eyes and slowed his breath. Suppose there were so many accidents you didn't have in a day, a week. Suppose there were near misses, close calls, some of which you didn't even notice. One of them would find you sooner or later.

He took Ani's packet of sandwiches out of his bag, unwrapping the carefully folded paper. Egg. And two slices of ham with a slice of tomato carefully between the two to try to stop it from making the bread soggy. She made them with love, she said. On a morning like this, he could almost taste it.

Yes, he would spread the universe beneath her feet, if it were his to spread — the

thousands of stars, the stretch of the sky, and the vast deep of the oceans it held and everything in them. If he were a different man, he would write her a poem. He would write her a poem about this place, its colors, its sounds, its shapes. The mountain, the water, the sky, and this nest of a village held safe by all three — she'd love that; it would make her smile from the deepest part of herself, the part that was his. He wondered about how he might start — but nothing came except the signal from the driver that the train was ready to go.

Mac finished his sandwich, flicked his light around to green, and leaned out of the window to taste the steamy air of the train as it pushed north.

Out along the horizon, a smudge of red cut through the darkness, a bright and glowing start to the next day. He thought of the two men he'd just met, the horror they had been carrying with them. He tried to imagine the sounds of war — of bombs and burning, of loss, of dying — and shook his head at it. The world couldn't come to that.

But the sun on the water reflected the stories of the doctor, of the poet: the sun on the water that morning looked like blood smeared on steel.

38

When he opens his eyes, the room quivers with a sharp green light. Roy blinks and blinks again. After the first blink, the green light fades down to darkness; after the second, he realizes he's in Iris's spare room, in Iris's house.

He blinks again. That green light: it must have leached out of his dream. His terrible dream. The guard's light green; the train coming on; and Roy himself riding fast towards the engine on a flimsy bike, trying to beat it, trying to best it, trying to fly across the tracks. He's dreamed this dream every night, every night for the three, four, five months now since the accident. He reaches for a glass of water, coughing as he takes too big a mouthful. From the hallway outside, he hears a clock's chime — three times — and he lies still a moment, wishing for the power to advance the time closer to dawn, before he lets himself confirm it with

the glowing green numbers on his watch.

Just gone three. The cold, quiet time. The left side of his body feels pummeled and bruised as if it had been buffeted by something with the force of a train.

Easing himself out of bed, Roy finishes the glass of water and gazes at the street. Three o'clock; he's slept just over four hours, but it's the longest stretch of sleep he's managed yet. And he's exhausted by the dream, the night, the waking.

He creeps through the dark house, out to the kitchen, refilling the glass and draining it again and again. *I am forty years old,* he thinks. *I may live another forty.* The idea is somehow untenable.

Back in his room, he feels around for clothes, boots, his coat and hat, in the darkness. His thumbs brush against his legs as he pulls on his trousers; his palms brush against his body as he pulls on his shirt. And in each touch, he feels papery skin against papery skin, as if the warmth, the blood, had already evaporated from his being.

Navigating the desk for his notebook, his pen, his hand finds the rectangle of the magazine that came with the previous day's post — his poem, his "Lost World," so distinct and incontrovertible in its regular

380

type. He should take it up to Ani now, he thinks; leave it in her mailbox for her to find in the morning.

It's breathtaking, the addictive powerlessness of unequal love, and the myriad explanations his mind can generate for Ani's ongoing silence. *Maybe Isabel didn't want another man in the way of her father's memory; maybe Ani didn't want to know.* The permutations of whether the girl even told her mother or not branch and multiply like the complex math problems he used to set, *when all you have to do is ask her yourself.* Easy to say at three in the morning, yet whenever he's seen Ani, he's stepped up to the precipice of this conversation, gulped, said nothing, and stepped back down, making his peace with himself with some line about her being his muse.

Bollocks: you don't dream of taking a muse by the hand, of holding her, of tasting her kiss — he makes himself stop, batting at his forehead like the dunderhead he is until his mind is blank again. And calm.

Later, he will take it to her later. No secrets this time; no sneaking around; no anonymity. Just him, Roy McKinnon, offering up this thing he has made. He lets his hand rest on the magazine, wondering what Anikka Lachlan will think of her mistake.

Well, his poem is beyond her now and out in the world. And he feels lighter for it.

He slips through the front door and across the road, tracing the waterline as he heads south along the sand and over the rocks. A single light from a ship pulses briefly on the line of the horizon and he watches it awhile, trying to remember the dots and dashes of Morse code. Perhaps it's a message for him, he thinks, trying to count a pattern of dots and dashes until he rubs his eyes and the light transforms into a regular pulse of flashes.

What are you thinking, mate? Why are you here?

He crouches down on the rocks, away from the onshore wind, and watches as the light disappears. As if there was a message; as if there was a sign. His back stiff against the hardness of the cliff's face, he flexes and tenses each of the muscles in his legs, trying to sit still a little longer. Some nights, he's fallen asleep down here, waking up with the gulls as the dawn rolls around. That bloke who gave his address as Thirroul Beach when he joined up for the war; maybe this was his very spot. Maybe this was the place that he thought of as home. *Guess he didn't get back,* Roy thinks out of nowhere, *or I'd've run into him by now.* He only realizes

he's crying when the tears penetrate his trousers' heavy fabric. He should build a cairn, he thinks then, and starts immediately, taking up the curved flutes of purple barnacle shells and smooth grey elliptical pebbles from the ground around him.

This do in remembrance of me.

Something moves along the sand, and Roy turns to see a fisherman casting out beyond the breakers. Balancing the last two pebbles on the mound, he gives it a salute. *There you are, mate,* he thinks, *home at last.* But before he turns to make his way along the beach, he crouches down again and scoops up handfuls of the stones, stuffing them into his pockets like candy or coins.

"Much biting?" he calls to the fisherman as he nears him, his fingers working the stones like a rosary.

"Bit of bream, bit of tailor," the man replies, indicating a bucket with his foot. "Where's your gear, mate?"

"Couldn't sleep," Roy says. "Just came out to stop myself staring at the ceiling." He loves these nocturnal meetings, their accidental connections and random conversations. He crouches again as the man's line tenses with a bite. "And another?"

"Bit of power in him," the angler agrees, reeling in the line and dropping this next

fish into his bucket. "Take one if you like; I've enough here to keep the wife busy awhile."

But Roy shakes his head. "Thanks though, I've got some walking to do before I head in." Tipping his hat to the fisherman, falling back into his stride. Ahead of him, the old jetty's pylons and crossbeams stand like a luminous forest of trunks and their branches, and as he nears them, he picks up speed, remembering his climb, his salty jump, when he first came home.

All right, he thinks, *come on* — springing along the sand as fast as he can, and up. *Do your St. Simeon again.* Thirty-nine years St. Simeon stayed up his pillar — *my whole life again, more or less.* It still feels an unconscionable time.

From the top, he counts the rhythm of the breakers, timing his breathing with their ebb and flow. Beyond their surge, something pale shimmers against the water, like a miniature iceberg, he thinks, although he knows that's as daft an analogy as looking for Morse messages from a passing ship. He squints, blinks, and squints again. *It's a bloody albatross,* and he wishes he was still standing with the other man, to have someone with whom he might share the sighting.

"Hey," he calls back along the beach,

pointing to the bird. "Hey look." But the fellow is too far away.

He watches as the albatross rises and falls on the ocean's tiny crests: wherever it's flown from, or is flying to, it's resting here, off the south coast of New South Wales. The distances it might have traveled; the expanses it might have seen. It would be something, thinks Roy, to be able to glide around and around and around the world, so rarely stationary, so rarely stuck on land. *That'd be the life,* he thinks, suddenly tempted to pack up his gear and move on. Whatever respite he had from coming here, from stopping awhile — he shivers in the cold air, and his torso keeps shaking, impossible to still.

But of course, to keep moving would be to move away from Ani Lachlan — *or your ideas of her, you yellowbelly,* he thinks, rubbing at his arms to try to stop their trembling. No, now that day is coming on, in no part of his imagination can he see himself approaching her, declaring himself — even managing to present her with the blessed magazine.

Damn it, man, you never even asked her on a day trip. Cross-legged up the pillar, he pulls the stones from his pockets one by one, flicking them down into the water

385

below. *She loves me; she loves me not; she loves me; she loves me not.* It's a fool's game of desire, but maybe there's as much joy in the act of loving as there is in being loved.

He pulls one last stone from his pocket, a perfectly fluted purple cone, and studies it awhile in the dim light. Out on the water, the albatross bobs gently and Roy remembers how once, on one of the worst days of his war, he'd happened to look up from his gun's sights at precisely the right instant to see a huge white ball of floss — feathers, he supposed, or some other sort of fluff — soft and gentle and floating above the mud. The impossibility of its purity, its fragility, its perfection. Now, with the purple shell balanced like a coronet on the plinth of his fingers, he pushes himself to his feet and stands on the pylon's top, holding the barnacle high and then tossing it higher again into the darkness. And as the little thing soars and tumbles through its arc, he sees its edges catch the light here and there, watches it rise up and drop all the way down, into the wide, dark ocean. He can see the albatross out there too, waiting just beyond the upright of the jetty's deepest stanchion, and he walks forward towards it, jumping between what's left of the jetty's

girders, its beams, its old tracks and sleepers.

Here I am, a railwayman at last, he thinks, and he laughs out loud at the idea of it. *A man of spectacular movement and action.*

The next pylon, he reckons, is a few feet away, and so on by regular gaps out into the water. He'd be tall enough, lithe enough surely, to spring out along this causeway — he balances, carefully, his arms out like a crucifix. And then he starts to run, out towards the horizon.

That phrase Frank had remembered — *a solid man; I was a solid man.* Roy laughs again as he feels himself surrounded by air. *There's nothing solid about me now.* In the water ahead of him, he sees a dark shadow like a right angle, and he remembers his hunt for the signs of hidden letters, remembers walking through the village as it slept, calling out rich words.

"*L,*" he shouts, for the fun of it. "Levity, luminous, lampyridine."

Leap.

On and on, faster and faster, his feet as light as Fred Astaire's. In the end, he couldn't have said if he jumped or fell. In the end, the fisherman said, it looked like he was flying.

On the last day of his life, Mackenzie Lachlan kissed his wife at the top of the steps, waved back to her from the corner of the street, and kept going without another thought. He walked most of the way to the railway with his daughter, telling her nothing stories about a tree here, a cloud there, the routes and runs his day would take. "And then your milkshake at the end, love: what'll you have, chocolate malted?" Her favorite; her automatic choice.

He did not hug her harder than usual when they parted. He did not kiss her one extra time, or call some message after her. He did not stand and watch her go, did not think about her future or her past. He simply hitched his bag onto his shoulder and walked down to the yards.

"Morning, Mac," his driver called. "A great day." And it was. It was. The sun was high and bright, the sky cerulean, and he

knew the ocean would be glittering when the train reached Scarborough, Clifton, Coalcliff.

"Great day," he agreed, checking his lamp, swinging up into the van.

"Thought of you this morning when I was coming in," the driver said. "In fact I almost came by and fetched you — they were out there again, a whole line of albatrosses as far as you could see. Reckon they stretched for a good three or four miles, just bobbing along on the water. A grand sight, Mac, magnificent."

And Mac laughed; let Ani have her phosphorescence. Let Isabel have her dolphins. What Mac wanted, more than anything else, was an albatross out on the ocean, or turning and gliding in flight.

"Reckon they'll be there when we get up the line?" he called and the driver shook his head. "Third time lucky, maybe." It was getting to be a joke between them — the birds coming, and settling, and Mac never quite in the right place at the right time to see them.

"Well, let's get on then, and fetch me next time, will you?" Mac added. "I'd get away early for that any day."

A harbinger of good fortune; a bright omen at sea. *Let's face it,* he thought, *a man*

needs all the luck he can come by.

So that later, when it happened, he saw this, the omen of the bird. He saw his wife, her hair shining, stepping out of the sunrise; he saw her eyes closed and dreaming on the night of their wedding. He saw her dancing through pools of light at the end of the war, and twirling on the ice, around and around. He saw himself talking about writing a poem — maybe he'd meant to; maybe he would. He saw himself running for a football, running with his daughter, running across a wide, green field, and then he was running along the uneven surface of the line's ballast. Running from this, whatever this was. Running from every accident he'd dodged and missed on every other day of his life. He saw all the things he wouldn't know about the future — Ani alone in a quiet room of books; Isabel practicing words on a page. He saw a man running along a railway line, running towards the sunrise. And then he was running along his own silver line of track, etched here between the ocean on one hand and the scarp high on the other.

Running through this place.

He saw all this in the blink of an eye, like fragments dislodged from his daughter's kaleidoscope.

After that, there was nothing but light, from white, through blue, and beyond.

On the first day of her first vacation, Ani is on the beach before the sunrise, watching its colors come up through gentle purples and silvers, and then a wide clear sky of perfect pale blue. She walks south along the sand, following the line of the tide so that her feet are brushed with the thinnest edge of the water's foam as each wave flows and ebbs. The ocean's still cold, although the year is touching summer, and she loves the slight shock of each ripple against her skin, the way her footprints disappear with each salty surge. Looking up from her feet a moment, she sees an albatross rise from the ocean — the power of it, and the majesty. The one bird Mac had always wanted to see on the coast. The one sight he'd always somehow missed.

She stands facing the brightness: she loves this moment, when the sun appears, loves the feel of the earth's ball rolling forward,

rolling on, turning itself in space.

Coming out of the grocer's the day before, Ani had met Mrs. Padman, one of the ladies from the church, and they'd stopped and talked awhile, of this and that, a baby born two streets down and someone's mother taken ill. There was a new roster being planned for the church's flowers, Mrs. Padman said, and she hoped she might be able to include Ani's name on it — no mention of why Ani had stopped doing this, of how long it had been, of whether Ani was ready to return. And Ani had smiled and nodded and said there were so many flowers in her garden at the moment — it seemed a shame that only she and Isabel were enjoying them.

Walking home with her flour and her sugar, a little bag of sweets for her daughter and her half a pound of tea, she realized it was the first meeting she'd had in the village streets where the weight of Mac, and what had happened, hadn't hung over the moment — where his story hadn't been there in the conversation, said or unsaid. Where she hadn't been spotlit by its circumstance, and raised up somehow, like someone famous — or infamous.

Now, under the first warmth of the sun, she feels light, and smiles. She thinks: *How dare you die.* But the force has gone out of

the phrase, and the words lie across the top of her imagination, thought, registered, but powerless beyond that.

In the pocket of her cardigan, she fiddles with an old library card on which she's jotted a shopping list, the soft pads of her fingers pushing against the sharp prick of the card's corners. *Imagine me, a librarian,* she thinks. *Imagine me, in charge.* All the things she'd never had to manage when there was Mac — bills and time and having coal delivered or the roof fixed and remembering which night the pan man came; all the things she'd never wanted to have to think about. And here she was, doing it all, and doing fine. She wants to feel proud of it, but the thought feels too close to being grateful for its circumstances — *Mac or a library; Mac or capability* — which is always an unthinkable thing.

Heading south along the beach, she scans the empty sand and then, before she can change her mind, runs forward and springs into a cartwheel. Another and another and another, although the last leaves her tumbled on the ground, gritty and laughing. She looks around again, not for any unwanted witnesses, but for wanted ones — Roy McKinnon is down here some mornings, and it's always lovely to talk with him

about the world. Even Frank Draper might have laughed at the silliness of it, if he'd been there. There's some kind of busyness a way away, at the foot of the headland beyond the jetty; Ani peers across the distance and turns back for home, too far away to pick out either the doctor or the poet among the fray.

Who'd have thought, she wonders, *what those two would be in my year?* Almost twelve months ago, they were newcomers in her world, slightly awkward at her Christmas lunch. This year, there was no question that they'd eat anywhere else. *And I will show him my poem,* she thinks, the first time she hasn't tagged it as Mac's. *It's such a beautiful thing.*

Walking on, Ani's foot scuffs something hard beneath the sand, and she leans down to work free a strange white shape, curled and twisted, turning it one way and then another until she realizes what it is — teeth! a little set of jaws! — and throws it away from herself, far out and into the ocean. Her hands rub furiously against her trousers, trying to erase the texture of the skeletal bone. There's a horrid taste in her mouth too, and she bends forward, spitting and spitting again to try to clear whatever it is.

Teeth; jaws: she can't begin to imagine what kind of creature they've come from — an animal? A fish? Some strange, snapping reptile? She shivers, wringing her hands in the sharp, salty water. That's why she hates Isabel's idea of Mac stuck under the water. There are too many things that can bite down there — bite him, tear at his body, and sever that lifeline that runs between them. Even the pretty-sounding stargazer her daughter mentioned turned out to have a horrible mouthful of teeth.

She washes her hands once more, rubbing them dry in her pockets. Her lightness has evaporated with the morning's haze: she's Ani Lachlan again, a widow, fixed and alone. It's never-ending, after all. She should go home and make her daughter her breakfast.

Climbing the cliff near the famous writer's house, she pauses, staring in at its deep, shaded veranda. If he hadn't happened on this village, if he hadn't happened on this house, what story would he have invented in those winter months instead — and would it have had anything to do with her?

A curtain flicks open at one of the house's windows and Ani turns hurriedly to give the appearance of looking out to sea. A man comes onto the veranda, and she thinks, for

an instant, that it's Lawrence himself, come back to life and come back to see what other story has been going on in this place in the space after his novel's last page.

A seagull shrieks, startling Ani as she comes on up the stairs. The man leans out towards the vastness of the sea, waving at Ani as she passes.

"A beautiful morning — we've got some view."

Ani waves back, nodding. "Perfect, isn't it? Bound to be a perfect day." She takes the last steps at close to a run, her lightness recovered again and flooding through her limbs.

She runs to the end of the street, around the corner, and back along to her own gate, bounding over its low fence and up the front stairs two at a time. She unlocks the front door and steps inside, closing it quietly and standing a moment in the reflected rose and blue of its two glass panels.

It's quiet in Isabel's bedroom, and dark, the blinds still drawn. Ani rests her hands on the high frame of the bedstead. Isabel is sleeping on her stomach, as she always has, her head turned slightly, and her hands up on her pillow.

Eleven years, thinks Ani. *I have stood and watched this baby sleep eleven years.* Isabel

stirs a little, and Ani creeps away, listening as her daughter coughs once, and settles. She opens the French doors onto the front veranda, letting in the first of the morning's sun. She'll make tea; she'll take it outside — it's the first day of her first vacation, and there's no rush. No rush. The sun sneaks across the boards of the veranda's floor; by the time she boils the kettle and soaks the leaves, it will have warmed the place where she can sit and gaze out at the ocean.

Which is where she is and what she's doing when the car turns into the street and draws up near her gate. When Frank Draper comes into her yard, and climbs her stairs, his hands held out towards her.

"Anikka," he says — he's never used her first name before — "I'm so sorry to be coming like this on such a gorgeous morning." And he sits down on the floor, before she can stand; sits down, cross-legged, facing her.

She wonders about the dust marking his nice suit. And she wonders, the question looping inside her head, what news he can possibly have brought, *because Isabel is safe inside; Isabel is asleep.*

As if nothing else mattered in the world.

"I've just come from Iris McKinnon's," he says at last. "I thought you'd want to

know. There was an accident, and Roy McKinnon . . ." He ducks, his face working silently. "Roy McKinnon has been drowned."

Watching him closely, watching the way his mouth twists at the end of the sentence, the way tears come into his eyes, Ani feels like some part of her is standing up, tall, looking down at him and looking down at herself as well. She's leaning towards Frank Draper, patting his hand, saying "there" and "shh" and "it's all right," like she used to say to Isabel when she was tiny and woke herself with the unknown trembling of a dark, bad dream. She sees herself doing this; she sees Frank Draper grab onto her hand and hold it, tight. She sees their heads close, his dark, and hers bright.

She sees them sit like this as the cicadas begin to sing.

The first man's hand I've held, she thinks from somewhere far away. She has never imagined it would be his. *I don't know what to think; I don't know what to do.*

But as she sits and grips the doctor's hand with hers, she remembers the minister, the hot, sweet, sugary drink he made her. And, "I'll get you some tea," she says, easing her fingers away. And she makes it hot and strong and sweet — makes it in the chipped

cup the minister had given her, as if that might be some important part of the ritual.

He drinks it in four or five scalding mouthfuls, blowing his breath out and wiping his hand across his eyes. "I thought you'd want to know," he says again, looking at her properly for the first time.

And she nods — *of course* — and says, "Poor Iris. I'll go down later. I'll take her some food." The commotion on the beach, she thinks suddenly, but doesn't want to ask. It feels discourteous somehow, or even cowardly, to have turned and walked away.

"No," says the doctor, "I don't think — no . . ." He's holding a large envelope out towards her; she opens it and sees a magazine, a strip of paper marking one page, and *"Lost World" — a new poem by Roy McKinnon.*

"I don't understand," says Ani slowly, her fingers rubbing at the page. "I mean, I knew he was writing again — he seemed pleased with what he was doing — and how awful to be stopped —" She strokes the paper awhile. "Such a curious title; I wonder how he came by it."

And then she looks at the poem's lines:

Let this be her.
A fold of light . . .

"I don't understand," she says again, her face pale and her fingers unsteady.

"He wrote it after Christmas." Frank Draper's voice is distant, somehow muffled. "I read it then — I told him it was good. He said he would show it to you. I mean, it's obviously about you."

"No." Ani closes the magazine, shaking her head. "No, my husband wrote this poem. Mac wrote this poem for my birthday before he died — he left it in a book for me; I found it on my shelf months later. Mr. McKinnon must have taken it; he must have copied it. Because they can't both have written the same poem, can they?"

There's a sudden movement in the yard, and Ani and the doctor both turn to see a magpie swoop in and settle. Ani holds fast to the magazine and its shockingly familiar verse, her eyes fixed on the bird, while Frank Draper worries at the skin around his thumbnail, pushing and chipping until the quick begins to bleed.

"Roy wrote it after Christmas," he says again. "He was anxious about showing you, but he said he thought he might leave it somewhere where you'd find it. I thought he'd probably slip it into one of his library books, see if you happened on it when you were packing them up. But he must have

401

brought it up here — maybe one night after the pictures, I don't know." He pauses, touches her hand. "Roy McKinnon wrote it, Ani, you know that. Your husband was a railwayman; he wasn't a poet."

Opening the magazine again, Ani follows the familiar words, a little less familiar, somehow, among the precise reportage of other articles, other words. "Mac told me once he wanted to write a poem," she says defensively. "And so I thought maybe he'd tried. It was beautiful, so beautiful." She watches a single tear — which must be hers — splash down onto the paper, darkening its color. "And it was mine."

The doctor leans forward, takes her hands again. "It's still yours, Ani. It's just from someone else — that's all."

"But I thought it was from Mac — I thought it was from him. What business does Roy McKinnon have thinking I look like an angel in a white dress and the sunshine?"

"Well, none, now, does he, but he thought the world of you — you must have known that." She can hear the impatience in his voice as he stands and raises his empty cup. "My turn to make the tea then?" And he disappears inside, leaving Ani and this newly dense idea alone in the morning.

She shifts the magazine, leafing through it at random. And when she finds the poem again, and reads it, it's Roy McKinnon's voice she hears, not some far-off trace of Mac's. *Of course my name wasn't in Mac's writing,* she thinks at last. *How could it be, when he didn't write it?* She pushes her nails into the palm of her hand like a run of sharp pins. "And the brooch," she says under her breath. "My Christmas brooch." The simple words stick in her throat.

Inside, through the open door, she can see the luminous wood of her little *bibliothèque* — no question he made that. She glances down at the page again and sees in tiny letters beneath its title, *For A.L.* A new and big thing that she was too afraid to see.

No question, no question at all.

She looks up as Frank comes out with the tea — "No milk or sugar in yours; I think I remembered it right?" — and wraps her hands around the cup's warmth as if it were the coldest winter's day.

"Thank you," she says — for the tea, for the poem, for whatever. The warmth burrows deep into her. The magpie begins to chortle, and she lets it finish before she speaks: "And Roy? What happened? Did he see this before he — before —"

There are dark smudges on the skin below

the doctor's eyes, and his eyes are red and rheumy. He leans into Ani's pause, taking a mouthful of his own tea and holding it in his cheeks awhile before he swallows and answers. "The magazine came yesterday, Iris thinks, and Roy went out last night. Hard to know what happened, except he drowned, fully clothed, with a few pebbles in his pockets — a fisherman saw him trying to run along what's left of the old jetty."

A great blast comes up from one of the railway's engines, and Ani starts, as surprised by its noise as if the train were in her very yard. "The first time I saw him, when he came home," she says as its sound fades away, "the first time I saw him, he was perched on one of those poles. I always wondered how he'd gotten down." Only later will she remember that Mac was there too; only later will she realize she's excluded him from the story.

The doctor sighs and wipes his eyes. "I was hoping for a happy ending," he says. "If I could manage it, surely anyone could." He frowns at her frowning, at her blank incomprehension. "You must have known, Ani. Every second gossip in this village has been talking about it for months. How long you'd wait. And what you'd wear." He laughs, but the laugh makes a cold and empty sound.

"You know how they are, how they all like to dream."

Ani picks up her teacup and is tempted for a moment to throw what's left of its liquid in his face. Then she moves her hand to throw it past him and away over the veranda's rail and onto the garden down below. "The year I've had, Dr. Draper, here, with my daughter, making sense of this strange new world. I've lost my husband. I have this job. I wake up in my own room, in my own house. And yet everything, everything is different. Meeting Mr. McKinnon, even meeting you; you were new people in my new world. And I appreciated that very much. I didn't think about much more than that. I paid no mind to what the village was plotting might happen next. I've just been trying to get us through the days, just me and Isabel, that's all." There are truths and untruths in this, she knows, but it feels too late to worry about any of them. And as she says her daughter's name, Isabel appears, lovely and smiling and half full of dreams.

"Bella." Ani reaches up to her girl. "You've had the loveliest long sleep. Dr. Draper's been here drinking tea with me. And now he's just on his way."

And she holds on fast to her daughter's warm hands.

"Ani," says the doctor, standing now and fumbling with his hat. "It's all right — I only meant . . ." And he sighs, pointing to the magazine. "I'll leave you this, then, and I'll leave you to your morning, Mrs. Lachlan."

From across the village comes the hard pull of an engine's brakes, and they both react, the doctor and the railwayman's wife. Frank Draper turns and walks away, still shaking his head as his car purrs and he pulls out onto the empty road.

Up on the porch, Ani keeps her eyes on the nothing of middle distance until the car has gone. She feels Isabel crouch beside her, sees her reach for the journal, and hears her gasp as she starts to read.

"The poem, Mr. McKinnon's poem, oh, and I — oh, Mum."

While Ani, leaning in, reads along, wondering what she might feel about any of this — not now, when everything seems pushed away and at arm's length, like trying to bring a line of type into focus, but some other time, on some other day. Then a sentence leaps at her from the facing page, its words wrapping around her, and she disappears into their world, enveloped and contained, lost to anything in this here or now, its chances, its hazards, its missed op-

portunities.

Overhead, the sun is still climbing, and as it catches the edge of a shiny tin roof across the street, Ani looks up from the page, staring straight at the bright disk until she's blinded by its glare. She reaches for her daughter's hand again, hanging on, holding on.

Somewhere in the world, the sun is always rising. Somewhere in the world, the day is getting light.

ACKNOWLEDGMENTS

The earliest drafts of this novel were completed under the auspices of a doctorate of creative arts at the University of Technology, Sydney. Thanks to Catherine Cole, Paula Hamilton, and Paul Ashton for their encouragement, guidance, and supervision both ahead of the project's beginnings and throughout its span.

The epigraph from Stephen Edgar comes from his poem "Nocturnal," originally published in *History of the Day* (2009), and is reproduced here with his permission.

The poem "Lost World" — written specifically for this novel — also came from the talented agency of Stephen Edgar, without whom Roy would never have found such an elegant and appropriate voice. I cannot thank him enough for his enthusiasm and generosity in this.

The research for this novel drew on a large number of written sources, and quotes

several — most crucially D. H. Lawrence's *Kangaroo* and Charlotte Brontë's *Jane Eyre.* The text also refers to articles from *Smith's Weekly,* 18 March 1944 (the story of the engine driver and his blackberries); the *National Geographic* of November 1947 (the northern lights); and *The Sydney Morning Herald,* 14 June 1949 (the newspaper Roy reads on the train). The other poems referred to in the text are Siegfried Sassoon's "Everyone Sang," Elizabeth Barrett Browning's "How Do I Love Thee?," and two by William Butler Yeats — "On Being Asked for a War Poem" and "Aedh Wishes for the Cloths of Heaven."

The description of Ani Lachlan as "an angel from a lost world" was inspired by "Angel," a poem by Justin Moon; the librarian who wonders to Ani if paradise might be a library paraphrases Jorge Luis Borges's words from his *"Poema de los Dones"* [Poem of the Gifts]; Roy borrows Heinrich Heine's words from his 1821 play *Almansor* when he talks about burning books; and the extracts on bathysphere diving are taken from William Beebe's 1934 memoir *Half Mile Down.* Joseph Davis's *D. H. Lawrence at Thirroul* was an invaluable reference and the source of the inspirational information that

Yeats's doctor, too, had found himself in this part of the world.

The idea for Frank Draper came originally from a conversation with Les Murray — for which many belated thanks.

Thanks to Julianne Schultz at *Griffith Review* for publishing an extract from the novel-in-progress in *GR30: The Annual Fiction Edition* (2010). Thanks to Caroline Baum, Sue Beebe, Tegan Bennett Daylight, Lilia Bernede, Ruth Blair, Ilithyia Bone, Leah Burns, Michelle de Kretser, Stuart Glover, Gail Jones, Richard Neylon, Daniel Perez-Bello, Mark Tredinnick, Brenda Walker, Geordie Williamson, and Charlotte Wood, and to Gail MacCallum, as always, for all their encouraging and helpful conversation and other things along the way.

Thanks to Allen & Unwin: to Jane Palfreyman, Clara Finlay, Ali Lavau, Kathryn Knight, and Louise Cornege in Sydney; to Clare Drysdale and Sam Redman in London. Thanks to Hannah Westland, Jenny Hewson, and Federica Leonardis at Rogers, Coleridge and White. And new thanks to Sarah Branham at Atria Books.

Thanks to the whole family — Hays and Beebes, but particularly Nigel Beebe and Huxley Beebe — for the time and space to complete this.

And thanks to Les Hay for not minding my imagining this story. It is for him.

This story is a work of fiction. Some of its locations do exist, as did the inspiration for some of its moments. But these events and their characters are the stuff of my imagination.

ABOUT THE AUTHOR

Ashley Hay is the author of six books including the nonfiction narratives *The Secret: The Strange Marriage of Annabelle Milbanke and Lord Byron* (2000), *Gum: The Story of Eucalypts and Their Champions* (2002), and *Museum* (2007; a collaboration with the visual artist Robyn Stacey).

The Body in the Clouds — her first novel — was shortlisted for a number of prizes including categories in the Commonwealth Writers' Prize and the New South Wales and Western Australian Premier's Awards. It was also longlisted for the 2011 International IMPAC Dublin Literary Award. *The Railwayman's Wife* — her second — was awarded the Colin Roderick Award by the Foundation for Australian Literary Studies, and won the People's Choice category in the New South Wales' Premier's Literary Awards. It was also longlisted for the Miles

Franklin award.

A former literary editor of *The Bulletin,* she contributes to a number of Australian publications including *The Monthly, Australian Geographic,* and *The Australian.* Her essays and short stories have received various prizes and listings, and have appeared in volumes including *Brothers and Sisters* (2009), *Griffith Review, The Best Australian Essays* (2003 and 2015), *The Best Australian Short Stories* (2012 and 2013), and *The Best Australian Science Writing* (2012). In 2014, she edited *The Best Australian Science Writing* anthology for that year, and in 2015 she was awarded the Australian Book Review/Dahl Trust Fellowship.

She lives in Brisbane.

The employees of Thorndike Press hope you have enjoyed this Large Print book. All our Thorndike, Wheeler, and Kennebec Large Print titles are designed for easy reading, and all our books are made to last. Other Thorndike Press Large Print books are available at your library, through selected bookstores, or directly from us.

For information about titles, please call:
  (800) 223-1244

or visit our Web site at:
  http://gale.cengage.com/thorndike

To share your comments, please write:
  Publisher
  Thorndike Press
  10 Water St., Suite 310
  Waterville, ME 04901